NAVIGATION AND GUIDANCE
IN SPACE

PRENTICE-HALL INTERNATIONAL SERIES IN SPACE TECHNOLOGY

C. W. Besserer and Floyd E. Nixon, Editors

PRENTICE-HALL, INC.
PRENTICE-HALL INTERNATIONAL, UNITED KINGDOM AND EIRE
PRENTICE-HALL OF CANADA LTD., CANADA

ALEXANDER AND BAILEY   *Systems Engineering Mathematics*
BAZOVSKY   *Reliability Theory and Practice*
ELLIS AND LUDWIG   *Systems Philosophy*
FOGEL   *Biotechnology: Concepts and Applications*
KOLK   *Modern Flight Dynamics*
LINDEN   *Printed Circuits In Space Technology*
LLOYD AND LIPOW   *Reliability: Management, Methods and Mathematics*
LOH   *Dynamics and Thermodynamics of Planetary Entry*
MACOMBER AND FERNANDEZ   *Inertial Guidance Engineering*
NELSON AND LOFT   *Space Mechanics*
ORDWAY, GARDNER, AND SHARPE   *Basic Astronautics*
ORDWAY, GARDNER, SHARPE AND WAKEFORD   *Applied Astronautics*
SAMARAS   *Applications of Ion Flow Dynamics*
SAMARAS   *Theory of Ion Flow Dynamics*
SCHLESINGER, et al.   *Principles of Electronic Warfare*
SLAGER   *Space Medicine*
STEARNS   *Navigation and Guidance In Space*
STILTZ (ED.)   *Aerospace Telemetry*

PRENTICE-HALL INTERNATIONAL, INC., *London*
PRENTICE-HALL OF AUSTRALIA, PTY., LTD., *Sydney*
PRENTICE-HALL OF CANADA, LTD., *Toronto*
PRENTICE-HALL FRANCE, S.A.R.L., *Paris*
PRENTICE-HALL OF JAPAN, INC., *Tokyo*
PRENTICE-HALL DE MEXICO, S.A., *Mexico City*

NAVIGATION AND GUIDANCE
IN SPACE

EDWARD V. B. STEARNS

Manager, Advanced Program Development
Space Systems Division
Lockheed Missiles and Space Co.

PRENTICE-HALL, INC.
ENGLEWOOD CLIFFS, N. J., 1963

To LARRY, BOB, and PATTI,
who will inherit the opportunities of the space age.

© 1963 by
Prentice-Hall, Inc.
Englewood Cliffs, N. J.

Library of Congress Catalog Card Number 63-10185

Printed in the United States of America

61070—C

PREFACE

In the preparation of this text on guidance and navigation of spacecraft, the goal was to present a discussion of the fundamental principles and broad techniques that are applicable to the art of navigation in space. This approach has been taken in preference to a presentation of detailed treatments of guidance instrumentation. Frequently the mechanization of a navigation system will be determined by the state of the instrumentation art at the time of a design freeze in the development of a particular system, or it will be determined by the optimization of some specific parameter of performance or logistics.

Man is now at the threshold of full development of his spaceflight capability. As the development proceeds, changes will, no doubt, be made in the precision that may be available from various sensors. These changes will have a profound influence on the instrument configurations that are found to be optimum for any given mission. Similarly, changing mission requirements will affect the weighting factors that will be assigned to the various logistical and economic parameters used to evaluate these systems. In short, what appears to be an ideal system in the context of one mission and time may well prove to be an inferior selection for another mission or another time period.

The literature contains many fine discussions of the dynamics of spacecraft in free flight and in the powered trajectories of spaceflight. Each of these is presented in the context of some specific field of celestial mechanics or dynamics. These treatments, prepared in varying degrees of rigor, frequently treat the motion of a spacecraft as that of a particle in free-fall under the influence of a gravitational field. The guidance, or navigation of such a craft, in distinction, must deal with the techniques that are required to determine the position and course of the spacecraft and subsequently to calculate the maneuvers that the craft must execute in order to correct this course. The objective of these corrective maneuvers

v

is to yield a new trajectory that will carry the vehicle to the intended terminal point.

Following the traditional approach that separates *guidance* from *control*, the discussions of this book will be concerned with the techniques for supervision of the trajectory and the means by which the deviations of the actual flight path may be detected to be different from some acceptable or *nominal* trajectory. It is not necessary, in general, that the spacecraft be returned to the nominal trajectory or that the trajectory of the craft be compared to the nominal one. In some cases, depending on the mission, this may prove to be convenient, however, in many examples, the trajectory will be recognized to be a function of many variables and our studies will permit adequate flexibility to allow for changes in path while assuring ultimate arrival at a pre-established destination at the end of a prescribed interval of time.

At the outset, it became apparent that one of the more difficult aspects of preparing the text for this book would be the very breadth of the subject that one embraces under the title of space navigation. To treat such a broad subject in a single volume and to treat it in the depth that will be required as the subject develops is just not possible. We have chosen, instead, to face this broad subject and to treat this breadth in enough detail that the reader will be able to relate the various branches of space navigation to each other and to recognize the general characteristics of each field. The value of a deeper treatment at this time is perhaps doubtful in view of the remarks that have been made in the previous paragraphs.

This work would not have been possible if it had been necessary to rely on the notes and researches of the author alone for the material. It has been necessary, from time to time, to draw from the work of others. Where this is possible, we have referenced these works and an adequate bibliography has been provided. It has not always been feasible to include reference to every pertinent work, paper, report, or book on each subject. Such omissions that have occurred are with the deep regrets of the author.

Special acknowledgments are due to the author's close colleagues and associates who have aided and assisted through their generous interest, discussions, comments, and suggestions.

EDWARD V. B. STEARNS

Menlo Park, California

CONTENTS

I

INTRODUCTION TO SPACEFLIGHT

Soon man will seriously plan personal visits and explorations to the planets and even to extragalactic destinations. Recently, the suggestion that man might venture into space and perhaps visit the Moon was considered most visionary and even a little foolish. However, concrete plans are underway for man's ventures at exploring cis-lunar space and even landings on the Moon. Before man, himself, penetrates very far beyond the orbit of the Moon, probes and unmanned exploratory reconnaissance vehicles must be dispatched in considerable numbers to various regions of the solar system and thence to study the Planets. All of these missions, whether manned or unmanned, will require development of new techniques for navigation of spacecraft. Space navigation will be seen to depend largely on celestial mechanics and the theory of orbits in a gravitational field. This will remain so as long as propulsion is a limiting factor in defining the regime of spaceflight, and the greatest part of the work that is done on transporting a spacecraft is done by the action of gravity forces rather than by the propulsion system of the craft itself. As the work done by the gravity fields becomes less and less effective when compared to the work of the propulsion system, the relative influence of orbit mechanics on the art of space navigation will also diminish.

The advent of the space age has brought forth a requirement for the development of techniques for the control of spacecraft in flight, to provide direction to the propulsion systems of these craft, and to generate steering commands which will direct the spacecraft over vast distances from the point of departure

1

to the destination. Some of these techniques will be discussed in the following chapters. Of course, the full context of spaceflight is so great that it would not be possible to treat such a broad field as space navigation in a single volume. There are, however, some general principles which will be shown to apply to several different environments of spaceflight. Emphasis will be placed upon the navigation aspects of the various missions and upon fundamental principles in order to relate the missions and the techniques to one another.

After a brief introduction to spaceflight and the application of the principles of navigation to space missions in Chapter 1, we will discuss the characteristics of space orbits and the applicable dynamical relations in Chapter 2. Chapter 3 will deal with the instruments for space navigation and the systems for their use. These systems will be treated in more or less general terms in order that the reader will be prepared to recognize their application to the flight missions which will be discussed in subsequent chapters.

Chapter 4 deals with guidance for ballistic missiles as the most primitive application of spaceflight. It is shown in this chapter that, while the spaceflight segment of the ballistic missile trajectory may be treated in a straight-forward manner, that the ascent and re-entry segments of the trajectory present major constraints to the flight system. The methods for calculation of ballistic free-flight trajectories will be related to the errors which occur in the flight conditions at the time of burn-out of the propulsion system. A brief discussion of re-entry trajectories and guidance in re-entry flight is presented.

Chapter 5 deals with the earth satellite and its special problems of guidance and navigation. The ascent trajectory and guidance into orbit are discussed. The problems of attitude control of an artificial earth satellite are also treated in this chapter. A section deals with the interesting problem of determination of the ephemeris of a satellite using measurements and observations which may be made by the occupant of the orbiter. Rendezvous and orbit maneuvers are also discussed in some detail.

Chapter 6 deals with interplanetary navigation. The general characteristics of interplanetary flight paths are discussed and some navigational relations are presented to show how flight paths may be chosen. Errors in interplanetary flight and the correction of orbits through the use of mid-course maneuvers is treated in some detail. The final correction, or homing phase, is developed thoroughly enough to permit a description of a navigation system which is proposed for this application.

The problems of lunar flight have been deferred for discussion in Chapter 7. While these flights occur in space closer to the earth than interplanetary flights, some special problems which do not appear in general interplanetary flight will arise. The three-body nature of the lunar flight trajectory is discussed as is the relative motion of the elements of the Earth-Moon system. A means for the application of linearized methods to this non-linear problem is proposed.

The age-old philosophical discussion of interstellar travel is the subject of some speculation in Chapter 8. A collection of tables, constants, and useful mathematical relations have been prepared and are presented in the Appendix.

1.1 GENERAL INTRODUCTION

The rate of development of spaceflight techniques is so fast that it has not been possible to present a thorough treatment of the techniques of navigation and guidance for application to operations in space. We have tried, however, to suggest some ideas which are related to the requirements of spaceflight and which will need development in the near future. The point of view which has been taken frequently is that of an individual navigator in the spacecraft. The problems are discussed as though he were faced with their solution; the concepts which are developed in this book may equally well be applied to an automatic computing device which has been programmed to navigate a craft with precision. The development of sensors and new methods for processing information will influence the mechanization of the techniques which will be discussed here. Consequently, we have tried to emphasize principles without specific relation to systems design; attention has been held to the *requirements* of guidance and navigation.

There has also been no attempt to present a rigorous discussion of the celestial, or orbital, mechanics of spaceflight since the depth of the mathematics would tend to obscure the principles in their application to the problem at hand. Sufficient mathematical treatment has been presented however to provide continuity and to permit the reader to evaluate the methods which are discussed in the text.

A vast range of problems will be encountered in the practice of space navigation; this is largely the result of the variety of situations that will be encountered as we explore deeper and deeper into space. In its usual sense, the term *spaceflight* refers to any form of directed travel outside of the Earth's atmosphere. We may consider space, then, to include the entire universe outside of a tiny sphere that is about 200 miles larger in diameter than the Earth. This definition leads us to include near earth orbiting bodies, the trajectories of lunar and interplanetary probes and vehicles, and even the motions of interstellar bodies. These will each be treated in their turn, although the problems of interstellar travel will admittedly be discussed in generalities. This is perhaps appropriate considering the current prospects of such missions.

Navigation, in the usual sense of the word, deals with the observation and measurement of the current position and velocity of a vehicle and the extrapolation of these data to determine future position. To do this, one must employ the dynamical laws that govern the motion of the craft in the environment under consideration. In this book, that environment is space with the many important variations that this implies. The term *guidance*, as we shall apply it here, will refer to a specialized form of navigation that is considered to be automatic in its application of commands to the autopilot or control system of the spacecraft.

In his historic role on the seas and in the air, the navigator performs his functions by observing his position, course, and speed. From these data, he extrapolates his future position using known laws of motion that are applicable to his craft and determines if he will, indeed, arrive at his destination. In the event that the result of his extrapolation is negative, a modified course is computed to place the craft at the destination. This correction is then transmitted to the helmsman, or pilot, as the case may be, and the navigator proceeds to compute such useful operational data as his expected time of arrival, fuel consumption rates, refuelling requirements, and so forth. After notifying the craft commander of such hazards as may be indicated on his charts and as a result of his observations and calculations, the navigator is free to concern himself with more routine tasks until the next periodic navigational check is required.

Traditionally, the communication between the navigator and the helmsman, or pilot, is periodic and seldom involves any active feedback of information. One might account for this as the result of the differing magnitudes of the time constants that govern the steering and navigational control of the craft. The relatively low speed of an ocean ship, or an aircraft, gives rise to long transit times, of the order of hours or even days, while the stability of the craft requires that steering control, as felt by the pilots, have operating periods not to exceed several seconds, or in the case of ocean vessels several minutes. With this disparity of time constants, designers were clearly justified to consider the navigation and steering functions to be *uncoupled* and hence to allow them to be performed with little reference to one another. The introduction of high performance aircraft and later the unmanned aircraft and missiles has increased velocity and modified craft dynamics to bring the navigational time constants into the same spectral regions as those for steering control. This situation gave rise to the requirements for automatic navigation systems in which the man played little or no part on board the craft. Man's role in these craft might be to calculate trajectories or steering programs in advance of flight or perhaps to perform a pilot-navigator's role through two-way transmission of data. These craft and their characteristics of coupled time constants for navigation and control produced the concept of continuous supervision of an automatic navigation, or *guidance*, system. The techniques of guidance engineers and designers can still be seen to be derived from the arts of the navigators who preceded them. Although some of the similarities are so subtle as to be unrecognizable to any but a trained observer, the analogies are, nonetheless, present.

The advent of rockets and ballistic missiles with their guidance cycles confined to a period of a few seconds, or at most a few minutes, in the flight, brought about still another step in the direction of closer coupling. During the brief guidance interval, a lapse of guidance functions would permit accumulation of an error in course that could not be corrected within the limitations of the fuel on-board the vehicle; indeed an erroneous guidance command could be expected to produce catastrophic results. In this environment, the dynamics of the craft have assumed a commanding influence on the selection of a flight path, or trajectory, and the functions of *guidance* and *control* for ballistic rockets are so intimately associated that they can scarcely be distinguished to be different on a technological basis. This strait-jacketing of navigation reached a pinnacle with the need for pre-calculated ICBM trajectories which could, at most, be perturbed only slightly for purposes of navigational control.

Now the coming of the popularly heralded space age presents the possibility for the practitioners of the guidance and navigation arts to emerge from this confined state and to contemplate advanced forms of vehicles in spaceflight in near earth orbits and traveling to more distant lunar and interplanetary destinations. Flight times for these vehicles will be relatively long with respect to man's reaction time and, what is more important, the stability periods will once again be short relative to the navigation periods and course observations may be made as desired with corrections applied at convenient times. Certainly, some maneuvers and rendezvous operations will require, for brief periods, that the craft be placed under the control of a machine that has more favorable response times, but in general, navigation in deep space may be handled on a periodic basis under the control of a human operator if this is desired.

For many space applications, the term *navigation* may be applied. Indeed, *navigation* carries a nautical connotation and some purists have suggested the term *astrogation* which has some etymological basis. However the term *aerogation* has not received wide use for the aerial forms of navigation; consequently this work will follow suit and consider the term *navigation* to apply to space as well as to sea, land, and air applications. We shall employ the words *guidance* and *navigation* somewhat interchangeably with an occasional conscious selection made to emphasize the presence, or lack, of continuous supervision.

In the practice of space guidance, trajectory predictions are made and a new trajectory must be computed to correct the flight path to bring the craft to its destination. A freedom of technique exists regarding whether to deal with a totally new trajectory or whether to apply the theory of perturbations and correct the flight path slowly. In performing his task, the navigator must recognize certain constraints. First, the new trajectory must be one which is permissible within the laws of motion as dictated by the forces acting on the vehicle and the modifications to these motions resulting from the thrusting system within the vehicle. A second constraint is that impulsive changes in position should not be considered as allowable maneuvers; time must not be treated as an adjustable coordinate but as the independent variable. Maneuvers will thus be restricted to changes in velocity which will, in many cases, be treated as though they were impulsive changes. A further constraint arises when, at times, it becomes necessary to recognize certain operational limitations that apply to the vehicle and, because of these, we find it necessary to modify or delay execution of the navigational commands.

Frequently, a navigation computation will be simplified if a special celestial, inertial or local coordinate reference frame is introduced for purposes of the calculation. A guidance command, stated in such a reference, will be meaningless to a control system that has been mechanized to operate in some other reference, for example, a body-fixed system. When a situation like this arises, we shall place the responsibility for translation of the command on the guidance system or the navigator as the case may be. Accordingly, it will not always be possible to avoid some discussion of automatic flight control systems and we will probably not always draw the line between guidance and control in the same place. The reader will be left to make his own evaluation of where these lines must be drawn according to the specific application at hand.

A number of working rules have been presented to define the way in which we shall discuss guidance and navigation. Major interests will be directed toward the means to determine errors that occur in the current trajectory and the means for calculation of corrective commands. To do this requires that the mathematics of celestial and orbit mechanics be employed. This is an exacting science in itself and involves extensive calculations to obtain solutions to the n-body problem. The approach that is used here is that the ultimate solutions of space navigation must not rely on such complex methods of calculation. We feel that a return to the use of iterative methods must be effected. Until propulsion techniques permit such freedom, space navigation will remain in a restricted state. The orbit mechanics that we will discuss in this book are presented with this in mind and it is presumed that the iterative methods will be used wherever possible. It has been felt necessary to include a discussion of orbit mechanics however, in order to permit the assumption of a *standardized reader* who is familiar with at least a minimum of the mathematical theory of orbits.

While the theory and analysis of a guidance method is interesting in itself, the discussion of theory would not be complete without a clearly defined concept for its instrumentation. We have frequently suggested configurations of such instruments, but do so with the full realization that techniques will vary somewhat from discipline to discipline and perhaps a suggested solution could be instrumented more effectively with techniques other than those discussed. The reader will be left to make his own extrapolation in many of the examples that are presented. Guidance and navigation deals with the measurement of and operations for, the control of position vectors and their time derivatives —velocity and acceleration. Naturally, then, the instruments that will be discussed will be those that are concerned with the measurement of, and mathematical operations on, these quantities. In particular we shall examine the application of self-contained systems and, to a lesser degree, we shall consider earth-based systems employing radio and radio-optical sensing methods.

1.2 THE SPACE ENVIRONMENT

Before presenting a discussion of the many techniques which apply to navigation in space it is well to consider the environment of space and to establish some general rules which apply to the motions of spacecraft. In the previous section, a definition of *space* was suggested. This is very broad and includes virtually the entire universe outside of the atmosphere of the Earth. With the exception of the last chapter, which deals with interstellar travel, this book will restrict attention to flight within the Solar System. Our knowledge of the space environment becomes most speculative for regions beyond this limitation. Flights outside of the Solar System seem, at this time, to require motivation and technological advances which we can not now predict.

One might exercise a kind of *partitioning* of the Solar System for purposes of guidance and navigation; in so doing the boundaries which will be established can not be sharp, they must, in fact, be rather diffuse. These boundaries will be useful since they permit separation of space into several regions where the the dynamical laws of motion are reasonably uniform. For example, the flight of a satellite or ballistic missile is strongly influenced by the gravitational field of the Earth and a reasonable estimate of its trajectory may be obtained even though the gravitational fields of the Sun and the Moon are neglected. The gravity of these distant bodies need be considered only if extreme precision of results is required. On the other hand, if we are considering an interplanetary flight, the effects of the gravity field of the Earth will be seen to be important initially as the vehicle departs the vicinity of the Earth. However, as the flight progresses it will be shown that the Earth's field may be neglected. Primary consideration is then shifted to the gravity field of the Sun. Later still, the gravity field of the destination planet will dominate and all others may be neglected. The definition of the boundaries for these transitions will be discussed later.

It seems useful at this time to discuss some of the geography—perhaps "heliography" might be a better term—of the Solar System. Within the scale of the Solar System, the Earth is in relatively intimate communication with its nearest neighbors and the Sun. Figure 1.1 illustrates that if we were to map the Solar System in three dimensions and omit the extreme planets, Mercury and Pluto, the remaining planets would be confined very nearly to the ecliptic plane. The *ecliptic plane* may be defined as the plane containing the Earth's orbit.

With the exception, again, of Pluto and Mercury, the planetary orbits are all very nearly circular. The greatest eccentricity among the remaining planets is 0.093—the orbit of Mars—which indicates that the maximum and minimum distances of the planet from the Sun differ from one another by about 25 per cent of the mean distance. To a fair degree of approximation, navigation within the Solar System may be considered as being confined to the ecliptic plane and the orbits of the planets may be considered to be circular. This approximation will, of course, be valid only if we confine our interests to the major planets and exclude the extreme planets, Mercury and Pluto. The restriction suggested is not really limiting, the environments of these extreme planets are rather forbidding and the desire to visit them may be limited. The temperature on Mercury is estimated at 600°F and its atmosphere is negligible; the temperature on the side away from the Sun approaches absolute zero. The estimated temperature on Pluto is in the neighborhood of 400°F below zero which suggests that whatever atmosphere it has is frozen.

While many useful navigational relations may be developed and used, employing the plane model of the Solar System, it is frequently necessary to consider

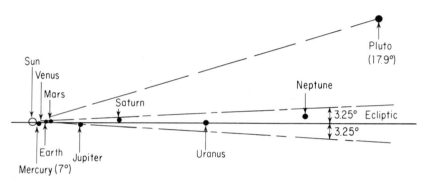

Fig. 1.1. Right: Navigation within our solar system can be considered as confined to the ecliptic plane of the earth's rotation about the Sun—only Mercury and Pluto are substantially outside this plane.

the inclination of the orbits. For example, in calculating the optimal transfer orbit between two planets whose orbits are inclined to one another in a flight where the arrival or the departure is substantially separated from the node of the orbit plane a large inclination angle may be required for the transfer orbit. This is illustrated in the sketch of Figure 1.2. This distribution of gravity fields through the Solar System is of interest to space navigation. This distribution is indicated in Figure 1.3: the acceleration due to solar gravity has been plotted as a function of the distance from the Sun. Solar distance is given in terms of astronomical units (one astronomical unit is equal to approximately 93,000,000 miles, the mean radius of the orbit of the Earth). Along the curve of solar gravity, spikes appear indicating local regions of high gravitational acceleration. They show the acceleration due to the gravity of the various planets. Of course, it is highly improbable that, at any time, all of the planets will be aligned in a single plane as might be inferred from Figure 1.3. Nevertheless, the graph serves to indicate the great distances which must be traversed between

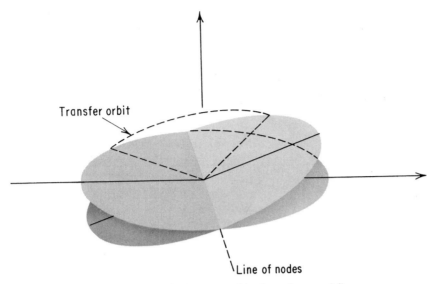

Fig. 1.2. Transfer between orbit planes (non-nodal).

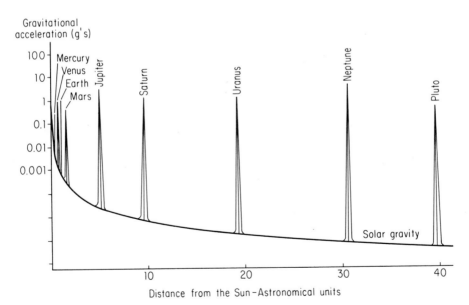

Fig. 1.3. Gravity fields in the solar system.

planets; in these intervals the only gravity force of significant magnitude is that which is due to the Sun. In the vicinity of the individual planets, however, consideration must be given to the influence which the separate gravity fields have on the motion of the spacecraft.

The data given in Figure 1.3 is sometimes presented in terms of an energy level diagram in which the potential energy of each point in the composite gravity field is shown. This form of presentation is given in Figure 1.4.

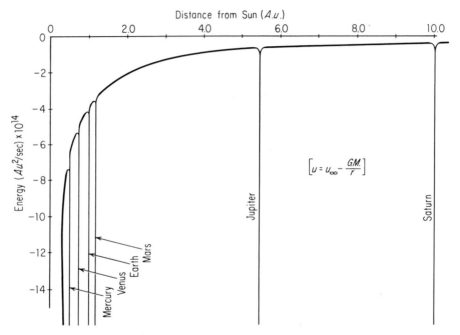

Fig. 1.4. Potential energy field of the solar system. (Referenced to energy level at infinity).

A spacecraft in flight in a gravity field will experience two balancing forces. The first is that due to gravity and acts "downwards" toward the center of the gravity field. The second force is the result of the centrifugal acceleration arising from the tangential velocity component of the motion. These forces are in balance as

$$f_{\text{resultant}} = m\ddot{a}_{\text{radial}} = mg - \frac{mv^2}{r}$$

The radial acceleration will vanish when the spacecraft is in a stable circular orbit; that is when $v = v_{\text{circular}}$

$$g = \frac{v^2_{\text{circ}}}{r}$$

$$v_{\text{circ}} = \sqrt{\frac{g}{r}}$$

For every point in a gravity field, the potential energy of a massive body relative to the point at the center of the force field will be given by

$$E_{\text{pot}} = mgr$$

If a spacecraft at a point under consideration were given a velocity impulse such that its kinetic energy would be equivalent to this potential energy, the craft would escape from the gravity field in which it resides. This escape velocity will then be found from the equation

$$\tfrac{1}{2}mv^2_{\text{escape}} = mgr$$

$$v_{\text{escape}} = \sqrt{2gr}$$

The velocity required to escape from the various planets and that required to orbit and to escape from the Sun's gravity field is shown as a function of the distance from the planet to the Sun in Table 1.1.

Table 1.1. Surface Gravity Field and Escape Velocity for Various Solar System Bodies

Planet	Distance from Sun (A.U.)	Diameter of Planet (st. mi.)	Surface gravity (ft/sec^2)	Escape velocity (ft/sec)
Sun	—	864,100	900.0	2,020,000
Mercury	0.387	3,194	10.45	13,109
Venus	0.723	7,842	28.30	33,697
Earth	1.000	7,926	32.16	36,677
Moon	—	2,159	5.19	7,693
Mars	1.524	4,263	12.95	16,825
Jupiter	5.202	82,229	85.27	197,700
Saturn	9.539	74,937	37.62	119,200
Uranus	19.182	33,181	33.85	72,490
Neptune	30.058	30,882	47.61	82,380

Pluto is not included since data are not available regarding the radius of Pluto.

The flight regimes of space travel are illustrated in Figure 1.5. The presentation shown in this figure was suggested by the work of Sanger (Reference 1.1). Earth orbital and earth escape velocities are shown as functions of altitude. The approximate boundaries for the limit of aerodynamic flight and the heat boundary for aircraft structures are shown. The altitude–velocity regime of ballistic rockets is shown; it is bounded by the curve of orbital velocity and the aerodynamic limit. An arbitrarily chosen lower limit for velocity has been chosen to close the region. The flight regime of space travel is enclosed within the dark boundaries. It is defined by a velocity which is greater than orbital

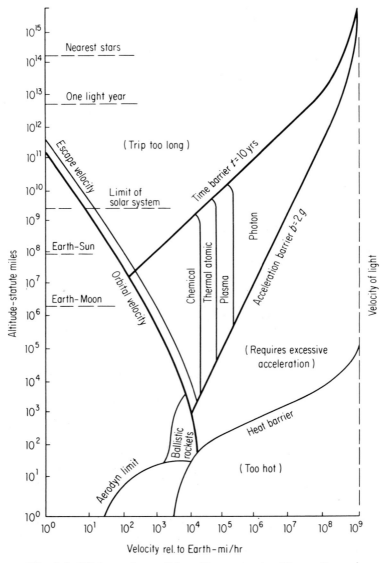

Fig. 1.5. Flight regimes of Aero/Astro–nautics (Eugen Sanger).

with altitudes falling below a limit which is defined by a *time barrier*. This time barrier represents the altitude and velocity for a 10 year round trip from the Earth. An *accleration barrier* is drawn to close the region; this boundary has been chosen as the altitude–velocity line representing the locus of points corresponding to a continuous acceleration of $2g$'s (64.4 ft/sec²). The space flight regime has been subdivided into regions which appear to be most favorable for the application of various propulsion systems on the basis of the estimated velocity ranges which are most applicable to their individual characteristics.

1.3 THE NATURE OF GRAVITATION

In the practice of space navigation it is frequently necessary to predict the future positions of one or more bodies moving in a space trajectory. These predictions will be shown to depend upon applications of celestial mechanics and celestial mechanics will, in turn, be shown to be a study of the relative motions of bodies under the influence of gravitational forces. These forces produce accelerations of the bodies on which they act. Gravitation is a mutual attraction occurring between masses which acts on all such masses with a force varying directly as the product of the masses inversely as the square of their distances apart. This law was first clearly formulated by Sir Isaac Newton but the fact of the action indicated was more or less clearly recognized by others before him.

The law of gravitation states that two masses M_1 and M_2, located at distance d from one another, will experience an attractive force

$$F = \frac{GM_1M_2}{d^2}$$

where

G is a constant for all kinds of matter—the universal gravitation constant.

The acceleration of M_2 towards M_1, or the force acting on it by M_1 per unit mass will be

$$f = \frac{F}{M_2} = \frac{GM_1}{d^2}$$

The exact determination of the value of the gravitational constant G has been the subject of many experiments. This constant which may be considered to present the attraction between two unit masses separated by a unit distance has a currently accepted value of

$G = 6.670 \times 10^{-8} =$ attraction, in dynes, between two one-gram masses one centimeter apart.

Perhaps more useful information is conveyed by the constant of the gravitational field for the various celestial bodies. The gravitational field constant k is defined in terms of the force per unit mass (specific force) acting on a test mass, it is

$$f = \frac{k}{d^2}$$

and

$$k = GM_1$$

The value of k for several bodies of the Solar System is shown in Table 1.2.

Table 1.2. Gravitational Parameters for Various Bodies
of the Solar System

Body	M_{Body}/M_{Earth}	Gravity constant k (ft³/sec²)	Gravity acel. at 45° Lat. (ft/sec²)
Sun	3.3253×10^5	4.6898×10^{21}	—
Mercury	0.0543	7.64539×10^{14}	11.36
Venus	0.8136	1.14499×10^{16}	27.67
Earth	1.000	1.407528×10^{16}	32.25
Moon	—	1.7270×10^{14}	5.32
Mars	0.1077	1.51520×10^{15}	13.19
Jupiter	318.35	4.46723×10^{18}	90.79
Saturn	95.30	1.33776×10^{17}	41.81
Uranus	14.58	2.04599×10^{17}	31.44
Neptune	17.76	2.42259×10^{17}	36.82
Pluto	0.8312	1.1697×10^{16}	12.93

The path of a body in motion under the influence of gravity forces is called its *orbit*. A body in such motion is said to be in *free fall*. In a central force field, i.e., a field in which only a single massive body contributes to the gravity, all orbits will be shown to be conic sections—ellipses, parabolas, or hyperbolas. Special cases will occur as radial motion and as circular orbits.

Kepler suggested that the planets move in orbits about the Sun under the influence of some kind of force exerted by the Sun but the laws of motion were not developed nor were Kepler's ideas of force clear enough to be stated precisely. Kepler did, however, state three laws of motion, these are

1. The orbits of the planets are ellipses with the Sun at one of their foci
2. The radius vector of each planet sweeps over equal areas in equal times
3. The ratio of the squares of the periods of two bodies is equal to the ratio of the cubes of the semi-major axes of their orbits.

The three Kepler laws may be recognized as special cases of Newton's three fundamental laws of mechanics. Newton's laws are:

The Law of Inertia: A body not subject to a force continues in a state of rest or of straight-line uniform motion.

The Definition of Force: A body which is subject to a force undergoes an acceleration. The force equals the product of body mass multiplied by the acceleration.

The Principle of Action and Reaction: For each force exerted by a mass A on a mass B there exists a corresponding equal and oppositely directed force exerted by B on A.

The application of the laws of Kepler and Newton to the prediction of the motions of celestial bodies and of spacecraft will be the subject of Chapter 2. These will also be discussed in more or less detail throughout the text.

1.4 THE SPACE NAVIGATION PROBLEM

Navigation and guidance in space will be characterized as dealing with the supervision of the trajectory of a vehicle in an interorbital transfer. Discussions of interorbital exchange problems will be presented in considerable detail in subsequent chapters with reference to several aspects of space flight. For purposes of the discussion here, we will introduce some important simplifications which may not always be employed. Interplanetary transfer is frequently discussed as a problem whose purpose is to determine the minimum energy orbit which will carry a spacecraft between two circular orbits which lie in a common plane. Reference to Figure 1.1 indicates that this is perhaps a reasonable approximation since the orbits of most of the planets are inclined only slightly to the ecliptic plane.

The nature of interplanetary paths, or orbits, in plane transfer has been the subject of literature in astronautics for many years (cf. Reference 1.2). The road to another member of the Solar System is a departure from the axiom of geometry stating that "the shortest distance between two points is a straight

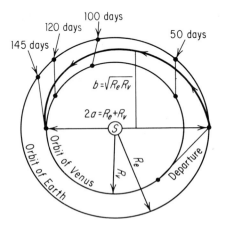

Fig. 1.6. Simplified Hohmann transfer to Venus.

line". Rather than the path of shortest distance, interplanetary flights will be concerned with the paths requiring the least energy. As an example, suppose we were to plan a trip to Venus, the orbit might be as shown in Figure 1.6. Venus is in an orbit which is nearly circular and about 25 million miles closer to the Sun than is the Earth, this orbit is inclined to the ecliptic by an angle of 3.24°. Hohmann (Reference 1.2) specified the minimum energy path between two planets which are moving in circular orbits which are confined to the ecliptic plane. It is an ellipse, tangent to the two circular orbits, having a major axis containing:

1. The Earth at the time of departure
2. The Sun
3. Venus at time of arrival.

The geometric properties of the transfer ellipse will be

$$\text{Major axis} = a = R_E + R_V$$
$$\text{Minor axis} = b = 2\sqrt{R_E R_V}$$

where

$R_E =$ distance from the Sun to the center of the Earth at the time of departure (or arrival).

$R_V =$ distance from the Sun to Venus at the time of arrival (or departure).

The time in transit depends upon the Sun's gravity field and is determined from a relation which will be developed in Chapter 2. The transit time is

$$T = \pi\sqrt{\frac{a^3}{k}}$$

where k is a constant of the gravitational field of the Sun. The value of the solar gravity constant is approximately $k = 4.69 \times 10^{21}$ ft³/sec².

If a Hohmann orbit were to be followed, the spacecraft would be injected into a transfer orbit to Venus by deceleration to give it a velocity which is about 0.8 miles per second less than the orbital velocity of the Earth ($v_E = 18.5$ miles per sec). This maneuver requires a velocity impulse in the retrograde direction (counter to the direction of the Earth's orbital velocity) giving the vehicle escape energy and a residual velocity, after escape, of 0.8 miles per sec. This residual velocity is called *hyberbolic excess velocity*, v_∞. The total impulse required, if it were all applied at sea level, may be estimated on an energy basis, neglecting the effects of air drag, as

$$\Delta v = \sqrt{v^2_{\text{esc}} + v^2_\infty} \approx \sqrt{49.0 + 0.64} = 7.04 \text{ mi/sec}$$

This impulse, applied at sea level, will provide the craft with the minimum perturbation to the orbit of the Earth which will place it on a elliptical trajectory intersecting the orbit of Venus. If the launching time of the space ship has been scheduled so that the craft arrives at the orbit of Venus at the time when Venus is at the proper position in its orbit, the ship will be captured by the gravity field of Venus and will descend to the surface under the influence of that gravitational field.

The complete one-way passage, defined in this manner, takes 145 days. A small maneuver may be required at arrival in order to assure capture and to provide a safe landing, these will be discussed in later chapters but will not concern us here. The return voyage will be made in a similar manner but it cannot be initiated until about 110 days have passed. The delay is necessary in order that the relative positions between the planets will be such that the Earth and the spacecraft will be in position for capture of the craft by the Earth's gravity field when the craft returns to the orbit of the Earth. The complete round trip from Earth to Venus in this manner will require a total of 400 days (1 year and about 1 month).

The Hohmann orbit described above will provide approximations which are useful for many purposes, however they are developed on the basis of planets which travel in circular orbits confined to the ecliptic plane. The small inclinations of the planetary orbits may actually require major departures from the Hohmann orbits. Except for flights which originate and terminate at the nodal points, there can be no co-tangential transfer between non-coplanar orbits. Depending upon the longitude of the departure point relative to the line of nodes, the inclination of the transfer orbit may depart considerably from the plane of the ecliptic. The inclination of the transfer orbit may in some cases exceed the relative inclination of the two orbits involved, this is illustrated in Figure 1.2. Changes in orbit inclination require relatively large velocity increments, consequently these have a major effect on orbit optimization. In order to minimize the total, or characteristic, velocity of the inter-orbital transfer the optimum orbit will frequently not be co-tangential nor will they be half-period orbits as described by Hohmann. Further discussions of this will be presented in Chapter 6.

1.5 CLASSIFICATION OF SPACE NAVIGATION PROBLEMS

The general subject of space navigation involves a very broad range of problems. Each of these is characterized by the environment in which it arises; we have chosen to discuss several of these problems in the context of those individual environments. The various problems which will be discussed are listed below.

1. *Ballistic missiles:* These are particles flying in orbits outside of the atmosphere of the Earth but restrained to the Earth by its gravity field. An important element of their military significance is derived from their

low maneuverability characteristics. Ballistic missiles are set into motion towards their targets through the use of rocket boosters. Thereafter they proceed on their orbits under the sole influence of the Earth's gravitational field. Guidance for these missiles is confined to the precise control of their booster rockets during the brief thrust program. This is done in such a way as to set the missile in motion with an orbit terminating at the desired point on the surface of the Earth. Guidance will normally make allowances for the systematic effects due to the atmosphere and to the displacement of the target due to rotation of the Earth.

2. *Earth satellites:* These vehicles are in free fall orbital flight about the Earth but the orbits have sufficient altitude over their entire cycle so that the vehicle remains free of the appreciable atmospheric drag—in this sense the orbits may be considered to be stable. These orbits are described, mathematically, by a set of parameters. Each of these parameters may be measured by observations made on the satellite in motion. The orbit is determined by the flight conditions (position and velocity) at the time of injection into orbit and, if these are known, the orbit may be calculated. Guidance for these vehicles is concerned with the measurement of position and velocity at the time of orbit injection. Some special problems of maneuvering satellites require a post-injection guidance but this may be considered as a special case associated with injection into a new orbit. These maneuvers, and their determination, will be treated along with the other problems of satellite navigation.

3. *Lunar flight:* A flight to the Moon involves departure from the gravitational field of the Earth and subsequent capture by the Moon's gravity field. Such a flight proceeds along a highly eccentric ellipse having the Earth at one focus; as the vehicle approaches the Moon, lunar gravity forces increase in magnitude until they finally surpass the waning forces due to the Earth's gravitation. During the greatest part of a lunar trajectory, it is necessary to treat the motion as a three-body problem and simple dynamical approximations are not available. Guidance for lunar flights is therefore concerned with measurement of position and velocity to establish the orbit injection conditions for a suitable lunar transfer orbit and the subsequent estimation of the orbit. Prediction of future positions and velocities are required to provide the means for in-flight corrections and landing guidance.

4. *Interplanetary flight:* Interplanetary flights differ from lunar flights in two important ways. First, the vehicle may be considered to actually *escape* from the influence of the Earth. Second, the entire flight may be analyzed as a series of segments, each of which is itself a two-body flight. The first segment is that of injection into, and flight in, an Earth-centered hyperbolic escape orbit. The second segment is orbital flight in the gravity field of the Sun. The third segment is hyperbolic (or perhaps parabolic)

approach to the destination planet. While it is theoretically possible to inject a vehicle into an Earth escape orbit carrying the vehicle into the near vicinity of the destination, there are practical limitations to this. Thus interplanetary guidance will involve an orbit injection control system but it will also include techniques for midcourse determination of the trajectory and the computation of corrections. Landing guidance will also be required as an aid to conversion of the transfer ellipse into a suitable approach hyperbola.

5. *Interstellar flight:* A vehicle in interstellar flight may be considered to have escaped completely from the Solar System. Thus it may be treated as though it were entirely free from all external forces, gravitational and otherwise, except when it approaches the vicinity of a star or star system.

1.6 CLASSIFICATION OF NAVIGATION AND GUIDANCE SYSTEMS

The purpose of a navigation system has been defined to be the measurement of the trajectory of a vehicle in space and the subsequent specification of the changes to that trajectory which will bring the vehicle into juxtaposition with a predetermined target or objective point. The trajectories, of course, are functions of the position and velocity vectors of the craft. These vectors are usually observed with relation to some convenient reference frame; the guidance systems for consideration must then be capable of measuring both the position and the velocity of the craft with respect to the selected reference frame. Computations may then be performed on the results of these measurements for the purpose of estimating the relative motions of vehicle and target.

The laws of relative motion in space will generally take their most simple form when the reference frame is a non-rotating (inertial) one moving with one of the bodies which is under consideration. Much of the hardware which will be discussed will be concerned with the establishment of such an inertial reference frame. These systems are inevitably known as *inertial systems* because of their dependance on inertial instruments which are employed to maintain this reference. The true inertial system is one in which this reference is maintained by a set of gyroscopic instruments, variations exist where celestial and Earth trackers, sensors, or scanners are employed to supervise the inertial components. While they are not true inertial systems, these latter nonetheless have many properties in common with inertial systems and hence are frequently classed as inertial.

Many spaceflight applications will have particular interest in navigation systems which involve a complex of ground observing stations. These stations are employed to measure the flight coordinates of the spacecraft as a function of time. The tracking data which is derived from these stations are then processed through real-time computing networks to obtain parameters of the orbital motion. Systems of this kind are known as *ground based systems*. In their conventional form, observations are made of distance, azimuth and elevation angles, velocities, and times; these measurements may be made through application of radar and optical techniques of instrumentation. The ground based systems have been devised to operate in a variety of configurations in which various measurements are made. Some of the most interesting of these configurations will be described and analyzed in Chapter 3.

In some situations it will be convenient to employ systems which do not require external cooperation of active system elements of any kind; these will be known as *self-contained systems*. Of course, an inertial system which operates entirely with reference to its own gyroscopes and accelerometers will fall into this class of system. In addition radio, radar and optical systems which do not require a set of cooperating elements to be placed at convenient points will be considered to be self-contained. As an example, a system using a celestial body tracker (or star tracker) or one employing "skin" tracking of a planet will be considered to be self-contained.

Once the reference system has been established in which the measurements of position and velocity will be made, it is necessary to determine the position of the craft and the destination relative to this reference frame. Navigation requires extrapolation of this motion to describe the future relative motion in the vicinity of the target. In the event that the motions of one body are known, or may be computed, the problem will be reduced to one of measuring position and velocity of the other relative to the chosen reference frame. Frequently this is accomplished through the use of radar or optical devices. For example, the craft may carry a light, a radar transponder beacon, or some other co-operating component; such a system is considered to be an *active system* since it depends upon the *active* cooperation of the beacon.

Both the self-contained and the active systems will be considered for many space applications. A landing on Earth, for example, may be accomplished by the use of an active guidance system in which a ground based radar system tracks the approaching vehicle and its transponder beacon. Such a system cannot be expected to be satisfactory as a landing aid for use in an exploration of other planets. While active systems may be the most important systems in the near future, it is apparent that distant space missions and manned missions of many kinds will require the application of both active ground based systems and self-contained systems.

1.7 GENERAL PROPERTIES OF ROCKET PROPULSION

In most cases which will be considered, the propulsion to be used for driving spacecraft and for the application of corrective maneuvers will be rockets. Some very general principles of propulsion using rockets will be discussed below.

The thrusting force of a rocket engine will be proportional to the rate of burning of the rocket propellant, W

$$T = I_{sp}\dot{W}$$

where the proportionality factor is the specific impulse, I_{sp}. The specific impulse is measured in pounds of force per pound (weight) of propellant burned per second; dimensionally this may be represented as unit of seconds. The specific impulse is a function of the propellant-oxidizer combination employed, their mixture ratio, the chamber pressure, the nozzle expansion ratio, and so on. Some typical values of vacuum I_{sp} for common fuel-oxidizer combinations are shown in Table 1.3.

The acceleration which is experienced by a vehicle employing thrusting devices is, of course, given by

$$a = \frac{T}{M} = \frac{I_{sp}g\dot{W}}{W}$$

The velocity attained under the acceleration may be computed by direct integration of the non-gravitational acceleration as sensed by an accelerometer.

$$\Delta V = \int_0^t \frac{I_{sp}g\dot{W}}{(W_0 - \dot{W}t)}\,d\tau$$

For many cases which are of interest, gravity and I_{sp} may be considered to be constant during the burning interval, t_b, and the burning rate, W, is a constant function of the fuel pumping rate. Under these assumptions, the integral of the acceleration yields the following estimate of the fuel required to effect a given velocity increment.

Table 1.3. THEORETICAL VACUUM SPECIFIC IMPULSE (CHAMBER PRESSURE AT 1000 PSI)

Oxidizer	Fuel	$\dfrac{Wt(oxid)}{Wt(fuel)}$	Specific impulse $I_{sp}(sec)$
Oxygen	Ammonia	1.30	285
Oxygen	R.P.–1	2.24	286
Oxygen	UDMH	1.39	295
Oxygen	Hydrogen	3.40	388
Chlorine Trifluoride	50 per cent UDMH 50 per cent Hydrazine	2.16	279
Red Fuming Nitric Acid	UDMH	2.46	267
Red Fuming NA	Hydrazine	1.23	277
Nit. Tetroxide	Hydrazine	1.08	283
Nit. Tetroxide	R.P.–1	3.46	263
Fluorine	Hydrazine	1.83	334
Fluorine	Hydrogen	4.54	398

$$W_b = W_0 e^{-(\Delta V/g I \mathrm{sp})}$$

where

W_b = the fuel burned during the maneuver.

As an example, if a vehicle traveling in an interplanetary orbit were to compute that a correction is required indicating a change in velocity of 0.035 miles per second (0.5 per cent of the velocity of the Earth in its orbit about the Sun), the fuel consumed in the maneuver would be about 2.4 per cent of the initial weight of the vehicle. This has been calculated on the basis of a fuel which has a specific impulse of 240 seconds. To emphasize the importance of such a maneuver, should such a correction be required at repeated intervals, the amount of fuel used may be estimated from the formula

$$W_b = W_0 f \sum_{i=1}^{n} (1 - f_i)^{n-1}$$

where

f = the fractional weight of the vehicle consumed in fuel at each maneuver
n = the number of intervals considered.

REFERENCES

1.1. Sanger, Eugen; *Sources of Radiation for Photonic Jet Propulsion.* Proceedings of the IXth Congress, International Astronautical Federation, Amsterdam, 1958.

1.2. Hohmann, W.; *Die Erreichbarkeit der Himmelskorper*, R. Oldenburg, Munich, 1925.

1.3. Berman, A. I.; *Physical Principles of Astronautics*, John Wiley, Inc., New York, 1961.

2

ORBIT CHARACTERISTICS

Navigation of spacecraft requires a capability to observe and calculate the orbit in which the craft is moving. It is subsequently required that the orbital flight be extrapolated to prediction of positions in the vicinity of a terminal, or rendezvous, point. The orbit changes which are required to adjust this rendezvous must be accomplished to complete the navigation task. This chapter will discuss spaceflight orbits and their calculation; some approximations which are useful in the determination of transfer maneuvers will also be discussed. The material presented here is not a rigorous treatment of the subject of orbit mechanics. The reader who wishes more detailed treatment is referred to the standard texts on orbit and celestial mechanics. It is felt that the requirements of navigation will ultimately be met by a "closed loop" technique in which a series of observations and orbit correction maneuvers are made so that the actual trajectory converges on the desired trajectory.

Following a brief general discussion of methods for orbit calculation we will discuss the mathematics of the motions of a spacecraft in free fall. This is followed by a treatment of the time-position relations which are developed from integration of the time equation. Orbit transfer maneuvers are presented in a general summary manner and a short discussion of perturbation techniques with non-gravitational forces concludes the chapter.

An orbit will be fully specified when all of the forces which will act on the body under consideration during its orbiting flight are known and can be computed for every point along the way. The calculation of space trajectories, or orbits, is a highly specialized art of which a complete discussion is beyond the scope of this book. Many situations will permit the use of the first-order techniques which are described in this chapter directly while others, for which these techniques are approximations, will require that first-order methods be applied with caution. In these events, it will almost always be possible to apply numerical approximations using the standard methods of astronomy. The approximate trajectories and sensitivity coefficients which reflect the variation of the trajectory with several parameters will be employed then in place of the analytical representations indicated in the following paragraphs.

2.1 THE CALCULATION OF ORBITS

It is a relatively straight-forward problem of numerical integration to calculate a space trajectory if the forces acting on the spacecraft are fully known. In very general terms, the trajectory equations will have the mathematical form

$$\mathbf{R} = \mathbf{R}(q_i, \dot{q}_i, \ddot{q}_i; t) \qquad i = 1, 2, 3 \qquad (2\text{-}1)$$

where the q_i represent the generalized coordinates which specify the craft position in some convenient three dimensional reference frame. From time to time, specialized situations will arise which permit the use of convenient forms of the trajectory equations which are, perhaps, more familiar. These equations may be integrated in closed form and have been studied in detail as problems of classical mathematics and orbit mechanics.

The motions of a spacecraft are in direct response to the forces which act on it. The forces which act on such a craft in motion can be classified into the following four groups:

1. *Driving forces*: These are usually propulsion forces and are applied in a systematic way. The term *thrust* is normally applied to this class.
2. *Forces which are a function of position*: In this class are forces of gravitational, electrostatic, and magnetic origin. Forces arising from the pressure of incident radiation should also be included.
3. *Forces which are a function of velocity*: This class is generally known as *drag forces*. It includes forces which are of an aerodynamic .nature, also electromagnetic forces and momentum exchanges arising from collisions in space.
4. *Forces which are a function of acceleration*: The most important forces in this class are the familiar inertial reactions.

In space trajectory work, forces arising from gravitational fields and inertia reactions are certainly the most significant of the last three of these. Nevertheless, recent spaceflight experiments have demonstrated that drag forces as well as gravitational perturbations due to non-central force fields are of considerable importance. (Reference 2.5.) While the acceleration arising from these sources may be quite small, they will act over extremely long periods of time and, as a result, their effects may be far from negligible.

A precision trajectory calculation involves the consideration of many complex forces but the use of simplified analytical representations of these forces is justified when considering navigation and to demonstrate the principles involved in space guidance. When required, the analytical approximations may be replaced by numerical functions which provide sufficient accuracy. Certain situations will arise where the perturbative forces are small enough to justify their being neglected over large regions of space. A notable example of this is the mid-course flight of an interplanetary vehicle when it is at great distance from any planet or satellite. Furthermore, in a situation where periodic navigational checks are planned, perturbative forces may be neglected provided their effects are small during the navigation time interval.

Consider, for example, a spacecraft departing the Earth. This craft will experience an acceleration due to the Earth's gravity; the magnitude of this acceleration may be computed from

$$g = g_0\left(\frac{R_0}{R}\right)^2 \qquad (2\text{-}2)$$

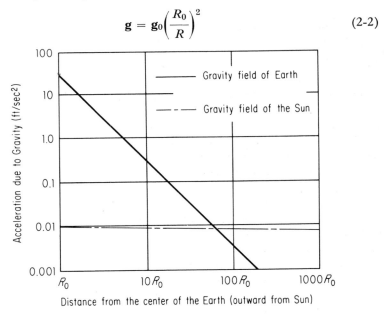

Fig. 2.1. Acceleration due to the gravity of the Earth and Sun.

At a distance of 100 times the planet radius from the earth (approximately 400,000 miles) this represents an acceleration of $10^{-4}g$ or about $1/6$ of that due to the gravity field of the Sun at the orbit of the Earth, see Figure 2.1. If this acceleration were to be neglected for an hour (3600 seconds) the resultant error in computation of position would be about 4 miles. If this same acceleration were neglected for about 100 hours, however, the resultant error would be approximately 40,000 miles. The decision as to "smallness" in this regard will be determined not by the trajectory errors which result from the perturbations, but by the magnitude of the energy required for a corrective maneuver. In many instances, it should be noted, the corrective maneuvers will require velocity increments which are less than those given to the vehicle as it traversed the perturbing force field. This is due to the fact that corrections will usually be made on the basis of placing the vehicle on a new course which will carry it from where it is now to its intended destination. Corrections will not normally be made to return the spacecraft to its original course.

In their most common form, the differential equations for a trajectory may be represented by a summation of the forces acting on a vehicle; symbolically, this may be represented by

$$F = \sum K + \sum P \qquad (2-3)$$

where

K represents the Keplerian forces (gravity)

P represents the perturbation forces.

In general, the perturbation forces are too complicated to be expressed concisely. Also, the motions of a craft under the influence of the gravity force fields of several centers of attraction is too complicated for solution in closed form. One of the most important problems of modern astronomy and astrophysics is the determination of the detailed form of the terms on the right hand side of Equation (2-3) and the development of techniques for the numerical integration of the resulting expression. The complexity of this problem gives rise to the oft-made statement that trajectory calculation is an art rather than an exact science.

A very important situation which arises commonly in the study of space travel is that in which a vehicle of very small mass is moving in relation to another body having very large mass; these two bodies interact mutually through their gravitational fields. A summation of the forces which act on such a vehicle provides an equation which, when integrated with appropriate initial conditions, will fully describe the motion of the vehicle. Subsequent discussions of this chapter will deal with the solutions of Equation (2-3) under special conditions which are of particular importance.

2.2 MOTION UNDER FREE FALL

The most common mathematical model of a spacecraft in motion is that of free fall. To analyze this motion, it is necessary to consider a particle moving under the influence of a single gravitational force field in which the gravity due to a single source, such as the Sun, is the only appreciable force acting. This two-body problem may be considered to be one of a single body which moves in a central force field; the second body is taken to be the Sun in our example. The force field moves with it, consequently the motion of this body need not be given special consideration. The position of a spacecraft in such a field may be described by a position vector $\mathbf{R}$ which is drawn from the center of the attractive force field outward to the craft. The position vector is related to the accelerations acting on the vehicle by the relation

$$\mathbf{R} = \mathbf{b} + \mathbf{g} \tag{2-4}$$

where

  $\mathbf{b}$ represents the non-gravitational acceleration (for our example, $\mathbf{b} = 0$)
  $\mathbf{g}$ represents the gravitational accelerations acting on the vehicle.

When the equation of motion is written in terms of acceleration as in Equation (2-4) rather than in the more familiar form which involves forces, constant vehicle mass is implied. Under ordinary conditions, a spacecraft in free fall will indeed have constant mass. No requirement will exist for ejecting or jettisoning of expendables, nor will there be a need for the use of rocket propellants in substantial quantities during free-fall. Any momentum changes will be the direct result of interactions of the gravity field and the mass of the spacecraft.

The choice of acceleration as a variable permits some convenient simplifications of the equations which follow since mass does not appear explicitly. Some confusion might arise when the energy and momentum expressions appear since they will not contain mass terms. This is because, in reality, the parameters developed in this way will represent *specific momentum* and *specific energy*. These may be interpreted as the momentum and energy, respectively, of a particle with unit mass in the orbit. This concept will prove to be a convenience for guidance and navigation purposes since the calculation of these important trajectory parameters will be independent of the configuration of the spacecraft.

The gravity acceleration in the central force field of the Sun, or one of the planets, may be represented mathematically as a radial term which satisfies the inverse square law as given in Equation (2-2)

$$\mathbf{g} = -g_0 \mathbf{R} \frac{R_0^2}{R^3} \tag{2-5}$$

substituting into the equation of motion, Equation (2-4),

$$\mathbf{R} + \omega^2 \mathbf{R} = \mathbf{b} \tag{2-6}$$

where

$$\omega^2 = g_0 \frac{R_0^2}{R^3}$$

$$\mathbf{b} = 0$$

It is possible to suggest a convenient interpretation for the coefficient ω as defined in Equation (2-6), it may be considered to represent the orbit angular velocity of a particle in a circular orbit at a distance R from the center of a force field in which the acceleration due to the gravity is g_0 at a distance of R_0. This concept will be made clear in a later section. In the hypothetical case of a satellite in a circular orbit at the surface of the Earth

$$\omega = \sqrt{\frac{g_0}{R_0}} = 1.24 \times 10^{-3} \text{ sec}^{-1}$$

A convenient relation may also be noted regarding the orbit period of the satellite in a circular orbit of radius R,

$$T = \frac{2\pi}{\omega} = 2\pi \sqrt{\frac{R^3}{g_0 R_0^2}}$$

$$T_0 = 2\pi \sqrt{\frac{R_0}{g_0}} = 5064 \text{ sec} = 84.4 \text{ min}$$

While these relations involving ω are useful for the purpose of making physical interpretations of the meaning of the parameters, it must be recalled that the significant quantity is the gravitational acceleration as expressed by the left hand side of Equation (2-5).

The vector differential equation form of Equation (2-6) can be rewritten as a set of scalar differential equations which relate the vector components of the acceleration to the motion of the craft. In the case of the problem under consideration, two dimensions only need to be studied. The choice of a coordinate reference frame may be made so that the motion will occur in the orbit plane. Consider, now, the motions of a spacecraft moving in a plane orbit described in polar coordinates having the origin at the center of the force field. In order to solve the vector Equation (2-6) it must be resolved into its scalar component equations. This resolution yields three second-order differential equations whose solution contains six arbitrary constants. It will be shown that these parameters (called *natural parameters*) may be stated in terms of the three components of the orbit angular momentum vector, the energy of the particle in orbit, the orientation of the line of apsides, and the time of passage of the periapsis. In the two dimensional example, which will be discussed presently, only four constants of integration will arise; this is because the angular momentum vector is fully described by a single scalar number giving its magnitude.

When the two-dimensional resolution of the vector Equation (2-6) has been effected, the scalar differential equations are written as

$$\ddot{r} - \dot{\theta}^2 r = g \tag{2-7}$$

$$\frac{d}{dt}(r^2\dot{\theta}) = 0 \tag{2-8}$$

Where the coordinates r and θ are defined as shown in Figure 2.2.

The second Equation, (2-8), expresses the principle of conservation of angular momentum which is applicable to orbits where gravitational accelerations are the only ones applied. The first integral of Equation (2-8) may be written at once, it is

$$r^2\dot{\theta} = h \qquad\qquad (2\text{-}9)$$

where

> h represents the angular momentum of a particle with unit mass (specific angular momentum).

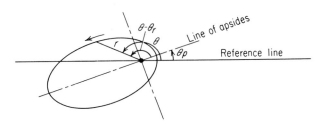

Fig. 2.2. Two-dimensional orbit.

The gravitational acceleration is inversely proportional to the square of the radial coordinate and may be written

$$g = -\frac{k}{r^2} \qquad\qquad (2\text{-}10)$$

where

> $k = GM$ is a constant of the gravity field
> $G =$ the universal gravity constant, approximately given by
> $\qquad 6.670 \times 10^{-8}$ dyne cm^2/gm^2
> $M =$ the mass of the attracting body.

After substitution of the relations in Equations (2-9) and (2-10), Equation (2-7) takes the form

$$\ddot{r} - \frac{h^2}{r^3} = -\frac{k}{r^2} \qquad\qquad (2\text{-}11)$$

Employing a relationship which is commonly used for differential equations of this kind, Equation (2-11) may be converted to a first order differential equation in r; the relation is

$$\ddot{r} = \frac{d\dot{r}}{dt} = \frac{dr}{dt}\frac{d}{dr}(\dot{r}) = \tfrac{1}{2}\frac{d}{dr}(\dot{r}^2)$$

Equation (2-7) may then be written

$$\tfrac{1}{2}\frac{d}{dt}(\dot{r}^2) - \frac{h^2}{r^3} = -\frac{k}{r^2} \tag{2-12}$$

This equation may be integrated immediately yielding

$$\dot{r}^2 = \frac{2k}{r} - \frac{h^2}{r^2} + 2E \tag{2-13}$$

It may be noted at this point that the constant of integration, E, represents the specific energy of a body moving in orbit, this energy is referenced such that the energy of a stationary body at infinity will vanish.

$$E = \tfrac{1}{2}\left(\dot{r}^2 + \frac{h^2}{r^2}\right) - \frac{k}{r} \tag{2-14}$$

$$= \tfrac{1}{2}v^2 - \frac{k}{r}$$

2.2.1 The Orbit Equation

At this point in the development, it will be convenient to eliminate the time variable from the differential equations of motion and to develop a special relationship which is called the *orbit equation*. Re-arranging the terms in Equation (2-13), it may be written with its variables separated

$$dt = \frac{dr}{\sqrt{2E + 2k/r - h^2/r^2}} \tag{2-15}$$

The time variable may now be eliminated making use of Equation (2-9) which may be written in the form

$$dt = \frac{r^2}{h}\,d\theta \tag{2-16}$$

The combined equations provide the resultant expression

$$d\theta = \frac{h\,dr}{r^2\sqrt{2E + 2k/r - h^2/r^2}} \tag{2-17}$$

It is possible to integrate Equation (2-17) directly after making the familar change of variable $r = u^{-1}$ which gives

$$d\theta = \frac{-h\,du}{\sqrt{2E + 2ku - h^2u^2}} \tag{2-18}$$

which, when integrated, yields

$$\cos (\theta - \theta_p) = \frac{u + k/h^2}{k/h^2 \sqrt{1 + 2Eh^2/k^2}} \tag{2-19}$$

where

$(\theta - \theta_p)$ is the position angle as measured from the periapsis of the orbit, it is known to the astronomer as the *true anomaly*.

Upon re-arrangement and changing the variable back to r, Equation (2-19) will be in the form

$$\frac{1}{r} = \frac{k}{h^2} \left[1 + \sqrt{1 + \frac{2Eh^2}{k^2}} \cos (\theta - \theta_p) \right] \tag{2-20}$$

Now, we recall that the general expression for a conic section with one focus at the origin is

$$\frac{1}{r} = \frac{1}{p}[1 + e \cos (\theta - \theta_p)] \tag{2-21}$$

where

e is the eccentricity
p is the semi latus-rectum of the conic.

By analogy, then, the orbit can be identified as a conic having one focus at the origin of the selected coordinate reference frame and with eccentricity

$$e = \sqrt{1 + \frac{2Eh^2}{k^2}} \tag{2-22}$$

and the semi latus-rectum is

$$p = \frac{h^2}{k} \tag{2-23}$$

The properties of the orbit will depend upon the magnitude of the eccentricity e, and hence the energy of the motion, according to the following table:

$$
\begin{array}{lll}
e \geqslant 1 & E > 0 & \text{the orbit is an hyperbola} \\
e = 1 & E = 0 & \text{the orbit is a parabola} \\
e \leqslant 1 & E < 0 & \text{the orbit is an ellipse} \\
e = 0 & E = \dfrac{-k^2}{2h^2} & \text{the orbit is a circle.}
\end{array}
$$

Many of the properties of the free-fall orbit, or trajectory, may be derived from the descriptive terms of analytical geometry; the sketch of Figure 2.3 shows the generalized conics and their geometric relations. The properties of orbits have received considerable study and, as a result, certain parameters have been defined and named for particular application and use.

The orbit equation is most commonly written in the form

$$r = \frac{p}{1 + e \cos(\theta - \theta_p)}$$

(2-24)

where

θ and θ_p are both measured from some convenient reference line. (See Figure 2.3.)

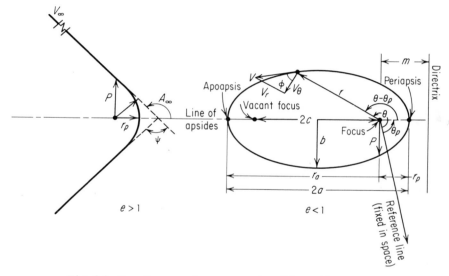

Fig. 2.3. Coordinates and parameters describing orbit motion.

The line of apsides is that line for which $\cos(\theta - \theta_p) = \pm 1$, and the periapsis distance is given by

$$r_p = \frac{p}{1 + e}$$

(2-25)

The apoapsis distance is given by

$$r_a = \frac{p}{1 - e}$$

(2-26)

The length of the line of apsides of an ellipse is also known as its major axis;

this is usually stated in terms of the semi major axis, a:

$$a = \tfrac{1}{2}(r_p + r_a)$$

$$= \frac{p}{1 - e^2} \qquad (2\text{-}27)$$

$$= \frac{-k}{2E}$$

The eccentricity of the orbit may be related to its geometrical parameters through the following relationship

$$e = \frac{r_a - r_p}{r_a + r_p} = \frac{p}{m} = \frac{c}{a} \qquad (2\text{-}28)$$

where

$a =$ the semi major axis
$c =$ the semi-distance between the foci
$m =$ the distance from the focus to the directrix.

Using the relations that have been established, other parameters of the motion may be calculated. For example, the escape velocity, v_e, is that velocity for which a parabolic orbit is obtained, for example $E = 0$;

$$\tfrac{1}{2}v_e^2 - \frac{k}{r} = 0$$

$$v_e = \sqrt{\frac{2k}{r}} \qquad (2\text{-}29)$$

Other examples of orbital relationships are tabulated without development in the appendix.

Three orbit parameters have been developed above, they are sometimes called the *natural orbit parameters* since they arise as constants of integration. These are sufficient to define the shape, orientation, and location of an orbit in a plane. Two additional parameters, making a total of five, are required to define an orbit in free-space and a sixth will serve to locate the spacecraft in the orbit. Recall that the three parameters that have been developed are

1. The angular momentum, h. (Since this is indeed a vector its components define a plane in space and represent three parameters in total.)
2. The orientation of the line of apsides
3. The semi-major axis of the orbit, a.

The sixth parameter, the time that has elapsed since passing periapsis, t_p, is required in order to locate the craft in the orbit. It will be the subject of the discussions of the next section.

The first of the natural parameters listed above, the angular momentum, is, in fact, a vector quantity which represents three parameters. In a three dimensional example, the angular momentum vector serves to define the plane of the orbit. The second parameter, θ_p, defines the orientation of the orbit in the plane defined by h. The orbit energy, E, is directly related to the semi-major axis of the orbit; taken with the other orbit parameters, it defines the shape of the orbit.

A parameter which is commonly used is the *true anomaly*, A_t. The true anomaly is related to the natural parameters by the relation

$$A_t = (\theta - \theta_p)$$

where

θ = the angle between a convenient reference line in the plane of the orbit and the radius vector to the spacecraft.

The true anomaly measures the arc traversed by the spacecraft since passing the periapsis; this measurement is given in angular units.

2.2.2 THE TIME EQUATION

The orbit equation was obtained when Equations (2-15) and (2-16) were combined and the resulting differential equation was integrated. The orbit equation serves to define the shape and orientation of an orbit in space but it is not sufficient to specify the location of an orbiting object along the trajectory as a function of time. In order to compute this time dependance, it is necessary to integrate Equation (2-16); this yields the time equation. In order to do this, it is convenient to introduce a new variable called the *eccentric anomaly*, A_e. The eccentric anomaly will be related to the true anomaly, A_t, and will be defined as the integration procedure is discussed.

Recall the first integral of the angular momentum equation:

$$r^2 \frac{d\theta}{dt} = h \tag{2-16}$$

which may be written directly in the form

$$dt = \frac{r^2}{h} d\theta = \frac{h^3 \, dA_t}{k^2 (1 + e \cos A_t)^2} \tag{2-30}$$

Now, before proceeding, we shall define a new variable—the *eccentric anomaly*. The eccentric anomaly is an angle which is chosen to permit the orbit equation to be written with the transcendental functions in the numerator rather than in the denominator. Hence the eccentric anomaly, A_e, is defined by the relations

$$r = \frac{p}{(1 + e \cos A_t)} = a(1 - e \cos A_e) \tag{2-31}$$

Since the semi latus-rectum, p, is given by $p = a(1 - e^2)$, the eccentric anomaly may be related to the true anomaly through the relations

$$\sin A_e = \frac{\sqrt{1 + e^2}\, \sin A_t}{1 + e \cos A_t} \tag{2-32}$$

$$\cos A_e = \frac{e + \cos A_t}{1 + e \cos A_t} \tag{2-33}$$

$$\sin A_t = \frac{\sqrt{1 - e^2}\, \sin A_e}{1 - e \cos A_e} \tag{2-34}$$

$$\cos A_t = \frac{\cos A_e - e}{1 - e \cos A_e} \tag{2-35}$$

When the orbit which is under consideration has eccentricity greater than unity, the values of A_e will be imaginary. However, Equations (2-32)–(2-35), shown above, are still valid and the resulting hyperbolic sines are used. The numerical relations between the eccentric anomaly and the true anomaly are illustrated in the graph of Figure 2.4.

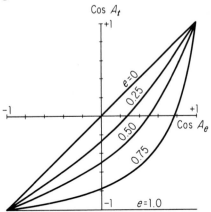

Fig. 2.4. Relations between cosine of true and eccentric anomaly.

The eccentric anomaly is adequately defined above to permit it to be expressed algebraically; it serves the very useful purpose in permitting the statement of the orbit equations in a form in which the trigonometric functions are confined to the numerator. It will be of further use to mention here the geometrical significance which may be attached to the eccentric anomaly. The construction of Figure 2.5 will be used to demonstrate this; from the geometry of the construction, it is apparent that

$$a \cos A_e = ea + r \cos A_t \tag{2-36}$$

The properties of a conic as defined in Equation (2-24) give

$$r = \frac{a(1 - e^2)}{1 + e \cos A_t}$$

which may be substituted for r in Equation (2-36) to provide the relation

$$\cos A_e = \frac{e + \cos A_t}{1 + e \cos A_t}$$

which is identical with Equation (2-33) as given above. This same relation may also be derived directly from the algebraic definition of the eccentric anomaly as it was expressed in Equation (2-31).

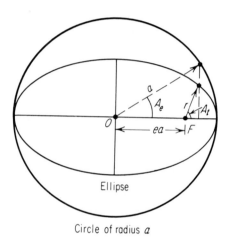

Fig. 2.5. Geometric construction of eccentric anomaly.

Returning, now, to the integral of the time equation, the eccentric anomaly may be substituted for the true anomaly in equation (2-30). This yields the differential form

$$dt = \frac{h^3(1 - e \cos A_e)}{k^2(1 - e^2)^{3/2}} \, dA_e \tag{2-37}$$

where

$k = $ a constant of the particular gravity field in which the motion is occurring; $k = g_0 r_0^2$.

Now, in order to simplify the integration it is desirable to define a constant factor n such that

$$n \overset{\Delta}{=} \frac{k^2(1 - e^2)^{3/2}}{h^3} = \sqrt{\frac{k}{a^3}}$$

This factor, n, is frequently called the *mean motion*. Substituting it into the time Equation (2-37), the equation becomes

$$dt = \frac{1}{n}(1 - e \cos A_e)\, dA_e$$

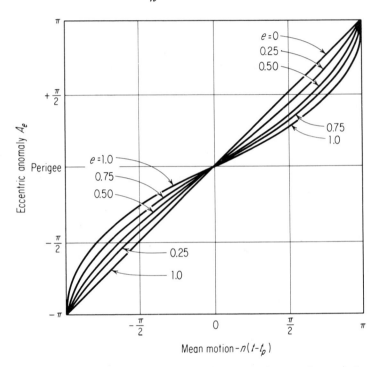

Fig. 2.6. Mean motion in orbit as a function of eccentric anomaly.

which may be integrated directly yielding

$$(t - t_p) = \frac{1}{n}(A_e - e \sin A_e) \tag{2-38}$$

Figure 2.6 shows a graph of the eccentric anomaly presented as a function of an independant variable which has been chosen to be $n(t - t_p)$.

   The integral of the time equation, as expressed by (2-38), may be used to determine the orbit period of any space vehicle or celestial body provided it is in a closed orbit. The body under consideration has completed its closed orbit when the true anomaly has traversed the angle of 2π radians. When $A_t = 2\pi$, then, $(t - t_p) = T$, the orbit period. Further, when $A_t = 2\pi$, $\cos A_t = 1$ and Equation (2-35) states

$$\frac{\cos A_e - e}{1 - e \cos A_e} = 1$$

solving, $A_e = 2\pi$. The period then is obtained by substitution into Equation (2-38), above; the orbit period is, then

$$T = \frac{2\pi}{n} = 2\pi\sqrt{\frac{a^3}{k}} \tag{2-39}$$

which illustrates the Kepler law and states that the period of an orbit is dependant only on the major axis of that orbit and the gravitational constant, k, of the field in which the motion occurs.

2.3 ORBIT TRANSFER

The problem of orbit transfer involves the determination of an orbit suitable to accomplish transfer of one body, which is moving in a dynamical orbit, to the position which is occupied by another orbiting body. The most straight-forward example of this comes to mind when we consider a space vehicle which has determined the parameters of its orbit and must now compute a new orbit in order to effect transfer to its destination. The destination might be the moon, another satellite or space vehicle, or it might be another planet. Several variations of this problem will arise in the context of different navigation problems. Indeed, the reader will recognize the transfer problem as a central problem in the guidance and navigation of space vehicles. We will discuss a few examples of transfer here to introduce the general nature of the techniques which may be applied to its solution. It will not be possible to present a general solution to orbit transfer, mathematically it is indeterminate; however, some special cases are of particular interest and will be discussed in considerable detail in later chapters.

Although its general form is indeterminate, the transfer problem may be solved when suitable constraints have been added. Typical examples of these constraints are:

1. Minimum transfer energy
2. Minimum transfer time
3. Transfer in a specified time interval, for example, to effect rendezvous with a moving point.

Solutions to the problem of orbit transfer has been the subject of many recent works, cf. Reference 2.7. A complete discussion is beyond the scope of the present work. However we will show how orbit transfer may be treated as a series of distinct individual steps. These will be analyzed by approximate methods which recognize some of the limitations which will apply to real situations.

In order to construct an orbit which will effect transfer from P_1 on the first orbit to P_2 on the same or a second orbit, the transfer orbit must satisfy the following two equations:

$$r_1 = \frac{h^2/k}{1 + e \cos (\theta_1 - \theta_p)}$$

$$r_2 = \frac{h^2/k}{1 + e \cos (\theta_2 - \theta_p)}$$

where

the parameters h, e, and θ_p all refer to the transfer orbit.

It is apparent, on inspection of these equations, that they are insufficient to specify the three parameters which appear in them. An infinity of orbits will satisfy these equations unless an additional constraint is imposed for their solution. Some examples of these constraints have been discussed above; if the position in the orbit where rendezvous is initiated or completed is important, an additional parameter, (t_p) is required. This would introduce the need for still another constraint.

While a broad spectrum of orbit transfer problems may be described, they may all be placed into one of five distinct groups. These groups are listed and described below.

1. *Point to point transfer:* The orbit is required which will transport a spacecraft from one point in space to another point in the same gravity field. The ballistic missile is characteristic of this group. See Figure 2.7a.
2. *Inter-orbital transfer:* A vehicle which is in flight on one orbit is required to change to another specified orbit. Examples are the injection of a satellite into orbit and the elevation of a low altitude satellite to a higher altitude. P.E. See Figure 2.7b.
3. *Inter-orbital rendezvous:* This is the change of a vehicle from a specific stable orbit to a specified moving point in another orbit. The most important examples of this are the transfer of a spacecraft from the vicinity of one planet to the vicinity of another planet and the mission of satellite rendezvous. See Figure 2.7c.
4. *Navigational adjustment:* A vehicle in flight on an orbit which is designed to effect the required transfer, detects that a small change in the orbit parameters is required in order to complete the transfer mission. This is typified by the problem of mid-course correction in an interplanetary transfer. See Figure 2.7d.

5. *Interplanetary transfer*: This is a complex of several different transfers. An interplanetary vehicle must leave the Earth in an hyperbolic escape arc, enter the elliptic midcourse trajectory about the Sun, and finally descend on the destination planet along a second hyperbolic trajectory. See Figure 2.7e.

Since the transfers of the first group involve only two points in a central force field, the transfer may be described in a single plane. The other groups, however, involve two or more orbits. Each of these orbits will have its own angular momentum vector, no two of these are necessarily colinear and the orbits need not be coplanar. The initial orbit, the transfer orbit, and the final orbit may all lie in different planes. Frequently, two or more orbits will contain the same attractive force center as a common point, each pair of orbits such as this will contain one or more points, called *nodes*, where one orbit passes through the plane of the other orbit. The line which is defined by the intersection of the two orbit planes is thus called the *line of nodes*.

Space maneuvers and orbit transfers may generally be accomplished by the use of one or more of the four maneuvers listed below.

1. Change of orbit plane
2. Transfer orbits within a plane. (Change size, shape, or orientation of the orbit.)
3. Advance, or retard, the position of the space vehicle in its orbit
4. Final closure. (Final closure, sometimes known as *homing* will not be discussed here but will be left for discussion in Chapter 6.)

The specific mission context in which these maneuvers are performed will exert a major effect on the detailed nature of the maneuvers which are required. Some general considerations regarding these maneuvers will be discussed in the following sections.

2.3.1 CHANGE OF ORBIT PLANE

The plane of an orbit may be defined as the plane which is normal to the orbit angular momentum vector. A change in the plane of an orbit is then equivalent to a change in the direction of the angular momentum vector which is associated with that orbit. Non-gravitational accelerations can be applied to the spacecraft to produce changes in the angular momentum vector. These may be determined quantitatively through application of the vector equation

$$\dot{\mathbf{h}} = \left(\frac{d\mathbf{h}}{dt}\right)_{\text{ref}} + [\mathbf{l} \times \boldsymbol{\Omega}] = \frac{d}{dt}[\mathbf{v} \times \mathbf{r}] \qquad (2\text{-}40)$$

Since, for the present, we wish to examine the maneuvers which are required to change *direction* of the angular momentum vector rather than its magnitude,

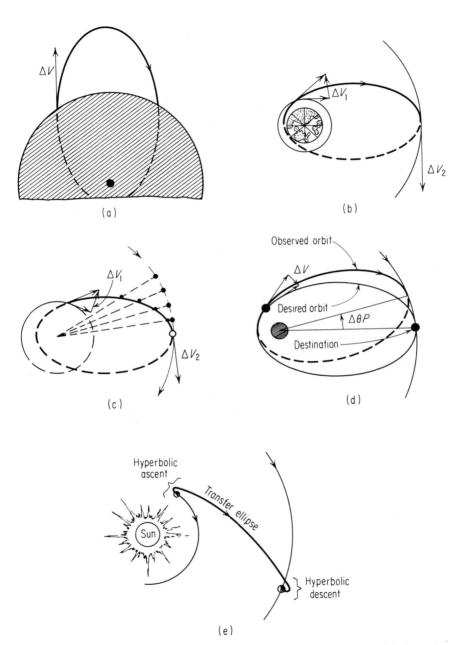

Fig. 2.7. Illustration of transfer orbits (a) point to point transfer (b) inter-orbital transfer (c) inter-orbital rendezvous (d) navigational adjustment (e) interplanetary transfer.

we shall consider only the case where

$$\left(\frac{dh}{dt}\right)_{\text{ref}} = 0$$

In order to proceed, let a coordinate reference frame be defined as embedded in the orbit plane such that:

z' is directed along the angular momentum vector of the orbit under consideration

y' is directed along the line of nodes which is the line common to the orbit plane and the plane of the desired motion

x' is directed so as to form a right-handed set.

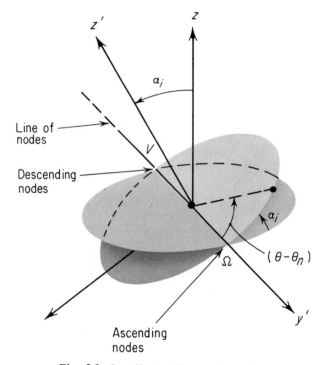

Fig. 2.8. Coordinate reference-plane change.

This coordinate reference is illustrated in Figure 2.8. With reference to this frame, the motion of the spacecraft will be such that $z' = \dot{z}' = 0$ and the accelerations acting on the craft will be due to gravity and to thrust.

The non-gravitational accelerations in the plane of the orbit will also vanish since the only change they can impose on the angular momentum vector is a change in magnitude, consequently $\dot{v}_{x'} = \dot{v}_y = 0$. The application of Equation (2-40), above, to define a plane change maneuver for a circular orbit gives rise to the relation

$$\dot{\mathbf{h}} = [\mathbf{h} \times \boldsymbol{\Omega}] = \frac{d}{dt}[\mathbf{v} \times \mathbf{r}] \qquad (2\text{-}41)$$

which may be resolved into differential equations that relate the scalar components. The vector cross products involved may be expressed as follows

$$[\mathbf{h} \times \boldsymbol{\Omega}] = \mathbf{i}(- h\Omega_{y'}) + \mathbf{j}(h\Omega_{x'}) \qquad (2\text{-}42)$$

and

$$\frac{d}{dt}[\mathbf{v} \times \mathbf{r}] = \mathbf{i}(- \dot{v}_{z'}y') + \mathbf{j}(\dot{v}_{z'}x') \qquad (2\text{-}43)$$

Combining these Equations, (2-42) and (2-43), the component differential equations become

$$h\Omega_{y'} = \dot{v}_{z'}y' = \dot{v}_{z'}r \cos(\omega t + A) \qquad (2\text{-}44)$$
$$h\Omega_{x'} = \dot{v}_{z'}x' = \dot{v}_{z'}r \sin(\omega t + A) \qquad (2\text{-}45)$$

The rate of change of the orbit plane will be given by the angular velocity, $\boldsymbol{\Omega}$, of the reference frame, the components of $\boldsymbol{\Omega}$ are

$$\Omega_{x'} = \frac{\dot{v}_{z'}r}{h} \sin(\omega t + A) \qquad (2\text{-}46)$$

$$\Omega_{y'} = \frac{\dot{v}_{z'}r}{h} \cos(\omega t + A) \qquad (2\text{-}47)$$

Interpretation of these equations indicates that $\Omega_{x'}$ represents a precession of the nodes and that $\Omega_{y'}$ represents change in the angle of inclination, A_i, between the existing orbit and the desired orbit plane. Accordingly, Equations (2-46) and (2-47) indicate that when thrusts are applied normal to the orbit plane they will induce a motion which is a combination of precession of the nodes and a change in the orbit inclination. Changes in the orbit inclination will be the sole result when the thrust is applied in the vicinity of the nodes as well as normal to the plane of the orbit. When a velocity increment which is intended to change the orbit plane is applied to the spacecraft at some point in the orbit which is remote from the nodes between the existing and the desired orbit, the maneuver will be inefficient because part of the velocity increment of the maneuver will go to precessing the nodes rather than to changing the orbit plane to the desired one.

The velocity increment which is required to effect a maneuver is frequently called the *characteristic velocity*. The characteristic velocity for a plane change maneuver may be related to the rocket fuel required to make the maneuver through the rocket equation; this velocity may be calculated by integration of Equation (2-47)

$$\Delta A_i = \int_0^t \Omega_{y'}\, d\tau = \frac{r\Delta v_{z'}}{h}\cos(\omega t + A) \tag{2-48}$$

where

$\Delta v_{z'}$ = the characteristic of the maneuver
ω = the angular velocity of the spacecraft in its circular orbit
A = the angle around the orbit from the line of nodes, $A = 0$ if $t = 0$ at the line of nodes.

The graph of Figure 2.9 shows the characteristic velocity required to make a 10 degree change in the orbit inclination angle. These are displayed as a function of the position angle measured from the line of nodes. These graphs represent Equation (2-48) which is adequate for estimation of the characteristic velocity when the specified change in the inclination angle is small so that the sine of the angle may be considered to be equal to the angle itself, for example, $\Delta A_i \leqslant 10$ degrees; within this range, the characteristic velocity will be directly proportional to the magnitude of the change in the orbit inclination. Larger changes in the orbit plane, when made as impulsive changes which take place at the node, may be calculated for all orbits, whether or not they are circular, by application of the law of cosines, for example

$$(\Delta v^2) = v_1^2 + v_2^2 - 2v_1 v_2 \cos \Delta A_i \tag{2-49}$$

where

v_1 = the orbit velocity of the craft before the maneuver
v_2 = the orbit velocity of the craft after the maneuver.

If $v_1 = v_2$, the velocity magnitude will be unchanged and the only effective change in the state of the spacecraft will be the desired change in the orbit plane. The other orbit parameters will, consequently, remain unchanged. For this case, then, we may rewrite Equation (2-49) as

$$(\Delta v^2) = 2v^2(1 - \cos \Delta A_i) \tag{2-49}$$

and

$$\frac{\Delta v}{v} = \sqrt{2(1 - \cos \Delta A_i)} = 2 \sin \frac{\Delta A_i}{2}$$

This expression is illustrated in the graph of Figure 2.10.

2.3.2 INTRA-PLANE CHANGE OF ORBIT

After completion of maneuvers to effect the change of orbit plane, it may still be necessary to make additional maneuvers to change the orbit of a spacecraft to permit the craft to meet its destination in another orbit which is located in the newly established plane. The problem, in its most general form, constitutes the core of interplanetary navigation and is beyond the scope of the present chapter, see Chapter 6. Nevertheless, it will be useful to discuss an important special case here; this will be the example of transfer between two circular orbits.

In the example selected, it will be desired to analyze the transfer of a spacecraft which is in flight in a circular orbit to a new orbit which is also circular.

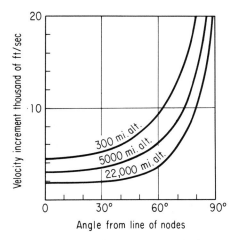

Fig. 2.9. Velocity increment required to change orbit plane inclination by 10°— (circular orbits).

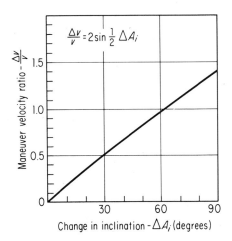

Fig. 2.10. Velocity ratio required to make a change in orbit inclination at the node.

Assume that the first orbit has radius r_1 and the second orbit is a circle of radius r_2, the transfer is illustrated in Figure 2.11. From the geometry, the apsidal radii must necessarily satisfy the following relations (for an inward transfer)

$$r_p = a(1 - e) \leqslant r_2 \qquad (2\text{-}50)$$

$$r_a = a(1 + e) \geqslant r_1 \qquad (2\text{-}51)$$

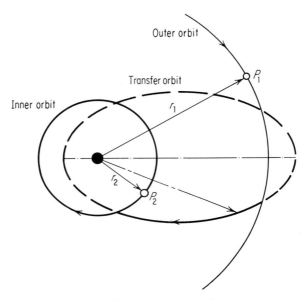

Fig. 2.11. Inter-orbit transfer.

As a matter of convenience, these equations may be normalized, using the relations $r_2/r_1 = n$ and $a/r_1 = q$. Accordingly,

$$q(1 - e) \leqslant n$$

$$q(1 + e) \geqslant 1$$

from which may be derived the following expressions for the eccentricity

$$e \geqslant \frac{q - n}{q} \qquad (2\text{-}52)$$

$$e \geqslant \frac{1 - q}{q} \qquad (2\text{-}53)$$

In the event that an hyperbolic transfer were to be used, it would be necessary that

$$r_p \leqslant r_2$$

and

$$a(e - 1) \leqslant r_2$$

hence, it follows that for the hyperbolic transfer

$$e \leqslant \frac{n + q}{q} \tag{2-54}$$

The foregoing relations are applicable to inward transfers and have been discussed in detail in Reference 2.8. A similar set of relations may be developed for the case of outward transfers. These are

for elliptical transfers

$$e \geqslant \frac{n - q}{q} \tag{2-55}$$

$$e \geqslant \frac{q - 1}{q} \tag{2-56}$$

for hyperbolic transfers

$$e \leqslant \frac{q + 1}{q} \tag{2-57}$$

These relations, Equations (2-52)–(2-57) define a set of boundaries which restrict the permissible combinations of the parameters which will be involved in a given transfer. These bounds have been plotted and are shown graphically on an $e - q$ plane in Figure 2.12.

The energy, and hence the characteristic velocity, which will be involved in the various transfer maneuvers may be estimated for the exchanges described above. The energy of a spacecraft in a circular orbit is given by

$$E_1 = \tfrac{1}{2}v_1^2 - \frac{k}{r_1} = \tfrac{1}{2}\frac{k}{r_1}$$

thus,

$$v_1^2 = \frac{k}{r_1}$$

and, similarly

$$v_2^2 = \frac{k}{r_2}$$

The energy of the spacecraft in the transfer orbit will be a constant which satisfies the relations

$$E_t = \tfrac{1}{2}v_{0t}^2 - \frac{k}{r_1}$$

$$= \tfrac{1}{2}v_{ft}^2 - \frac{k}{r_2}$$

$$= -\frac{k}{2a}$$

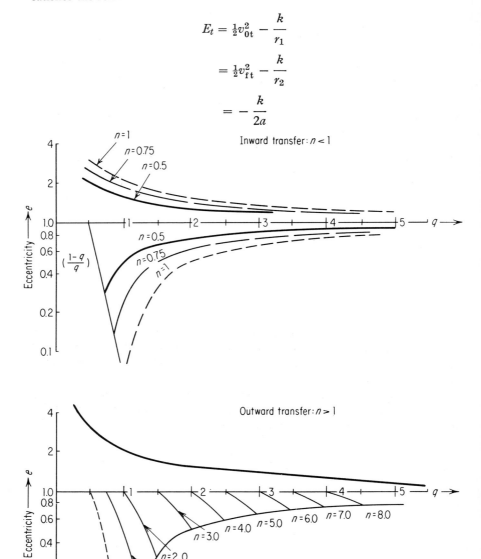

Fig. 2.12. Boundaries of permissible transfer between circular orbits.

It follows from the above that

$$v_{0t}^2 = k\left(\frac{2}{r_1} - \frac{1}{a}\right)$$

$$v_{ft}^2 = k\left(\frac{2}{r_2} - \frac{1}{a}\right)$$

These equations may be normalized; as before, $n = r_2/r_1$ and $q = a/r_1$. As a result, we obtain

$$v_1^2 = nv_2^2$$

$$v_{0t}^2 = v_1^2\frac{2q - 1}{q}$$

$$v_{ft}^2 = v_1^2\frac{2q - 1}{nq}$$

Consequently, the velocity increment required at the first impulse maneuver will be given by

$$\Delta v_1 = v_{0t} - v_1$$

$$= \frac{v_0^2 - v_1^2}{v_{0t} + v_1} = \frac{v_1^2}{v_0 + v_1}\left(\frac{q - 1}{q}\right) \tag{2-58}$$

After a similar development, we obtain

$$\Delta v_2 = \frac{v_2^2}{v_{ft} + v_2}\left(\frac{q - n}{q}\right) \tag{2-59}$$

Now, the direction of the velocity of the spacecraft in the initial and final circular orbits will be perpendicular to the radius vector at the point of departure and the point of arrival. The direction of the velocity vector of the spacecraft in the transfer orbit will be tangent to the orbit at the point under consideration at any particular instant. If the angle between the tangent to the orbit and the radius vector is given by ϕ, then

$$\tan \phi = -r\frac{dA_t}{dr}$$

where

$$r = \frac{a(1 - e^2)}{1 + e \cos A_t}$$

and $A_t = $ True Anomaly. Hence

$$\tan \phi = -\left(\frac{1 + e \cos A_t}{e \sin A_t}\right) \tag{2-60}$$

In order to specify a transfer maneuver, it will be necessary to compute the vector which represents the difference between the velocity vectors describing the motion of the spacecraft in the orbit before the maneuver and after the maneuver respectively. A similar determination will be required for the terminal adjustment into the final orbit. The characteristic velocity for the transfer will be given by the scalar sum of the two velocity increments. The velocity maneuver which is required at the initial departure is given by (See Figure 2.13)

$$\Delta v^2 = v_1^2 + v_{0t}^2 - 2v_1 v_{0t} \cos\left(\phi - \frac{\pi}{2}\right)$$

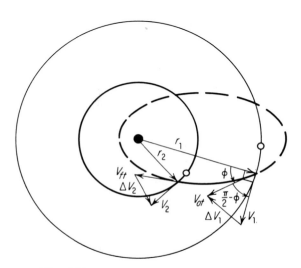

Fig. 2.13. Velocity increment for maneuver.

but we may make the substitution

$$\cos\left(\phi_1 - \frac{\pi}{2}\right) = \sin \phi_1$$

$$= (\cot^2 \phi_1 + 1)^{-1/2}$$

$$= \frac{1 + e \cos A_t}{(e^2 \sin^2 A_t + 1 + e \cos A_t)^{1/2}}$$

The velocity increment may then be stated in the form

$$\Delta v_1^2 = v_1^2 + v_{0t}^2 - 2v_{0t}v_1 \frac{a(1 - e^2)}{r_1(e^2 \sin^2 A_t + 1 + e \cos A_t)^{1/2}}$$

which, after considerable manipulation may be reduced to

$$\frac{\Delta v_1^2}{v_1^2} = 3 - 2[q(1 - e^2)]^{1/2} - \frac{1}{q} \tag{2-61}$$

In a similar manner we obtain

$$\frac{\Delta v_2^2}{v_2^2} = \frac{1}{n}\left\{3 - 2\left[\frac{q(1 - e^2)}{n}\right]^{1/2}\right\} - \frac{1}{q} \tag{2-62}$$

The characteristic velocity for the complete transfer will be given by the sum of the two impulsive velocity increments, for example

$$v_c = \Delta v_1 + \Delta v_2$$

The characteristic velocity for a transfer by elliptical orbits will be given by:

$$v_c = v_1\left[\sqrt{3 - 2[q(1 - e^2)]^{1/2} - \frac{1}{q}} + \sqrt{\frac{3 - 2[q(1 - e^2)/n]^{1/2}}{n} - \frac{1}{q}}\,\right]$$

For a transfer by hyperbolic orbit, the characteristic velocity is:

$$v_c = v_1\left[\sqrt{3 - 2[q(e^2 - 1)]^{1/2} + \frac{1}{q}} + \sqrt{\frac{3 - 2[q(e^2 - 1)]^{1/2}}{n} + \frac{1}{q}}\,\right]$$

2.3.3 Determination of Transfer Time

The time required to effect a transfer between specified points in space may be evaluated using the integral of the time equation, see Section 2.2.2. The time which has elapsed since the orbiting craft passed periapsis is given in terms of the parameters of the orbit in which it is flying by the equation which has already been developed

$$(t - t_p) = \frac{1}{n}(A_e - e \sin A_e) \tag{2-38}$$

where the parameters are those of the orbit in which the spacecraft is moving.

The transfer time, Δt, will be given by the difference between the time computed by Equation (2-39) for the two points of interest in the transfer, that is

$$\Delta t = (t_2 - t_p) - (t_1 - t_p) = (t_2 - t_1)$$

Consequently,

$$\Delta t = \frac{1}{n}[A_{e2} - A_{e1} - e(\sin A_{e2} - \sin A_{e1})] \tag{2-63}$$

where

    A_{e1} = the eccentric anomaly at the first point of interest; r_1, θ_1.
    A_{e2} = the eccentric anomaly at the second point of interest; r_2, θ_2.

Equation (2-63) may be applied to the problem of transfer between circular orbits as discussed in the previous section. The eccentric anomaly of the initial (departure) point is given in terms of the orbit parameters as

$$A_{e0} = \cos^{-1}\left(\frac{a - r_1}{ae}\right) = \cos^{-1}\left(\frac{q - 1}{qe}\right)$$

Similarly, the eccentric anomaly at the terminal (arrival) point will be given by

$$A_{ef} = \cos^{-1}\left(\frac{a - r_2}{ae}\right) = \cos^{-1}\left(\frac{q - n}{qe}\right)$$

From trigonometry,

$$\sin A_{e0} = \sqrt{1 - \left(\frac{q - 1}{qe}\right)^2}$$

and

$$\sin A_{ef} = \sqrt{1 - \left(\frac{q - n}{qe}\right)^2}$$

From these we may compute the value of the transfer time, it is

$$\Delta t = \frac{1}{n}\left[\cos^{-1}\left(\frac{q - n}{qe}\right) - \cos^{-1}\left(\frac{q - 1}{qe}\right) - \frac{1}{q}\left(\sqrt{q^2(e^2 - 1) + 2q - n^2}\right.\right.$$
$$\left.\left. - \sqrt{q^2(e^2 - 1) + 2q - 1}\right)\right]$$

In terms of the period of the transfer orbit, this may be written as

$$\frac{\Delta t}{T} = \frac{1}{2\pi}\left[\cos^{-1}\left(\frac{q - n}{qe}\right) - \cos^{-1}\left(\frac{q - 1}{qe}\right)\right.$$
$$\left. - \frac{1}{q}\left(\sqrt{q^2(e^2 - 1) + 2q - n^2} - \sqrt{q^2(e^2 - 1) + 2q - 1}\right)\right] \quad (2\text{-}64)$$

A similar expression may, of course, be developed for the case of hyperbolic transfer in which the circular trigonometric functions are replaced by hyperbolic functions.

It is perhaps interesting to note at this point that, for elliptical transfer orbits, a useful approximation may be obtained by neglecting the radical terms in Equation (2-64). Thus,

$$\frac{\Delta t}{T} \approx \frac{1}{2\pi}\left[\cos^{-1}\left(\frac{q - n}{qe}\right) - \cos^{-1}\left(\frac{q - 1}{qe}\right)\right]$$

The configuration of the system of orbiting bodies at the time of the initial maneuver will be shown to be closely related to the selection of a transfer orbit. If a rendezvous type trajectory is required, then the destination point should be chosen such that the destination body will just arrive at the destination point at the same time as the arrival of the spacecraft in the transfer orbit. This is illustrated in Figure 2.14. The Figure shows the initial and final orbits and the transfer orbit. The inter-orbital transfer time is given by

$$\Delta t = \left(\frac{1}{n} A_{etf} - A_{et0} - e_t(\sin A_{etf} - \sin A_{et0}) \right)$$

$$= \frac{1}{n_t} \left\{ \cos^{-1} \frac{e_t + \cos A_{t2f}}{1 + e_t \cos A_{t2f}} - \cos^{-1} \frac{e_t + \cos A_{t10}}{1 + e_t \cos A_{t2f}} \right.$$

$$\left. - e_t \sqrt{1 + e_t^2} \left[\frac{\sin A_{t2f}}{1 + e_t \cos A_{t2f}} - \frac{\sin A_{t10}}{1 + e_t \cos A_{t10}} \right] \right. \quad (2\text{-}65)$$

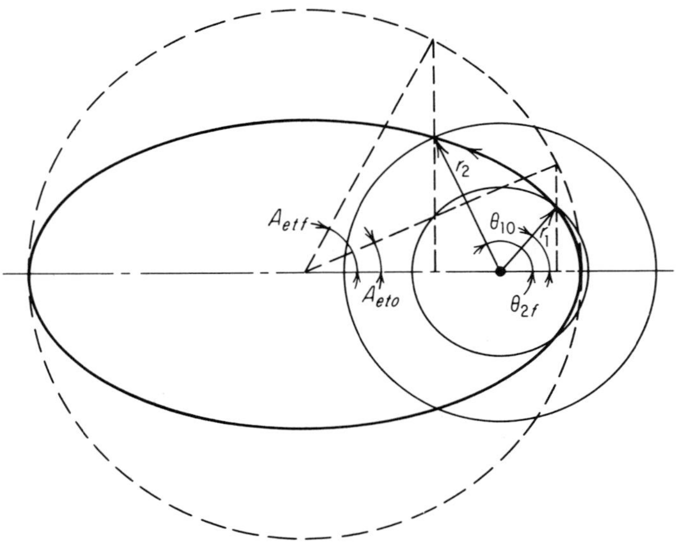

Fig. 2.14. The geometry of orbit transfer.

These relations will be the subject of further discussions in Chapter 6. It may be noted here that, even after the initial and final orbit points have been selected, the transfer time and hence the transfer orbit geometry is not determined until three additional parameters have been selected. These parameters are

the mean motion (n_t) of the transfer orbit
the eccentricity of the transfer orbit
the orientation of the line of apsides of the transfer orbit.

2.3.4 ADVANCE/RETARD IN ORBIT

Frequently, spacecraft maneuvers may be required to advance (or retard) the position of a craft in the orbit in which it is currently in motion. The only change in orbit parameters desired is a change in the time of passing periapsis. Such a change may be accomplished by transferring the craft to place it in an exchange orbit which has a period that is different from that of the original orbit; no change in plane need be involved. An exchange orbit of the kind required will intersect the original orbit at one, or more, points as shown in Figure 2.15. Through appropriate choice of the exchange orbit, the desired change of phase will be accomplished. The change may be made quickly at a relatively high cost in maneuver energy; conversely, the change may be made slowly at as small an increment of velocity as is desired. The time for the change becomes large without limit as the energy increment is made arbitrarily small.

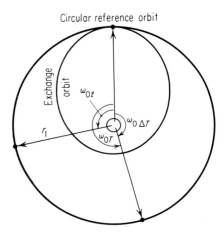

Fig. 2.15. Advancing phase in orbit.

The time which is required to effect the change in phase of an orbiting spacecraft will depend upon the relative periods of the original orbit and the exchange orbit. The principle involved in the maneuver will be illustrated by an example in which a vehicle is considered to be traveling in a circular orbit. The position occupied by the spacecraft in its circular orbit will be defined by means of a position (phase) angle relative to a reference line by

$$\phi = \omega_0 t = \frac{2\pi}{T_0} t$$

where

ω_0 = the angular velocity of the spacecraft in its original, circular, orbit.

If, now, the spacecraft leaves its circular orbit and returns to the departure point after one cycle on the exchange orbit, the spacecraft will have changed its position relative to its initial point in the orbit. This change will be given by

$$\Delta\phi = 2\pi \pm \omega_0 T = 2\pi\left(1 \pm \frac{T}{T_0}\right) = \pm \omega_0 \Delta T \qquad (2\text{-}66)$$

where

T = the period of the exchange orbit

$\Delta\phi$ = the change in phase occurring during one period of the exchange orbit.

The selection of the algebraic sign in Equation (2-66) will depend upon the relative magnitude of the original and the exchange orbits. An exchange orbit of lesser period than the original orbit will give rise to an advance in phase of the spacecraft relative to its original motion, conversely an increase in period will lead to a retarding of the phase. The positive sign will apply to a decrease in orbit period and a negative sign will be used when the exchange orbit has a longer period than the original orbit. A similar analysis leads to more complex results when an elliptical reference orbit is used. Special variations of this technique may be used when the point at which the maneuver is made is not on the line of apsides for either the reference orbit or the exchange orbit.

Returning to the example illustrated by Figure 2.15 in which a change of phase is required of a vehicle which is traveling in a circular orbit, the maneuver velocity may be estimated through the calculation of the energy in the orbits before and after each incremental maneuver. This technique is not universally applicable to the determination of maneuver requirements; however it is applicable to the special case under consideration in which the transfer to, and from, the exchange orbit is accomplished by a tangential maneuver. The energy of the spacecraft in the orbit is given by

$$E = -\frac{2k}{a}$$

The energy is also related to the velocity by

$$E = \tfrac{1}{2}v^2 - \frac{k}{r}$$

The semi-major axis of the exchange ellipse will then be given by

$$a = -\frac{k}{2E} = -\frac{k}{(v^2 - 2k/r)}$$

The period of the orbit has been shown to be related to the semi-major axis of the orbit of motion, Equation (2-39) . It is

$$T = 2\pi\sqrt{\frac{a^3}{k}} = \frac{\pi k}{\sqrt{2E^3}}$$

Differentiating this expression, the change of period per unit change in energy is

$$\Delta T = \frac{-3\sqrt{2}}{4}\pi k E^{-5/2}\Delta E \qquad (2\text{-}67)$$

where

$$\Delta E = v\Delta v + \frac{k}{r^2}\Delta r$$

$\Delta r = 0$ for the impulsive maneuver

$$\Delta E = v\Delta v$$

Performing the substitution and rearranging the terms, the velocity increment is related to the change in orbit period by

$$\Delta v = \frac{-4E^{5/2}}{3\sqrt{2}\,\pi k v}\Delta T$$

The complete phase change maneuver will, of course, be given by

$$v_c = 2\Delta v = \frac{-8E^{5/2}}{3\sqrt{2}\,\pi k v}\Delta T$$

Recalling now Equation (2-66) above

$$\Delta T = -\frac{\Delta\phi}{\omega_0}$$

We may now state the characteristic velocity for a change in phase when executed by the maneuver described in Figure 2.16. It is

$$v_c = \frac{4\sqrt{2}E^{5/2}}{3\pi k v\omega_0}\Delta\phi \qquad (2\text{-}68)$$

2.3.5 Final Closure and Adjustments

After completion of a series of maneuvers such as those which have been described in the previous sections; for example, plane change, intra-plane orbit change, and phase change; it will frequently be necessary for a spacecraft to make final adjustments to the orbit in order to effect closure between the craft and its destination. These adjustments are necessary in order to account for small errors in the guidance and navigation and to make the small corrections in course which may be essential to avoid a destructive collision.

In the full context of space navigation, two very important situations will arise with respect to final closure, these are described below:

1. *Zero-g homing* (*docking*): This is the flight situation in which two small spaceborne bodies must make physical contact with one another. The initial situation is one in which both craft are in very nearly identical orbits, hence no *relative* gravity forces act on the two craft. (Relative gravity forces are described and discussed in Chapter 5.)

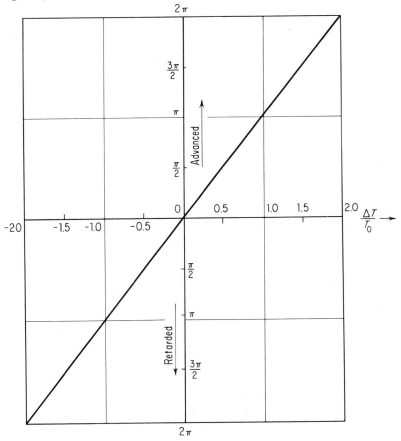

Fig. 2.16. Phase advancement.

2. *Homing in a gravity field*: This situation arises in lunar and interplanetary flight when a spacecraft is making final closure for landing on a massive body. The gravity field of the destination body strongly influences the trajectory of approach and navigation requires that this be taken into account.

Homing in a gravity field will be discussed in considerable detail in Chapter 6 when the techniques of interplanetary flight are presented. Consequently it will not be analyzed further here.

Zero-g homing, or docking, requires that the craft be placed on a course leading to a collision with its destination. This must be accomplished in a space environment where the forces on the craft are negligible with the exception of those which determine the trajectory. These forces act on both the bodies in a nearly identical manner. Forces for driving, steering, braking, and attitude control must all be generated by self-contained subsystems on the vehicle. The collision course may be established using a navigation criterion which is well known in nautical applications, for example the craft will be on a collision course with another body when the turning rate of the line of sight to that body vanishes. This navigation system has been mechanized in the *proportional navigation* systems of anti-aircraft missiles. In these missiles, the rate of change of the flight heading is made to vary in proportion to the rate of change of the tracking line, or line of sight to the target. The sense of the proportionality constant is selected so as to make the rate of change of the direction of the line of sight diminish. This flight doctrine leads to a collision course from an arbitrary set of initial conditions. The system has certain inherent singularities which are of tactical significance for anti-aircraft weapons but which need not concern us for the present discussions.

The design requirements arising from the need for physical contact in docking make it necessary that precision matching of velocity be provided to prevent destructive collisions of the two spacecraft. This portion of the operation requires special autopilot mechanization for use in a closed loop control system. Docking equipment which is closely associated with the details of the design of the craft and the docking operation is required also. But this is not related to the navigation of the craft and will not be discussed here.

2.4 MOTION UNDER NON-GRAVITATIONAL FORCES

Orbital motions which take place under the influence of non-gravitational forces or of gravitational forces arising from several independant sources are more complicated to define in mathematical terms than those which occur in an idealized inverse force field. In general, the equations of motion for a spacecraft which is subject to these complex forces will have the form

$$\ddot{r} - \dot{\theta}^2 r = -\frac{k}{r} + \sum_{i}^{n-1} \hat{\mathbf{r}}_i \cdot \mathbf{g}_i + C_D(r, \theta)\dot{r} + T(r, \theta, t) \tag{2-69}$$

and

$$r^2\dot{\theta} = \sum_{i}^{n-1} \hat{\boldsymbol{\theta}}_i \cdot \mathbf{g}_i + C_D(r, \theta)r\theta + T(r, \theta, t) \tag{2-70}$$

These equations are non-linear and, except for some special cases, can not be solved in closed mathemetical form. Some of these special cases are discussed in Reference 2.9. Standard methods do, however, exist for the solution of these non-linear problems but a complete discussion of them is beyond the scope of the present text. The brief discussion of perturbation methods which follows is intended to orient the reader to problems of this kind, for further material on this vast and specialized subject the reader is referred to standard works in celestial mechanics.

Equations (2-69) and (2-70) are non-linear. Equations of this type may generally to be integrated by the application of perturbation theory. In the perturbation method, only the departures from a reference orbit are integrated and these are subsequently added to the integral of the reference orbit. By use of this method, the number of computational iterations which must be used to obtain a given accuracy of solution is drastically reduced below that which would be required if the entire equation were to be integrated. Application of the perturbation techniques has the effect of reducing both the residual errors and the computational time. In both examples where the problem formulation is such that it is necessary to integrate the total forces acting on the spacecraft in the sense of Equation (2-3), a technique which is known to the astronomers under the name of *Cowell's method*, relatively large residual errors may occur even though many iterative calculations are employed. While the use of large scale electronic computing machinery makes the use of this method less objectionable than has been the case in the past, computational efficiency is still important and perturbation methods are used wherever they are applicable.

Two classes of perturbation methods are commonly used for orbit calculations. The first, called *Encke's method*, uses a reference orbit and deviations from this reference which are the result of perturbations are integrated in the computational process. If the reference orbit which is selected is a conic section, for example, only those deviations of the force from a central force field need be integrated as perturbations. These give rise to perturbative displacements from the reference conic which must be added to the displacements which are due to the motions of the craft in the reference orbit.

As an alternative approach, the continuous *rectification* (sometimes called correction) of a reference orbit is sometimes used. In this method, the rectified orbit is known as the *osculating orbit* and it is defined by a set of varying parameters which define the orbit so that at every instant of time the osculating orbit exactly describes the position and velocity of the spacecraft. This technique is known as *variation of parameters*. Suitable parameters for variation of a two-body central force-field ellipse are the eccentricity, the semi-major axis, and the argument to periapsis; these parameters are varied throughout the trajectory where perturbing forces are applied.

The reference orbit which is suitable for use in perturbation studies is chosen to be that orbit which best depicts the gross motion of the object under study while still providing mathematical convenience. All forces which are not directly taken into account in the integration of this reference orbit as it is stated mathematically are then categorized as perturbation forces. It is usually advisable, then, to employ a reference orbit which may be integrated in a closed form and which does not require numerical computation processes in its integration. These considerations have led astronomers to select the two-body Keplerian orbit as the reference orbit for the study of most problems of planetary motion. All forces which are exerted on the planet (or spacecraft) in the form of drag, light pressure, or gravitation from other planets are then included in the integration of the orbit as perturbation forces tending to change the parameters of the reference orbit. When integrated, the actual orbit which is followed will be defined as a tabulation of orbit parameters shown as a function of time, or position. These parameters may then be used to define the orbit of the spacecraft as a function of the pertinant independant variable. The orbit is described as an instantaneous (or osculating) orbit. A general study would provide the definition of all five natural parameters describing an orbit and a sixth parameter to determine the position of the craft within the orbit.

PROBLEMS

1. What is the acceleration due to the solar gravity at the orbit of Venus, Earth, Mars, and Jupiter? The following information is given.

Planet	Period	Mean Orbit Radius (A.U.)
Venus	224 days	0.723
Earth	365 days	1.00
Mars	687 days	1.524
Jupiter	4328 days	5.202

2. Compute the specific angular momentum of the Earth in its orbit about the Sun, of the Moon in its orbit about the Earth, and of an artificial satellite of the Earth in a circular orbit at 300 miles altitude.

3. Using the value of the universal gravity constant, $G = 6.670 \times 10^{-8}$ dynes cm^2/gm^2; radius of the Earth $R_e = 6378.4$ km, and the acceleration due to gravity at the surface, $g = 980$ cm/sec^2, compute the energy of an artificial satellite of the earth in a circular orbit at 300 miles altitude.

4. Find the specific energy of a spacecraft in a parabolic escape orbit, $e = 1$, having perigee at 300 miles.

5. A spacecraft is in a tangential transfer orbit between the orbits of Earth and Venus, see Figure 1.6. Find the apogee radius, perigee radius and the eccentricity of the transfer ellipse.

6. Compute the surface values of the escape velocity of the planets for which the following data are given.

Planet	Surface Gravity Earth = 1	Equatorial Radius Earth = 1
Mercury	0.38	0.39
Earth	1.00	1.00
Mars	0.39	0.52
Jupiter	2.65	10.97

7. Using the data that were obtained in the previous problem, calculate the constant, k, for the same planets. Find n, the mean motion, for each planet.

8. Graph the eccentric anomaly as a function of time for a spacecraft in an orbit about the Earth having eccentricity of 0.5 and perigee altitude 300 miles.

9. Compute the range of velocity increments and flight path angles applicable to permissible elliptical orbit transfers to Mars.

10. Compute the range of velocity increments and flight path angles applicable to permissible elliptical orbits for transfer to Venus.

11. Compute the range of transfer time for the orbits that were considered in Problem 9.

12. Compute the range of transfer time for the orbits described in Problem 10.

REFERENCES

2.1. Moulton, F. R., *An Introduction to Celestial Mechanics*, The Macmillan Co., New York, 1914.

2.2. Smart, W. M., *Celestial Mechanics*, Longmans, Green & Co., 1953.

2.3. Goldstein, Herbert, *Classical Mechanics*, Addison-Wesley Press Inc., Cambridge, Mass., 1951.

2.4. Ehricke, Krafft A., *Space Flight I. Environmental and Celestial Mechanics*, D. Van Nostrand Company, Inc., Princeton, New Jersey, 1960.

2.5. Sedov, L. I., *Dynamic Effects on the Motions of Earth Sputniks*, Proceedings of the IXth I.A.F. Congress, Amsterdam, 1958.

2.6. Browne, S. H. and J. J. Gilvary, Jr., *Theory of Blind Navigation by Dynamical Measurements*, The Rand Corporation, R-144, July 1949.

2.7. Lawden, D. F., *Optimal Programming of Rocket Thrust Direction*, Astronautical Acta, 1, 41–56, 1955.

2.8. Vertregt, M., *Interplanetary Orbits*, Journal of the British Interplanetary Society, Vol. 16, No. 6, Mar–Apr. 1958.

2.9. Baker, Robert, M. L., Jr., *Encke's Method and Variation of Parameters as Applied to Re-Entry Trajectories*, Advances in Astronautical Sciences, Vol. 3, Plenum Press, New York, 1958.

2.10. Baker, R. M. L. and Makemson, M. W. *Astrodynamics*, Academic Press, New York, 1960.

3

INSTRUMENTATION

In this chapter, some of the methods which may be used for measurement of orbit parameters will be discussed. In addition, brief mention will be made of the methods for handling and processing these data in order to determine the corrective maneuvers which will be required in order to permit the craft to complete its mission. The treatment given here will be limited in its scope and will approach the subject from the point of view of the navigation problem which was outlined in the first chapter. The reader is referred to appropriate texts and engineering reports for details regarding the methods and techniques. The application of these methods to the various situations which will arise in space will be discussed in the separate chapters of this book; here we shall treat the measurements which must be made and relate them to the more general properties of the instrument systems which may be used. We shall also discuss the operation of these instruments in the situations which are of major interest in space navigation.

Instrumentation systems will not generally be applied to direct measurements of orbit parameters. Rather, it is usually convenient to measure and record the values of coordinates from which the orbit parameters may be computed. This chapter will discuss the methods for measuring the coordinates describing the flight of a spacecraft and the subsequent computation of the parameters which describe its orbit. The concept of position vectors will be introduced and their use as applied to space navigation will be demonstrated. The techniques required to effect the vector transformations which are used in space flight will be discussed briefly.

Specific systems for use in tracking by means of range, angle and velocity measurements will be treated in some degree of mathematical detail. Self contained instrumentation systems will be introduced and the characteristics of these systems which make them particularly advantageous for certain missions will be presented. Finally a brief discussion will be presented of the methods for analysis of errors in space orbits. This is followed by a treatment of the requirements for corrective maneuvers and the means for their computation and application.

3.1 INTRODUCTORY COMMENTS

Before discussing the means to measure flight *coordinates* and their conversion into orbit *parameters*, it is appropriate to discuss the meaning of the two terms. The parameters and their interpretations were discussed in the previous chapter; these are quantities which have been shown to be convenient for description of a space orbit. The outstanding examples are the *natural parameters* which were shown to arise as constants of integration when the differential equations of motion of the spacecraft were integrated. The *coordinates*, on the other hand, are quantitites which describe the instantaneous state of the spacecraft in its flight; examples of coordinates are position, velocity, and acceleration. The coordinates may not be used individually to obtain the orbit parameters, however, they may be taken in groups to compute the parameters.

While it is usually desired to use the orbit parameters, since these may be used to describe the orbit completely, it will be shown that it is more convenient to measure coordinates of the spacecraft. The parameters of the orbit may then be calculated as functions of the coordinates. Three second-order differential equations were involved in the description of the orbit, hence six orbit parameters result. It will be shown that the parameters may be computed from any set of six independant coordinates. Additional coordinates may, from time to time, be used but this is to provide increased accuracy.

3.1.1 COMPUTATION OF ORBIT PARAMETERS FROM MEASURED DATA

The instrumentation of a space guidance system has the primary mission of performing those measurements which are necessary to permit calculation of the orbit parameters. These parameters and their significance were developed in considerable detail in the previous chapter; they are a set of numerical constants which define the orbit in which a spacecraft is moving and its position in that orbit. The parameters may be calculated from measured coordinates; for example, consider the following parameters and the definitions which are given.

1. The angular momentum vector

$$\mathbf{h} = \mathbf{r}_0 \times r_0\dot{\boldsymbol{\theta}}_0$$

2. The energy of the motion

$$E = \frac{1}{2}\left(\dot{r}_0^2 + \frac{h^2}{r_0^2}\right) - \frac{k}{r_0}$$

3. The orientation of the line of apsides (argument to periapsis)

$$\theta_p = \theta_0 - \cos^{-1}\left(\frac{h^2 - (k/r_0)}{ker_0}\right)$$

where

$$e = \sqrt{1 + \frac{2Eh^2}{k^2}}$$

4. The time since passing periapsis (epoch)

$$t_p = t_0 - \frac{1}{n}[A_{e0} - e\sin A_{e0}]$$

where

$$n = \frac{k^2(1 - e^2)^{3/2}}{h^3}$$

$$\sin A_{e0} = \frac{\sqrt{(1 - e^2)}\sin(\theta_0 - \theta_p)}{1 - e\cos(\theta_0 - \theta_p)}$$

It should be noted that the first of these four parameters has been stated in the form of a vector. In this form, the single vector, angular momentum, represents two additional parameters. The total number of parameters, then, is six. Three components of angular momentum define the plane of the orbit which contains the center of the force field and is normal to the angular momentum vector. The energy defines the size of the orbit and, with the angular momentum vector, it defines the orbit shape. The argument to periapsis defines the orientation of the orbit and the position of the spacecraft in its orbit is defined with relation to the epoch.

Frequently, a problem in space navigation will require calculation of the angle which is swept out by the line of sight from the primary focus to the vehicle during some known time interval. Problems of this kind will not require that the epoch, t_p, be calculated specifically. For example, the eccentric anomaly is related to the time since passing periapsis by

$$t_0 - t_p = \frac{1}{n}(A_{e0} - e\sin A_{e0})$$

and

$$t_1 - t_p = \frac{1}{n}\left(A_{e1} - e \sin A_{e1}\right)$$

hence

$$t_1 - t_0 = \frac{1}{n}\left[A_{e1} - A_{e0} + e(\sin A_{e1} - \sin A_{e0})\right] \quad (3\text{-}1)$$

The angle traversed in time $(t_1 - t_0)$ will be given by the difference in the true anomalies for these two times and may be calculated directly from the above using the relations given in Chapter 2.

During a free-fall flight, or a flight which approximates free-fall in a central force field, where no thrusts or other forces with components at right angles to the velocity vector of the spacecraft are acting, the motion of the vehicle can be considered to be planar. A reference frame may be selected which will permit the vector form of the angular velocity to be replaced with the more familiar scalar representation: $h = r^2\theta$.

The six scalar parameters which are listed above may be calculated from measurement of a correlated set of coordinates which specify the position and velocity of the spacecraft. Variations in these measurements may be applied; for example, data specifying two successive positions and the time interval between may be employed. Velocity and acceleration data may also be measured and integrated to obtain the orbit parameters. The design and selection of an instrumentation system will depend, to a degree, upon the nature of the flight which is under consideration and upon the expected time variations for the coordinates to be measured.

It will not always be convenient to measure range or range rate directly over the great distances which are involved in spaceflight. Consequently, it will be desirable to have available the means to eliminate the requirement for direct measurement of these quantities. The measurement of distances may be eliminated in the case of the Kepler orbits. The time derivative of the angular momentum is known to vanish, as a consequence

$$2\dot{r}r\dot{\theta} + r^2\ddot{\theta} = 0 \qquad (3\text{-}2)$$

This equation may be solved to provide the following for r;

$$r = \frac{-2\dot{r}\dot{\theta}}{\ddot{\theta}} \qquad (3\text{-}3)$$

Through the application of similar manipulations, it would be possible to eliminate the requirement for the measurement of $\dot{r}$ as a specific measurement. Indeed, astronomical determinations of orbits have been made for ages with the only measurements being those of angles and time intervals. Many combinations of coordinate measurements will serve to permit the calculation of the desired parameters, in general a set of six independent coordinates will be required. While the classical methods of astronomy have been proved satisfactory for that purpose, navigation in space will frequently demand that solutions for the orbit parameters be obtained in brief time intervals before excessive errors have accumulated. To do this will generally require that rates be measured directly and that measurements which the astronomers have not been using must be included in the space navigator's techniques.

Once the orbit parameters have been established, the orbit may be defined through the use of the orbit equation; (2-24)

$$r = \frac{h^2/k}{1 + e \cos (\theta - \theta_p)}$$

A time history of the spacecraft motion may be defined through the use of the relations involving the eccentric anomaly, Equation (2-38)

$$(t - t_p) = \frac{1}{n}(A_e - e \sin A_e)$$

When they are required, small extrapolations of the trajectory may be made using the convenient relation

$$\Delta\theta = \frac{[1 + e \cos (\theta - \theta_p)]^2 \, n \, \Delta t}{(1 + e^2)^{3/2}} \tag{3-4}$$

which may be derived from the time Equation (2-37). This relation assumes that the time rate of change of the true anomaly is constant over the interval of extrapolation. While this is true only for infinitesimal intervals of time or for circular orbits, that is $e = 0$, many useful approximations may be derived from applications of Equation (3-4).

3.1.2 POSITION VECTORS AND THEIR USE

The motion of an orbiting spacecraft may be described through the use of a vector which is drawn from the reference point outward to the position which is being defined, this is called a *position vector*. The convenience of the position vector concept results from the ease with which position and velocity of a particle may be calculated and manipulated by the application of the vector calculus. The analysis of the motions of a spacecraft may be reduced to problems of vector analysis. The position of a spacecraft at a point P is defined by the vector **r** as shown by Figure 3.1. The vector **r** is related to its cartesian components in an inertial reference frame by

$$\mathbf{r} = \mathbf{i}(r \cos \alpha \sin \eta) + \mathbf{j}(r \cos \alpha \cos \eta) + \mathbf{k}(r \sin \alpha) \tag{3-5}$$

The velocity of the spacecraft at P will be obtained by direct differentiation of the vector **r**;

$$\dot{\mathbf{r}} = \mathbf{i}(\dot{r}\cos\alpha\sin\eta + r\cos\alpha\cos\eta\dot{\eta} - r\sin\alpha\sin\eta\dot{\alpha})$$
$$+ \mathbf{j}(\dot{r}\cos\alpha\cos\eta - r\cos\alpha\sin\eta\dot{\eta} - r\sin\alpha\cos\eta\dot{\alpha})$$
$$+ \mathbf{k}(\dot{r}\sin\alpha + r\cos\alpha\dot{\alpha}) \tag{3-6}$$

Equation (3-6) may be stated in a different form as follows

$$\dot{\mathbf{r}} = \mathbf{v} = \mathbf{i}\dot{x} + \mathbf{j}\dot{y} + \mathbf{k}\dot{z}$$

Similarly, the acceleration $\ddot{\mathbf{r}}$ may be derived by a second application of term by term differentiation

$$\mathbf{a} = \ddot{\mathbf{r}} = \mathbf{i}\ddot{x} + \mathbf{j}\ddot{y} + \mathbf{k}\ddot{z} \tag{3-7}$$

The angular velocity of the position vector in space will be important in applications which will be discussed in later sections. It is designated by the vector ω and may be computed as shown below

$$\omega = \mathbf{i}\dot{\alpha}\cos\eta + \mathbf{j}\dot{\alpha}\sin\eta + \mathbf{k}\dot{\eta} \tag{3-8}$$

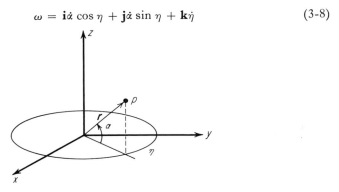

Fig. 3.1. The position vector.

3.1.3 REDUCTION OF AN ORBIT TO A PLANE

The free-fall orbit of a spacecraft in its central force field will be confined entirely within a plane; this is indicated by the principle of conservation of angular momentum. (Kepler's second law.) The plane of the orbit motion is defined as containing the velocity vector, $\mathbf{v}$ and the central point, or focus, of the force field. It may also be defined as the plane normal to the angular momentum vector. In central force field problems, it will always be possible to define a new coordinate system x', y', z' for which the angular momentum vector components $h_{x'} = h_{y'} = 0$. The following relations will obtain in this new reference frame (see Figure 3.2);

$$x' = r'\sin\eta'$$
$$y' = r'\cos\eta' \tag{3-9}$$
$$z' = 0$$

Differentiating these equations, we obtain the velocity components as the following expressions.

$$\dot{x}' = \dot{r}' \sin \eta' + r' \cos \eta' \dot{\eta}'$$

$$\dot{y}' = \dot{r}' \cos \eta' + r' \sin \eta' \dot{\eta}'$$

(3-10)

The acceleration components are given by

$$\ddot{x}' = (\ddot{r}' - r'\dot{\eta}') \sin \eta' + 2\dot{r}' \cos \eta' \dot{\eta}'$$

$$\ddot{y}' = (\ddot{r}' - r'\dot{\eta}') \cos \eta' - 2\dot{r}' \sin \eta' \dot{\eta}'$$

(3-11)

Where the notation which has been used is shown in Figure 3.2.

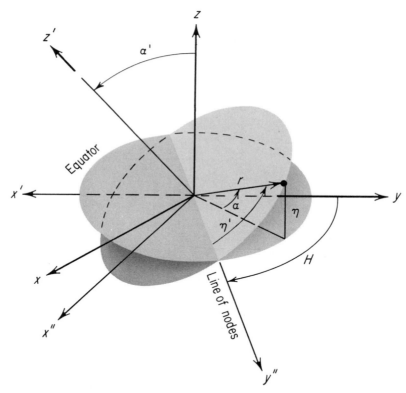

Fig. 3.2. The orbit reference system.

It may be noted here that, in the case of an orbit which is confined to the $x'y'$ plane, the angle η' will differ from the true anomaly, A_t, only by an additive constant.

The coordinate transformation from the x, y, z, reference frame to the

x', y', z' frame is accomplished by two successive rotational transformations. These are as follows

1. Rotate the frame about the z axis, an angle η placing the y' axis along the desired line of nodes.
2. Rotate an angle α' about the y' axis, the line of nodes.

This transformation may be defined mathematically by the matrix equation

$$x' = [A]x \tag{3-12}$$

where the matrix (A) will be given by

$$[A] = \begin{bmatrix} \cos \eta & \sin \eta & 0 \\ -\sin \eta \cos \alpha' & \cos \eta \cos \alpha' & \sin \alpha' \\ \sin \eta \sin \alpha' & -\sin \eta \sin \alpha' & \cos \alpha' \end{bmatrix} \tag{3-13}$$

The desired transformation will be obtained and $h_{x'} = h_{y'} = 0$ if the angles η and α' are selected such that

$$\tan \eta = \frac{-h_x}{h_y} \tag{3-14}$$

and

$$\tan \alpha' = \frac{h_x}{h_z} \sin \eta \tag{3-15}$$

The coordinates which are represented in this way may be considered to be a set of *normal* coordinates; most problems will be described in terms of these normal coordinates and, for the sake of convenience, the primes will be omitted from the notation.

3.1.4 OFFSET POSITION VECTORS

In many space problems, it will not be possible to measure **r** directly since it would require access to the origin of coordinates such as the center of the Earth, the center of the Sun, and so on. The measurement of such a position vector is frequently made by means of an *offset*. When an offset is used, the distance to the body in question is measured from some convenient point whose position relative to the central reference point is known and the desired position vector is calculated using vector analysis. If the offset measurement is made from a point at position given by **R**, and the measurement indicates a position vector **ρ** relative to the point at **R**, the desired position vector will be given by

$$\mathbf{r}(x, y, z) = \mathbf{R}(X, Y, Z) + \mathbf{\rho}(x_1, y_1, z_1) \tag{3-16}$$

The velocity and acceleration vectors are obtained by means of differentiation of Equation (3-16). The coordinate reference which is fixed at **R** will not, in general, be an inertial frame, consequently allowance must be made for its rotation. The relations of the coordinates are illustrated in Figure 3.3.

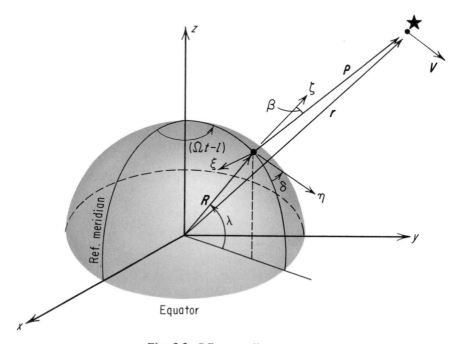

Fig. 3.3. Offset coordinate system.

An example which will demonstrate the method will be described. Consider a set of measurements of ρ which have been made from an Earth-fixed site. The center of the Earth is taken as the origin of coordinates and it is desired to convert the components of ρ to have reference to the origin at the center of the earth. The components of ρ are

$$x_1 = \rho \cos \beta \sin \delta$$
$$y_1 = \rho \cos \beta \cos \delta \qquad\qquad (3\text{-}17)$$
$$z_1 = \rho \sin \beta$$

The components of the position vector of the measuring site are the components of **R**, they are

$$X = R \cos \lambda \sin (\Omega t - l)$$
$$Y = R \cos \lambda \cos (\Omega t - l) \qquad\qquad (3\text{-}18)$$
$$Z = R \sin \lambda$$

where

l = longitude of the tracking station
λ = latitude of the tracking station

$$\Omega = \frac{2\pi}{24} \text{ hrs} = 75 \times 10^{-6} \text{ radians/sec}$$

The position vector, measured relative to a convenient reference frame, will require transformation to permit these measurements to be stated relative to another reference. For example, observations which have been made in terms of antenna coordinates at a tracking station must be transformed before they are stated as a set of coordinates which are referred to a geocentric inertial reference frame. This is accomplished by use of one intermediate set of Earth-fixed coordinates. In vector terms, the position of the spacecraft is given by

$$\mathbf{r}_I = \mathbf{R}_I + \boldsymbol{\rho}_I \tag{3-19}$$

where

$\mathbf{r}_I$ = position of the spacecraft relative to the geocentric inertial reference.
$\mathbf{R}_I$ = position vector of the tracking station relative to the inertial coordinate reference.
$\boldsymbol{\rho}_I$ = position vector of the spacecraft relative to the tracking station.

The vector Equation (3-18), above, may be rewritten in terms of Earth fixed vectors as

$$\mathbf{r}_I = [A](\mathbf{R}_{\text{earth}} + \boldsymbol{\rho}_{\text{earth}})$$

where the matrix, $[A]$, transforms a vector which is described in an inertial reference frame (geocentric) to one which is described in an equatorial Earth-fixed system.

A second transformation matrix, $[B]$, will be required to transform the Earth-fixed position vector of the craft to one which is stated in terms of the antenna axis. In short, the matrix $[B]$ describes the orientation of the tracking antenna reference frame with respect to the equatorial reference system, see Figure 3.4. In the terms which have been defined above, the position of the spacecraft will be given as

$$\mathbf{r}_I = [A](\mathbf{R}_{\text{earth}} + [B]\boldsymbol{\rho}_{\text{antenna}}) \tag{3-20}$$

In order to obtain the desired transformation, the matrix $[A]$ will represent the Earth's rotation, for example a rotation through an angle $(\Omega_e t - l)$ about the Z axis.

$$[A] = [(\Omega_e t - l)_Z] = \begin{bmatrix} \cos(\Omega_e t - l) & \sin(\Omega_e t - l) & 0 \\ -\sin(\Omega_e t - l) & \cos(\Omega_e t - l) & 0 \\ 0 & 0 & 1 \end{bmatrix} \tag{3-21}$$

The matrix $[B]$ represents a rotation of a displaced coordinate frame; this reference frame has its origin at the position indicated by $\mathbf{R}$ and has axes parallel to the Earth-fixed geocentric system (X', Y', Z'). This reference frame is

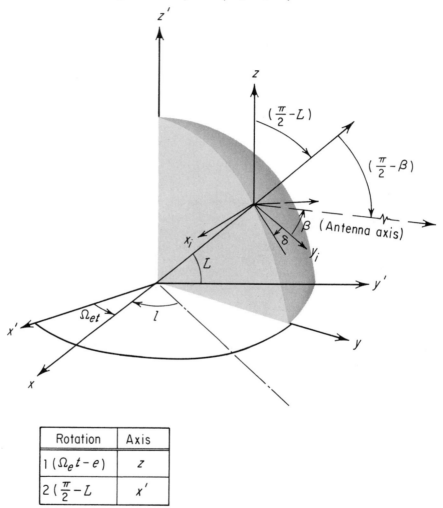

Rotation	Axis
$1\ (\Omega_e t - e)$	z
$2\ (\frac{\pi}{2} - L$	x'

Fig. 3.4. Transformation from geocentric inertial reference to antenna coordinates.

rotated through an angle $(\pi/2 - L)$ about the X' axis of the displaced reference frame. This transformation aligns the z_1 axis with the local vertical and places the x_1 axis in the plane containing the pole and the X' axis. This matrix may then be stated mathematically as follows;

$$[B] = \left[\left(\frac{\pi}{2} - L \right)_{x'} \right] = \begin{bmatrix} 1 & 0 & 0 \\ 0 & \sin L & \cos L \\ 0 & -\cos L & \sin L \end{bmatrix} \quad (3\text{-}22)$$

In order to compute the velocity of the spacecraft, it is necessary to determine the velocity of the tracking, or measuring site, relative to the center of the Earth and to add this to the velocity of the craft relative to the measuring site. The first of these terms is calculated as the derivative of $\mathbf{R}(X, Y, Z)$ under the restriction the $\dot{R} = \dot{\lambda} = \dot{l} = 0$. Consequently

$$\dot{\mathbf{R}} = \mathbf{i}\dot{X} + \mathbf{j}\dot{Y} + \mathbf{k}\dot{Z} \quad (3\text{-}23)$$

Where, from Equation (3-18)

$$\begin{aligned} \dot{X} &= R\Omega_e \cos \lambda \cos (\Omega_e t - l) \\ \dot{Y} &= -R\Omega_e \cos \lambda \cos (\Omega_e t - l) \\ \dot{Z} &= 0 \end{aligned} \quad (3\text{-}24)$$

Since the measurements of ρ are made with reference to the Earth-fixed local reference frame, which rotates in inertial space, the derivative of ρ must take account of this rotation. This is done through application of the theorem of Corriolis.

$$\dot{\rho} = \frac{d\rho}{dt} + (\Omega_e \times \rho)$$

The velocity components of $\dot{\rho}$ are thus computed as

$$\begin{aligned} x_1 &= \dot{\rho} \cos \beta \sin \delta - \rho \sin \beta \sin \delta \quad \dot{\beta} + \rho(\dot{\delta} - \Omega_e) \cos \beta \cos \delta \\ y_1 &= (\dot{\rho} - \rho\dot{\delta}) \cos \beta \cos \delta - \rho \sin \beta \sin \delta \quad \dot{\beta} + \Omega\rho \cos \beta \sin \delta \quad (3\text{-}25) \\ z_1 &= \dot{\rho} \sin \beta + \rho \cos \beta\dot{\beta} \end{aligned}$$

The position and velocity vectors of the craft relative to the geocentric inertial system are given by

$$\mathbf{r} = \mathbf{i}(X + x_1) + \mathbf{j}(Y + y_1) + \mathbf{k}(Z + z_1) \quad (3\text{-}26)$$

$$\dot{\mathbf{r}} = \mathbf{i}(\dot{X} + \dot{x}_1) + \mathbf{j}(\dot{Y} + \dot{y}_1) + \mathbf{k}(\dot{Z} + \dot{z}_1) \quad (3\text{-}27)$$

In general, space navigation problems will not require further differentiation to obtain acceleration terms. When these are required, however, they may be obtained by successive application of the techniques which have been described above.

3.2 VECTOR TRANSFORMATIONS IN SPACE NAVIGATION

The motions of Solar System bodies and spacecraft as they move about are determined by the gravitational forces which are exerted on these bodies;

in addition it is necessary to consider the perturbations due to non-gravitational forces acting on the bodies under consideration. Perturbing forces may arise as a result of

Rocket thrust

Momentum exchanges (for example, drag or meteoroid impacts)

Non-spherical properties of the gravity fields (for example, departure from a true inverse-square law central force field).

The structure of the Solar System makes it convenient, in many cases, to consider these motions as though they were occurring entirely in the field of one body or the other. Such an assumption can be justified as a mathematical approximation but this justification will be omitted here. As a result of this assumption it becomes convenient to describe the motion of the planets, satellites, and astronautical bodies in terms of coordinate reference frames which have their origins at the center of the applicable gravity fields. This section will discuss some of these reference frames as they are used in specific problems. The mathematical relations which obtain between the coordinates of an invariant vector when that vector is defined with reference to the different systems are also discussed.

The reference frames which will be discussed in this section will all be cartesian systems with their third, or z, axis aligned along the angular velocity vector which is of greatest interest in the motion. It will be taken as a convention to name these reference frames after the body which is found at the origin; an additional specification will indicate the plane of the x and y axes. Consequently, heliocentric systems have origin at the center of the Sun, geocentric systems are Earth centered, and so forth. Orbital systems have their x–y planes in the plane of the orbits under study, equatorial and ecliptic systems are those in which the named planes contain the x–y plane.

It would, of course, be impossible to define a single general purpose transformation of coordinates for all space navigation problems. However, an example which is considered to contain the important elements of most typical problems will be discussed below. Specific applications of the techniques to be presented will permit variations to be developed for individual cases as they arise.

Consider the example of a spacecraft traveling in an orbit about the Earth, and it is desired to transfer this craft to another planet, say to Mars. The motion of the craft in its orbit will be known as a result of observations which may have been made from an Earth-bound tracking system or a self-contained guidance system. Such a system will be assumed to contain computer elements to calculate the coordinates and the velocity of the craft with relation to an orbital reference frame which has its origin at the center of the Earth (a geocentric orbital reference system). In order to define the interplanetary transfer trajectory in a convenient manner, it will be necessary to discuss the motions of the craft in terms of a heliocentric-ecliptical reference frame. This transformation from a geocentric-orbital reference to a heliocentric-ecliptic system will be discussed in the following paragraphs.

The components of a vector, for example, the position or velocity of a point in an Earth referenced orbit, are given in a geocentric-orbital coordinate system and it is desired to define the vector and its components with reference to a set of heliocentric-ecliptic coordinate axes. Although a single tranformation is desired, it will be convenient to develop this transformation as a series of steps in which the desired vector undergoes a series of transformations from one coordinate reference frame to another. The reference frames to be considered are as follows:

Geocentric-Orbital System (See Figure 3.5)

Origin— center of the Earth
x axis— directed from the origin through the descending node of the orbit and the equatorial plane
y axis— directed so as to form a right handed set with x and z
z axis— directed outward from the origin along the positive sense of the orbit angular velocity vector

Geocentric-Equatorial System (See Figure 3.6)

Origin— center of the Earth
x' axis— directed outward from the origin to the descending node formed by a point on the equator of the Earth and the ecliptic plane
y' axis— directed so as to form a right-handed set with the x' and z' axes
z' axis— directed outward from the origin along the vector which represents the angular velocity of diurnal rotation of the Earth

Geocentric-Ecliptic System (See Figure 3.7)

Origin— center of the Earth
x'' axis—directed outward from the origin toward the first point of Ares, ♈ (the vernal equinox)
y'' axis—directed so as to make a right-handed set with x'' and z''
z'' axis—directed outward along the positive sense of the vector representing the velocity of annual rotation of the Earth about the Sun

Heliocentric-Ecliptic System (See Figure 3.8)

Origin— center of the Sun
X axis— directed outward from the origin toward the first point of Ares, ♈ (parallel to x'')
Y axis— directed so as to form a right-handed set with X and Z
Z axis— directed outward from the origin in the same direction as z''

Now, let the position of a spacecraft be defined by its position vector **r** and its velocity by a vector **v**. These may be specified relative to the various coordinate systems as follows:

$\mathbf{r}^0, \mathbf{v}^0$— position and velocity of the craft when expressed on the geocentric-orbital system

$\mathbf{r}', \mathbf{v}'$— position and velocity of craft expressed in geocentric-equatorial system

$\mathbf{r}'', \mathbf{v}''$—position and velocity of craft expressed in geocentric-ecliptic system

$\mathbf{R}, \mathbf{V}$— position and velocity of craft expressed in heliocentric-ecliptic system

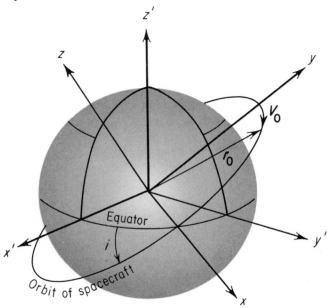

Fig. 3.5. Geocentric-orbital reference system.

The following general relations exist between the geocentric and heliocentric vectors

$$\mathbf{R} = \mathbf{R}_\oplus + \mathbf{r}$$

and

$$\mathbf{V} = \mathbf{V}_\oplus + \mathbf{v}$$

where

$\mathbf{R}_\oplus$ = the position of the Earth when defined relative to the heliocentric system

$\mathbf{V}_\oplus$ = the velocity of the Earth relative to a heliocentric reference

The vectors which describe the position and velocity of the Earth have components which may be expressed in the heliocentric-ecliptic system as follows

$$\mathbf{R}_\oplus = \begin{bmatrix} R_\oplus \cos \Omega_\oplus t_{\Upsilon} \\ R_\oplus \sin \Omega_\oplus t_{\Upsilon} \\ 0 \end{bmatrix} \begin{bmatrix} u_X \\ u_Y \\ u_Z \end{bmatrix} \tag{3-28}$$

$$\mathbf{V}_\oplus = \begin{bmatrix} V_\oplus \sin (\Omega_\oplus t_{\Upsilon} + \phi) \\ V_\oplus \cos (\Omega_\oplus t_{\Upsilon} + \phi) \\ 0 \end{bmatrix} \begin{bmatrix} u_X \\ u_Y \\ u_Z \end{bmatrix} \tag{3-29}$$

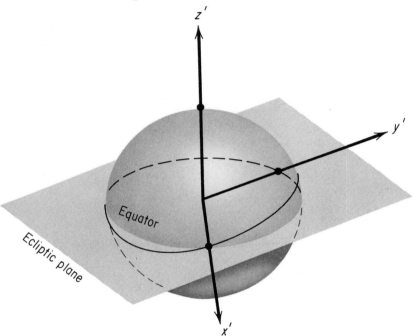

Fig. 3.6. Geocentric equatorial reference system.

where

u_X, u_Y, u_Z = the unit vectors in the directions of the coordinate axes of the heliocentric reference system

t_{Υ} = the time since the vernal equinox

ϕ = a time varying angle which accounts for the ellipticity of the orbit, for a circular orbit, $\phi = 0$

$\Omega = \dfrac{2\pi}{365}$ radians per day

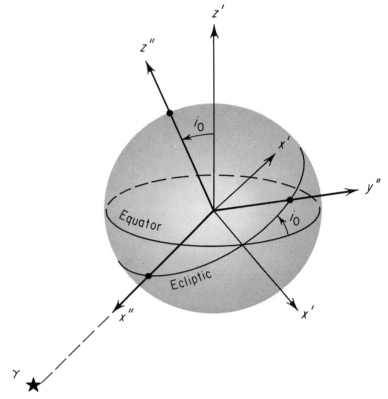

Fig. 3.7. Geocentric-ecliptic reference system.

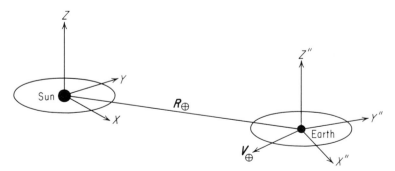

Fig. 3.8. Heliocentric-ecliptic reference system.

The transformations which are required within the geocentric group of reference frames will be discussed first. The steps required are given by two matrixes as follows

$\mathbf{r}' = [I]\mathbf{r}^0$ transforms $\mathbf{r}^0$ from a geocentric-orbital system to a geocentric-equatorial system

$\mathbf{r}'' = [II]\mathbf{r}'$ transforms $\mathbf{r}'$ from a geocentric-equatorial system to a geocentric-ecliptic system

The two matrixes indicated by $[I]$ and $[II]$ are taken to represent transformations through a set of Eulerian angles. The general transformation will be as shown in Figure 3.9. The rotation matrixes may be formed by standard methods such as those which are described in Reference 3.1; the general transformation may be summarized as follows:

$$[T] = \begin{bmatrix} \cos A_3 & \sin A_3 & 0 \\ -\sin A_3 & \cos A_3 & 0 \\ 0 & 0 & 1 \end{bmatrix} \times \begin{bmatrix} 1 & 0 & 0 \\ 0 & \cos A_2 & \sin A_2 \\ 0 & -\sin A_2 & \cos A_2 \end{bmatrix} \times$$

$$\begin{bmatrix} \cos A_1 & \sin A_1 & 0 \\ -\sin A_1 & \cos A_1 & 0 \\ 0 & 0 & 1 \end{bmatrix} \qquad (3\text{-}30)$$

When the operations indicated have been performed with the angles as tabulated in Figure 3.9. The transformation matrix will be

$$[T] = \begin{bmatrix} \cos A_3 \cos A_1 - \cos A_2 \sin A_1 \sin A_3 \\ -\sin A_3 \cos A_1 - \cos A_2 \sin A_1 \cos A_3 \\ \sin A_2 \sin A_1 \end{bmatrix}$$

$$\begin{array}{cc} \cos A_3 \sin A_1 + \cos A_2 \cos A_1 \sin A_3 & \sin A_3 \sin A_2 \\ -\sin A_3 \sin A_1 + \cos A_2 \cos A_1 \cos A_3 & \cos A_3 \sin A_2 \\ -\sin A_2 \cos A_1 & \cos A_2 \end{array} \Bigg] \qquad (3\text{-}31)$$

In the transformations which are of interest, we have chosen $A_3 = 0$, consequently $\sin A_3 = 0$ and $\cos A_3 = 1 : [T]$ may be written as

$$[T] = \begin{bmatrix} \cos A_1 & \sin A_1 & 0 \\ -\cos A_2 \sin A_1 & \cos A_2 \cos A_1 & \sin A_2 \\ \sin A_2 \sin A_1 & -\sin A_2 \cos A_1 & \cos A_2 \end{bmatrix} \qquad (3\text{-}32)$$

Now, substituting the specific values which are indicated in the table on Figure 3.9

$$[I] = \begin{bmatrix} \cos l_0 & \sin l_0 & 0 \\ -\sin l_0 \cos i_0 & \cos l_0 \cos i_0 & \sin i_0 \\ \sin l_0 \sin i_0 & -\cos l_0 \sin i_0 & \cos i_0 \end{bmatrix} \qquad (3\text{-}33)$$

$$[II] = \begin{bmatrix} \cos \Omega_\oplus t \Upsilon & \sin \Omega_\oplus t \Upsilon & 0 \\ -\cos 23\tfrac{1}{2}° \sin \Omega_\oplus t \Upsilon & \cos 23\tfrac{1}{2}° \sin \Omega_\oplus t \Upsilon & \sin 23\tfrac{1}{2}° \\ \sin 23\tfrac{1}{2}° \sin \Omega_\oplus t \Upsilon & -\sin 23\tfrac{1}{2}° \cos \Omega_\oplus t \Upsilon & \cos 23\tfrac{1}{2}° \end{bmatrix} \qquad (3\text{-}34)$$

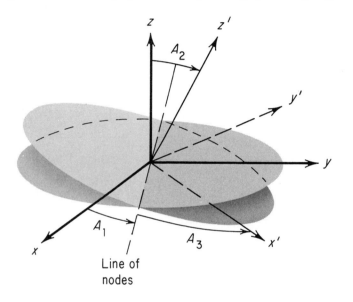

Transformation angles

Symbol	Definition	Value in $[I]$	Value in $[II]$
A_1	Longitude of line of nodes	l_0	$\Omega_\oplus t \gamma$
A_2	Inclination angle	i_0	$23\tfrac{1}{2}°$
A_3	Not applicable	—	—

Fig. 3.9. The general transformation.

The matrix for the geocentric transformation from orbital to ecliptic coordinates may now be obtained through application of matrix multiplication to Equations (3-33) and (3-34), for example

$$\mathbf{r}'' = [I][II]\mathbf{r}^0$$

This expansion will not be shown here but it may be developed readily by the reader if it is required.

The transformation to heliocentric coordinates is indeed a translational transformation, no rotations are indicated since the x'', y'', and z'' axes have been defined to be parallel to the XYZ system. The transformation, then, is represented by an operation of vector addition

$$\mathbf{R} = \mathbf{R}_\oplus + \mathbf{r}$$

Which may be expanded into matrix form as follows

$$\mathbf{R} = \begin{bmatrix} R_X \\ R_Y \\ R_Z \end{bmatrix} \begin{bmatrix} u_X \\ u_Y \\ u_Z \end{bmatrix} = \begin{bmatrix} R_\oplus \cos \Omega_\oplus t \varphi + r''_x \\ R_\oplus \sin \Omega_\oplus t \varphi + r''_y \\ r''_z \end{bmatrix} \begin{bmatrix} u_X \\ u_Y \\ u_Z \end{bmatrix} \qquad (3\text{-}35)$$

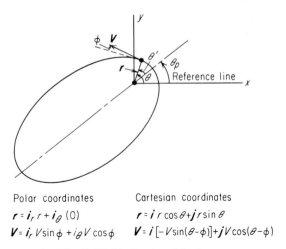

Polar coordinates

$r = i_r r + i_\theta (0)$

$V = i_r V \sin \phi + i_\theta V \cos \phi$

Cartesian coordinates

$r = i\, r \cos \theta + j\, r \sin \theta$

$V = i [-V \sin(\theta - \phi)] + j V \cos(\theta - \phi)$

Fig. 3.10. Motion in orbit plane.

Frequently, it will be convenient to state the position of a spacecraft in polar coordinates. These coordinates will be referred to the Sun or the Earth as a pole. For example, consider such a position vector when it is given with reference to a geocentric-orbital coordinate system; the velocity will also be given in terms of its magnitude, v, and a flight path angle φ. This is illustrated in Figure 3.10. The resolution of these polar coordinates into components which are related to the cartesian coordinate reference is shown in the figure. As a result of the definition of the orbital reference system, the nominal values of r_z and v_z will be zero. Any out-of-plane component of position or velocity will, indeed, represent error quantities in a navigation problem.

3.3. TRACKING SYSTEMS

Instruments which are designed to measure the trajectory (or track) of a moving craft are called *tracking systems*. Tracking systems may be designed to operate on optical, radar, or sonic principles among others. The most common systems employ radio or radar techniques. In this section our attention will be directed to selected systems for measurement of the position of a spacecraft relative to a center of a complex of tracking stations. Systems which make direct measurements of the velocity of a spacecraft will be discussed in a later section. Combined systems may, of course, be used to secure the advantages of both kinds of systems under certain circumstances.

In this section, tracking systems which determine position by the following means will be described and analyzed.

1. Spherical-polar systems: These measure the range to a spacecraft and note the azimuth and elevation angles of the line of sight from a convenient reference direction

2. Three dimensional-spherical systems: This class of system measures range to the craft from each of three stations in order to compute the position of the craft

3. Three dimensional-hyperbolic systems: These measure the difference in range from pairs of stations and compute position of the craft from these difference data (three stations are required).

Spherical-polar systems are of general interest since systems of this kind require a single tracking station for each independant determination of position. A typical example of the spherical-polar system is a fire control radar tracking station. Three dimensional-spherical (range only) systems are convenient where it is possible to transmit signals to a spacecraft and to note the time delay before receipt of the retransmitted, or reflected, signal. Thus range is measured without requiring precision measurement of directional data.

Three dimensional-hyperbolic systems are convenient for applications where three remote stations can transmit signals to the spacecraft which are subsequently retransmitted to a central master station. These signals are made coherent with a time reference in the master station and range difference data may be calculated for each pair of remote stations. Each range difference measurement places the spacecraft on the surface of a hyperbola. Three difference pairs will permit a unique position determination. This system permits precision calculation of position without requiring that absolute precision distance measurements be made.

Each of the systems to be discussed must be carefully considered with regard to the precision required and to the capability of the measuring equipment. Any real system will, of course, be characterized by the presence of a small but finite error, or uncertainty, in its measurements. These errors will be subject to a variation as a function of position of the spacecraft relative to the tracking station, or stations. This effect is geometrical in nature and must be considered in the selection of a tracking system for a specific application.

In addition to the above mentioned geometrical errors, each system will be subject to errors which may be classed as systematic and as random. The systematic errors may be removed through calibration of the system, the random errors, on the other hand, will require special attention and analysis for each installation and for each mission. The accuracy of the computed position will depend upon the particular parameters which are measured, the measuring system, and the location of the spacecraft with respect to the complex of measuring stations. It is characteristic of all such systems that the random errors in position which result from the random errors in measurement of parameters by the system will be increased, or diminished as a function of the position of the craft being tracked. The errors which result from a specific measurement will depend only partially on the accuracy of the equipment but in addition they will depend upon the relative configuration of the spacecraft and the measuring system. This configuration will determine the extent to which the geometric effects will influence the accuracy of measurements. As will be seen, a useful rule is that ground based measuring systems will exhibit errors which increase with increasing distances and with the presence of measurements which must be made over oblique angles. The measurement of position by the three techniques mentioned above will be discussed in some detail. The geometric effects on system accuracy will be discussed with relation to the first system only.

Velocity of a spacecraft may be computed from a pair of independant position measurements. From the calculus of continuous motions, velocity may be defined as

$$\mathbf{v} = \lim_{\Delta t \to 0} \frac{\mathbf{r}_2 - \mathbf{r}_1}{\Delta t}$$

When the motion is approximately uniform during a time interval τ, the velocity may be approximated as follows

$$\mathbf{v} = \frac{\mathbf{r}(t + \tau) - \mathbf{r}(t)}{\tau}$$

Some enhancement in accuracy may be obtained when several measurements and their time intervals are averaged. An interesting special case arises when a sequence of positions have been measured at uniform time intervals following a reference time t. The sequence is given as

$$\mathbf{r}(t), \ \mathbf{r}(t + \tau), \ \mathbf{r}(t + 2\tau), \ \mathbf{r}(t + 3\tau), \ \dots \ \mathbf{r}(t + n\tau)$$

and the average velocity over the interval $n\tau$ may be calculated as

$$\mathbf{v} = \frac{1}{n}\left[\frac{\mathbf{r}(t + \tau) - \mathbf{r}(t)}{\tau} + \frac{\mathbf{r}(t + 2t) - \mathbf{r}(t + \tau)}{\tau}\right.$$

$$\left. + \ldots \frac{\mathbf{r}(t + nt) - \mathbf{r}[t + (n - 1)\tau]}{\tau}\right]$$

$$= \frac{1}{n\tau}\sum_{i=1}^{n}(\mathbf{r}_i - \mathbf{r}_{i-1})$$

It is characteristic of this method of averaging that the effect of random errors in position measurement will be diminished in proportion to $\sqrt{n}$ when the velocity is calculated in this manner.

3.3.1 SPHERICAL-POLAR SYSTEM

This class of tracking system, in its most familiar form, consists of a single radar station. This station locates a point in space by measuring the slant range, the elevation angle and the azimuth angle of the line of sight. These three coordinates are adequate to specify the position in space that is occupied by the point being tracked. A right-handed coordinate reference frame such as the one shown in Figure 3.11 has been selected for the discussion of the spherical-polar system. The ground station is located at the origin of coordinates. From Figure 3.11, it may be seen that the spacecraft which is at P will be located in space by a position vector having components as follows

$$x = r \cos \varphi \cos \theta$$
$$y = r \cos \varphi \sin \theta \qquad (3.36)$$
$$z = r \sin \varphi$$

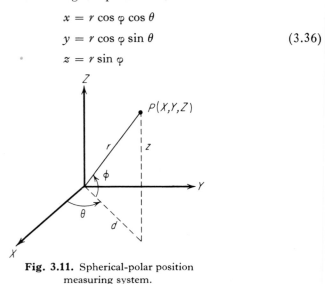

Fig. 3.11. Spherical-polar position
measuring system.

From the geometry, it is apparent that these may be stated in terms of cylindrical coordinates as

$$x = d \cos \theta$$
$$y = d \sin \theta \tag{3-37}$$
$$z = z$$

where

$$d = \sqrt{r^2 - z^2}$$

$$\cos \varphi = \frac{d}{\sqrt{d^2 + z^2}} = \frac{d}{r}$$

$$\sin \varphi = \frac{z}{r}$$

The accuracy of the component determinations will reflect the geometrical properties of the position errors. They are measured in terms of the statistical properties of the errors in position as indicated by the differentials in the components, for example, dx, dy, and dz. These differentials may be calculated as follows

$$dx = \frac{\partial x}{\partial r} dr + \frac{\partial x}{\partial \theta} d\theta + \frac{\partial x}{\partial \varphi} d\varphi$$

$$dy = \frac{\partial y}{\partial r} dr + \frac{\partial y}{\partial \theta} d\theta + \frac{\partial y}{\partial \varphi} d\varphi \tag{3-38}$$

$$dz = \frac{\partial z}{\partial r} dr + \frac{\partial z}{\partial \theta} d\theta + \frac{\partial z}{\partial \varphi} d\varphi$$

The partial derivatives shown in Equations (3-38) may be calculated with reference to Equations (3-36) and are given by the expressions

$$\frac{\partial x}{\partial r} = \cos \varphi \cos \theta$$

$$\frac{\partial x}{\partial \theta} = - r \cos \varphi \sin \theta$$

$$\frac{\partial x}{\partial \varphi} = - r \sin \varphi \cos \theta$$

$$\frac{\partial y}{\partial r} = \cos \varphi \sin \theta$$

$$\frac{\partial y}{\partial \theta} = r \cos \varphi \cos \theta$$

$$\frac{\partial y}{\partial \varphi} = -r \sin \varphi \sin \theta$$

$$\frac{\partial z}{\partial r} = \sin \varphi$$

$$\frac{\partial z}{\partial \theta} = 0$$

$$\frac{\partial z}{\partial \phi} = r \cos \varphi$$

As a result of making the indicated substitutions

$$dx = \cos \varphi \cos \theta \, dr - r \cos \varphi \sin \theta \, d\theta - r \sin \varphi \cos \theta \, d\varphi$$

$$dy = \cos \varphi \sin \theta \, dr + r \cos \varphi \sin \theta \, d\theta - r \sin \varphi \sin \theta \, d\varphi \qquad (3\text{-}39)$$

$$dz = \sin \varphi \, dr + r \cos \varphi \, d\varphi$$

Frequently, it will be desired to state the statistical nature of the geometrical contribution to the error in tracking in terms of a root mean square error (rms). If the errors in the measured coordinates are independant of one another, the rms errors in position will be computed from the expressions

$$dx_{\text{rms}} = \sqrt{\cos^2 \varphi \cos^2 \theta \, dr_{\text{rms}}^2 + r^2 \cos^2 \varphi \sin^2 \theta \, d\theta_{\text{rms}}^2 + r^2 \sin^2 \varphi \cos^2 \theta \, d\varphi_{\text{rms}}^2}$$

$$dy_{\text{rms}} = \sqrt{\cos^2 \varphi \sin^2 \theta \, dr_{\text{rms}}^2 + r^2 \cos^2 \varphi \sin^2 \theta \, d\theta_{\text{rms}}^2 + r^2 \sin^2 \varphi \sin^2 \theta \, d\varphi_{\text{rms}}^2}$$

$$dz_{\text{rms}} = \sqrt{\sin^2 \varphi \, dr_{\text{rms}}^2 + r^2 \cos^2 \varphi \, d\varphi_{\text{rms}}^2}$$

3.3.2 THREE DIMENSIONAL SPHERICAL SYSTEM (Range only)

A spherical surface in space may be defined as the locus of points which are equidistant from some fixed point. In a three dimensional spherical tracking system, three such surfaces each of which is defined as a surface having distance equal to the range measured to the spacecraft from each of three widely separated stations are used to define the position of a spacecraft. Three of these surfaces will intersect to define two points which are located symmetrically with respect to the plane defined by the centers of the three spheres. If it is assumed that an object, such as a spacecraft, is tracked by a system of this kind in which range data are the only kind to be collected and it is further assumed that the vehicle does not cross the plane of symmetry without being detected, the position of the craft will be determined uniquely. Otherwise, some means to resolve the ambiguity will be required.

The three dimensional spherical tracking system requires three range measurement stations; ordinarily these will be radio or radar stations. A right-handed reference system is employed for the derivation of the position equations, see

Figure 3.12. In the general case, coordinates of the spacecraft are $P(x, y, z)$ and the coordinates of the range measuring stations are $R_i(x_i, y_i, z_i)$ where $i = 1, 2, 3$.

Let r_1, r_2, and r_3 be equal to the distances of the object in space from the measuring stations R_1, R_2, and R_3 respectively. From the geometry of Figure 3.12, it follows that

$$r_i^2 = (x_i - x)^2 + (y_i - y)^2 + (z_i - z)^2 \tag{3-40}$$

The distance of each measuring station from the origin of coordinates is given by

$$d_i^2 = x_i^2 + y_i^2 + z_i^2$$

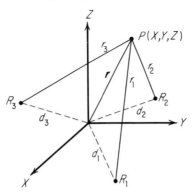

Fig. 3.12. Three-dimensional spherical system (range only).

The distance of the spacecraft at P from the origin is obtained from

$$r^2 = x^2 + y^2 + z^2$$

Squaring the terms of binomials as indicated in Equation (3-40) and using the relations of the following two equations one obtains

$$r^2 = r_i^2 - d_i^2 + 2(x_i x + y_i y + z_i z) \tag{3-41}$$

After some rearrangement of terms, this yields the relations

$$(x_2 - x_1)x + (y_2 - y_1)y + (z_2 - z_1)z = V_{12} \tag{3-42}$$

$$(x_3 - x_1)x + (y_3 - y_1)y + (z_3 - z_1)z = V_{13} \tag{3-43}$$

$$(x_3 - x_2)x + (y_3 - y_2)y + (z_3 - z_2)z = V_{23} \tag{3-44}$$

where the terms on the right hand side of these equations are defined as

$$V_{ij} = \tfrac{1}{2}[(r_i^2 - r_j^2) - (d_i^2 - d_j^2)] \tag{3-45}$$

In order to solve the above set of equations, we multiply Equations (3-42),

(3-43), and (3-45) by x_3, $- x_2$, and x_1 respectively and add the set. The result may be expressed conveniently in a determinant form as follows:

$$\begin{vmatrix} (x_1 - x_2) & (y_1 - y_2) \\ (x_3 - x_2) & (y_3 - y_2) \end{vmatrix} y + \begin{vmatrix} (x_1 - x_2) & (z_1 - z_2) \\ (x_3 - x_2) & (z_3 - z_2) \end{vmatrix} z = \begin{vmatrix} (x_1 - x_2) & V_{21} \\ (x_3 - x_2) & V_{23} \end{vmatrix}$$

$$(3\text{-}46)$$

Similarly, by multiplying Equations (3-42), (3-43), and (3-44) by y_3, $- y_2$, and y_1 respectively and adding we may obtain the following relation

$$\begin{vmatrix} (y_1 - y_2) & (x_1 - x_2) \\ (y_3 - y_2) & (x_3 - x_2) \end{vmatrix} x + \begin{vmatrix} (y_1 - y_2) & (z_1 - z_2) \\ (y_3 - y_2) & (z_3 - z_2) \end{vmatrix} z = \begin{vmatrix} (y_1 - y_2) & V_{21} \\ (y_3 - y_2) & V_{23} \end{vmatrix}$$

$$(3\text{-}47)$$

Equations (3-46) and (3-47) are linear expressions for x and y as functions of z, they may be written simply as

$$x = az + s$$
$$y = bz + t$$

where

$$a = \frac{-\begin{vmatrix} (y_1 - y_2) & (z_1 - z_2) \\ (y_3 - y_2) & (z_3 - z_2) \end{vmatrix}}{|D|}; \quad b = \frac{\begin{vmatrix} (x_1 - x_2) & (z_1 - z_2) \\ (x_3 - x_2) & (z_3 - z_2) \end{vmatrix}}{|D|}$$

$$s = \frac{-\begin{vmatrix} (y_2 - y_1) & V_{21} \\ (y_3 - y_2) & V_{23} \end{vmatrix}}{|D|}; \quad t = \frac{\begin{vmatrix} (x_1 - x_2) & V_{21} \\ (x_3 - x_2) & V_{23} \end{vmatrix}}{|D|}$$

$$|D| = \begin{vmatrix} (x_1 - x_2) & (y_1 - y_2) \\ (x_3 - x_2) & (y_3 - y_2) \end{vmatrix}$$

The coordinate z is determined by substituting Equations (3-46) and (3-47) into Equation (3-41) and rearranging the terms. The resulting equation is

$$(a^2 + b^2 + 1)z^2 + 2(as + bt - ax_i - by_i - z_i)z$$
$$+ (s^2 + t^2 + d_i^2 - r_i^2 - 2sx_i - 2ty_i) = 0 \quad (3\text{-}48)$$

The value of z is determined from solution of the resulting quadratic equation for any one of the three values of i.

It should be noted that these equations will be simplified if the coordinate system is chosen so that all of the receiving stations are in the x–y plane. In this case

$$z_i = 0$$
$$a = 0$$
$$b = 0$$

consequently

$$x = s$$
$$y = t$$
$$z = (2sx_i + 2ty_i + r_i^2 - d_i^2 - s^2 - t^2)^{1/2}$$

3.3.3. THREE-DIMENSIONAL HYPERBOLIC SYSTEMS

A hyperbolic position fix on a point in space will be obtained if the range difference measurements are noted with respect to the range from known and separate measuring stations. In the Raydist system (Reference 3.5), this range difference is measured by radio means and recorded in terms of phase in a signal carrier at the master stations. Three such independant range difference measurements must be made to calculate uniquely the position of an object in three dimensional space. In order to facilitate the development of the pertinent equations, a right-handed rectangular coordinate system has been used (see Figure 3.13). The z axis is vertical and the master receiving station is at the origin. The coordinates of the spacecraft are $P(x, y, z)$ and those of the slave stations are $R_i(x_i, y_i, z_i)$.

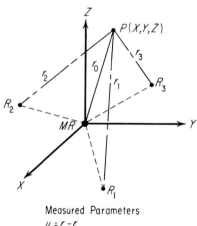

Measured Parameters
$$u_1 = r_1 - r_0$$
$$u_2 = r_2 - r_0$$
$$u_3 = r_3 - r_0$$

Fig. 3.13. Three-dimensional hyperbolic system.

In practice, position measuring systems of this kind will usually be established with their tracking stations in a nearly co-planar configuration. Little error will be introduced by the assumption that these stations are indeed confined to a single plane. This assumption greatly simplifies the mathematical analysis which will follow. For the co-planar configuration, the positions of the slave receivers are given by the points $(x_i, y_i, 0)$.

Let r, r_1, r_2, r_3, be the distances from the object in space to the master station and to each slave station respectively. It follows that the three measured range differences are given by

$$u_i = r - r_i \tag{3-49}$$

From Figure 3.13

$$r_i^2 = (x_i - x)^2 + (y_i - y)^2 + z^2 \tag{3-50}$$

and

$$r^2 = x^2 + y^2 + z^2 \tag{3-51}$$

The distances from the receivers to the master station are

$$d_i^2 = x_i^2 + y_i^2$$

now, from Equations (3-49) and (3-50)

$$r_i^2 = r^2 - 2u_i r + u_i^2 \tag{3-52}$$

Making substitutions from Equations (3-49) and (3-51)

$$x x_i + y y_i - r u_i = V_i \tag{3-53}$$

$$V_i = \tfrac{1}{2}(d_i^2 - u_i^2)$$

The values of x, y, and r may be obtained from Equation (3-53) with the values assigned to $i = 1, 2,$ and 3. The altitude z is obtained from Equation (3-50) after x and y are known.

It will be convenient to carry on the discussion from this point with a determinant notation. For this purpose, we make the following definitions

$$D = \begin{vmatrix} x_1 & y_1 & u_1 \\ x_2 & y_2 & u_2 \\ x_3 & y_3 & u_3 \end{vmatrix} \qquad D_y = \begin{vmatrix} x_1 & V_1 & u_1 \\ x_2 & V_2 & u_2 \\ x_3 & V_3 & u_3 \end{vmatrix}$$

$$D_x = \begin{vmatrix} v_1 & y_1 & u_1 \\ v_2 & y_2 & u_2 \\ v_3 & y_3 & u_2 \end{vmatrix} \qquad D_r = \begin{vmatrix} x_1 & y_1 & V_1 \\ x_2 & y_2 & V_2 \\ x_3 & y_3 & V_3 \end{vmatrix}$$

The Equations (3-53) have the following solutions in terms of these determinants

$$x = \frac{D_x}{D}$$

$$y = \frac{D_y}{D}$$

$$r = \frac{D_r}{D}$$

$$z = (r^2 - x^2 - y^2)^{1/2}$$

The Raydist system has the property that the recorded values of u_i are ambiguous by an integral number of wavelengths of the radio signal in use plus a fixed error which arises in the calibration of the equipment. When a minimum quantity of equipment is used, the ambiguity must be resolved by the use of a fix made by some auxiliary ground equipment. The absolute accuracy of the Raydist system is, then, limited by the fix accuracy which is obtained with this auxiliary system.

3.4 DOPPLER TRACKING TECHNIQUES

The frequency of an oscillatory signal which is detected at a receiver will appear to be different from that of the signal which is emitted when the transmitter and receiver have a relative velocity. This well known phenomenon of classical physics is called the *Doppler shift*; many applications have been made of the effect. These applications include such diverse uses as measurement of the rate of expansion of the universe and the apprehension of automobile speeders. Many examples of aircraft navigation devices which employ Doppler shift may be found. (Reference 3.6.) In its most simple form, the Doppler shift may be observed as the change of frequency of a pure C–W sinusoidal signal which is emitted by a source and received by an observer. Under the assumption that the emitted signal is a known, constant, frequency, the observer can specify the relative velocity component (for example the velocity component along the line-of-sight from the transmitter to the receiver) by measuring the received signal frequency and subtracting the known emitted frequency.

$$v_{\text{rel}} = \lambda_e(f_e - f_r) \tag{3-54}$$

where

f_e = the emitted frequency
f_r = the received frequency

Integration of Equation (3-54) will provide the separation distance from receiver to transmitter within an additive constant. Changes in separation distance may be calculated from the definite integral

$$s_1 - s_0 = \int_{t_2}^{t_1} \lambda_e(f_e - f_r)\, d\tau = \int_0^{t_1} \lambda_e \Delta f(\tau)\, d\tau \tag{3-55}$$

Since the signal frequency may be considered to be the time rate of change of phase of a sinusoidal signal, the integration of the Doppler frequency will be equivalent to a measurement of phase and hence to the measurement of range increments.

If the emitted signal is received by several observers each located at points which are known relative to one another and the received signals compared in frequency and phase with one another and with a reference signal which has been synchronized in both frequency and phase with the emitted signal, then the motions of the transmitter relative to the complex of receiving stations will be known except for certain ambiguities which may be resolved by special techniques. This forms the basis of the technique for tracking missiles and spacecraft through the use of Doppler radar or radio systems. Some special applications of this technique will be discussed in this section.

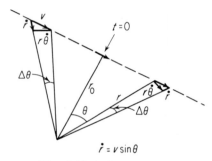

Fig. 3.14. Relative velocity.

The utility of Doppler measurements in application to satellite tracking is generally recognized; it finds uses in such systems as Minitrack (Reference 3.7). The development of the maser and the subsequent development of atomic clocks provide the means for generation of signals with very stable and precisely known frequencies. These will form the basis of some special and precise applications for the Doppler tracking systems. But first let us consider the basis of the design for such a system.

From geometry, one may derive that the relative velocity of two objects will vanish and reverse direction at the instant when the two are at their closest approach (see Figure 3.14). The time of closest approach, on a given pass, will be identified as the time when the Doppler shift passes through zero, for example when the received signal is identical in frequency and phase with the transmitted signal. Consider, as an example, the simplified model of a constant velocity satellite moving in orbit about a non-rotating Earth. In this example, a short segment of the trajectory may be approximated as a straight line. The radial component of the velocity will be given by

$$\dot{r} = V \sin \theta \tag{3-56}$$

where

$$\sin \theta = \sqrt{\frac{r^2 - r_0^2}{r^2}}$$

The Doppler frequency which is observed when this satellite is tracked by a fixed ground receiver will be

$$\Delta f = \dot{r}\lambda_e = \lambda_e V \sin \theta = \frac{\lambda_e V}{r}\sqrt{r^2 - r_0^2} \qquad (3\text{-}57)$$

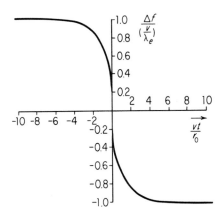

$$\frac{\Delta f}{\left(\frac{V}{\lambda_e}\right)} = \frac{1}{\sqrt{\frac{r_0^2}{vt^2}+1}}$$

Fig. 3.15. Universal doppler shift curve.

The time rate of change of the Doppler frequency will be of interest, it is given by

$$\frac{d}{dt}(\Delta f) = V\lambda_e \cos \theta \frac{d\theta}{dt} = \frac{V^2 r_0^2}{r^2}\lambda_e \frac{d\theta}{dt} \qquad (3\text{-}58)$$

It will be noted that the slope of the curve of Doppler frequency vs time vanishes as $r \to \infty$ or as $\theta \to \pi/2$; it is a maximum at $r = r_0$ or $\theta = 0$. Since the Doppler frequency is a function of two parameters (v, r_0) and the variable r, three measurements of Δf taken at different times will be sufficient to determine the velocity (and hence an estimate of the altitude) of the satellite and its distance of closest approach (cf. Reference 3.6). An example of a typical Doppler frequency versus time curve is shown in the form of a universal Doppler shift curve in Figure 3.15.

Additional measurements of the Doppler shift may be used to refine the values of the orbit parameters; the optimum use of the measured data will be the result of a least squares fit of the data to a theoretical curve of the form shown in Figure 3.15. The universal Doppler shift curve, must of course be corrected to account for non-circular orbits. The theoretical curve for the Doppler frequency may range from that which is illustrated above and applies to a straight line segment and constant velocity to a very complex model which accounts for the ellipticity of the satellite orbit, effects of Earth's rotation, refraction of the atmosphere, and so forth.

3.4.1 VELOCITY TRACKING SYSTEMS

One objective of a spacecraft tracking system is to determine the orbit elements of the trajectory on which the craft is traveling.   A system which can do this conveniently without making explicit measurements of position will be a useful

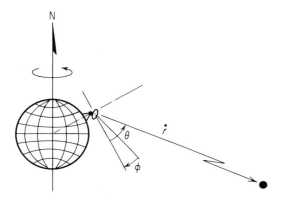

Fig. 3.16. Doppler tracking system.

tracking system in certain situations. A tracking complex of this kind will be discussed in the succeeding paragraphs; it consists of a Doppler radar to measure range rates and a direction finding system capable of indicating azimuth and elevation angles and their time derivatives. The tracking complex is illustrated by the diagram of Figure 3.16. The angular rates required may be sensed by special instruments mounted on the tracking antenna or telescope.

The spacecraft in its free-fall orbit will have constant momentum, hence

$$\dot{h} = \frac{d}{dt}(r^2\dot{\theta}) = 0 \tag{3-59}$$

consequently

$$2r\dot{r}\dot{\theta} + r^2\ddot{\theta} = 0 \tag{3-60}$$

hence

$$r = \frac{-2\dot{r}\dot{\theta}}{\ddot{\theta}} \qquad (3\text{-}61)$$

From this relation and the measurements of $\dot{r}$, θ, and $\dot{\theta}$ the six orbit parameters may be calculated using the relations which have been discussed in Section 3.1.

For purposes of tracking a vehicle in deep space, a directional tracking antenna which is slaved to the line of sight to the spacecraft will be useful. Doppler frequency shift may be used to measure range rate ($\dot{r}$) and the directional tracking loop will yield data regarding θ, $\dot{\theta}$, and $\ddot{\theta}$. The tracking stations will be located at the surface of the Earth and consequently the measurements must be corrected for the displacement between the orbit center and the tracking system. A convenient degree of approximation may be obtained by neglecting this displacement when tracking vehicles at a great distance from the Earth.

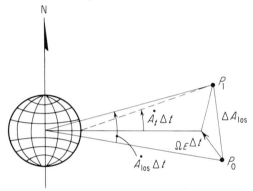

Fig. 3.17. Angle tracking.

A directional tracking system such as an antenna or a telescope which is slaved to the line of sight to a spacecraft will have angular velocity relative to a reference line fixed in the Earth that is approximately equal to the vector sum of the two angular velocities, that of the Earth and that of the position vector of the vehicle when drawn from the center of the Earth. This is stated in mathematical terms as follows

$$\dot{\mathbf{A}}_{los} = \mathbf{\Omega}_E + \dot{\mathbf{A}}_t$$

where

$\mathbf{\Omega}_E$ = angular velocity of the Earth
$\dot{\mathbf{A}}_t$ = rate of change of the true anomaly.

This is illustrated in the sketch of Figure 3.17. The degree of approximation will depend upon the extent to which the tracking station may be considered to be located at the center of the Earth. These approximations will introduce uncertainties in the position of the spacecraft that are of the same order of magnitude as the ratio of size of the Earth to the distance from the Earth to the spacecraft. Consequently this kind of tracking system will be appropriate mostly for satellites orbiting the Earth at distances which are many times the radius of the Earth. Similar applications may be conceived for a Doppler tracking system in an interplanetary flight environment where the tracking station, or stations, are located on selected planets. Such a tracking complex for Solar System use will not be able to take advantage of the approximation which has been discussed above.

3.4.2 Precision Frequency Measurements for Range Determination

The techniques of Doppler measurement may be applied to the measurement of range if a means is provided to resolve the ambiguity or "constant of integration" problem. This has been made possible as a result of some recent developments in electronics which make it possible to generate signal frequencies which are stable to within approximately one part in 10^{12}. This precision frequency may be used as the reference in the construction of a clock of extreme accuracy (see Reference 3.9). Clocks of this kind may be synchronized at some convenient time and will retain their synchronism within the accuracy of their frequency references to provide precision timing which is limited only by the special theory of relativity (Reference 3.10).

These precision clocks form the basis of a position determination system of the three dimensional spherical type (range only), these systems were analyzed briefly in Section 3.3.2. If a timing signal is emitted at time t_1 from a clock, it will be received and noted at the location of another clock at the time $t_1 + r/c$ where r is the distance between the clocks and c is the speed of propagation of the signal between the two clocks. Consider now a tracking system which consists of three stations each located on a single planet (presumably the Earth) and a synchronized clock which is carried in the spacecraft. Such a system will have the characteristics of the radar system described in Section 3.3.2.

The error in range measurements due to the lack of synchronism between two time standards will be given by $c\Delta t$ where Δt represents the accumulated relative time error between the two clocks under consideration, for example,

$$\Delta t = \int_0^t \frac{\Delta f}{f_0} d\tau = \frac{\Delta f}{f_0} t$$

where

$\dfrac{\Delta f}{f_0}$ is the long term relative error in the time standard

These errors have been tabulated for various space missions where the accuracy of the time standard is given by $(\Delta f/f_0) = 10^{-10}$ and are shown in Table 3.1.

Table 3.1.

Destination	Time of Flight	Resultant Range Error
Luna (Moon)	3 days	4.8 st. mi
Venus	150 days	590 st. mi
Mars	260 days	1010 st. mi
Jupiter	2.7 years	3900 st. mi

3.5 SELF-CONTAINED SYSTEMS

A self-contained system is one which requires no aid or active participation from elements which are external to the spacecraft. This definition includes inertial systems employing gyroscopes and accelerometers, it also includes systems which employ optical tracking of the stars and the planets. In addition, systems which make use of the electromagnetic energy which is reflected from a reference body will also be considered to be self-contained. Doppler systems and radar range systems which do not require special reflectors and cooperating beacons are thus included in this class of system.

The application of self-contained navigation systems to spaceflight will permit direct measurement of trajectory coordinates on board the craft and will frequently obviate the necessity for application of offset measurement techniques and special transformations. This leads to considerable simplification of the system, particularly with regard to the computation required. However, self-contained systems will generally have performance, accuracy, and flexibility which is restricted by the size and weight permissible on the spacecraft. Conversely, the use of large, permanent, installations of telescopes, radars, and computers will permit Earth-based systems to have more inherent accuracy than self-contained systems for many missions. Under certain circumstances, notably those in which the spacecraft is at very great distances from a tracking site, self-contained systems are expected to prove favorable in comparison to ground-based systems as a result of their ability to continually correct the course of a craft toward its destination.

The importance of the self-contained system is illustrated in Figure 3.18, as the spacecraft travels in its orbit, the measurement of its position vector ρ from the Earth to the spacecraft becomes increasingly less accurate. In the vicinity of the destination planet, it will become necessary to make final measurements for navigation and guidance with respect to that planet. The spacecraft will, perhaps, be a hundred million miles or more from the Earth. At the same time its distance from the destination planet may be of the order of one to one-half million miles. Clearly, the more accurate measurement can be made with respect to the destination planet. Measurement of position will generally include errors which are roughly proportional to the distance over which they are being measured. In addition, the uncertainty in our current knowledge of the scale of the Solar System is about 1 part in 10^4. This uncertainty in the magnitude of the astronomical unit gives rise to a corresponding uncertainty of about 10,000 miles in the positions of the near planets. The accuracy in navigation and control which is required for the terminal phase of an interplanetary flight will be of the order of a few miles depending upon the vehicle configuration, the destination, and many additional operational variables. Accuracy of the kind required will not generally be obtained using an Earth-based tracking of the spacecraft but can be obtained with application of a self-contained system which makes measurements relative to the nearest Solar System bodies.

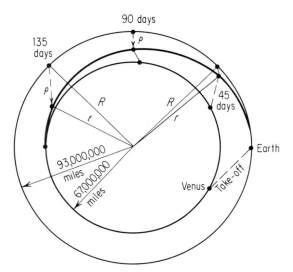

Fig. 3.18. Geometry for Homann Transfer—Earth to Venus.

3.6 ERRORS IN ORBIT CALCULATIONS

Often a guidance problem will be more closely concerned with the errors which arise in the determination of the trajectory parameters than with the computation of the trajectory itself. The determination of the errors in the trajectory parameters which are the result of the residual uncertainty in the guidance equipment is essential to the proper selection of a suitable guidance. Further, a study of the theory of errors in trajectories will permit the specification of the corrective maneuvers which are required to reduce the errors in the orbits to acceptably small values.

The position of a spacecraft in a idealized Keplerian orbit will be completely specified if a set of orbit parameters such as θ_p, t_p, **h**, and E have been specified. However, in many situations these parameters will not be known with precision. Uncertainty in future positions will be the result and the arrival of the craft at established destinations and rendezvous points will be in doubt. These uncertainties may be the direct result of errors in the measurements made by the guidance or navigation system at the time of injection into a free fall, or coasting, orbit. Another source of uncertainty in the orbit parameters will occur when the orbit in question passes through those regions of space where perturbations to the reference orbit occur causing the vehicle to deviate from an ideal orbit. Guidance, in the form of a ground-based tracking system or perhaps some self-contained system, may be employed to monitor the trajectory and to detect deviations from the ideal orbit and determine the corrections which are necessary. These corrections will involve applications of the theory of errors in orbits to provide for the extrapolation of present positions to determine the changes in the coordinates which will reduce the errors at a destination or reference point to an acceptable level.

The position of a spacecraft in an orbit whose parameters are known approximately can be specified as within a volume which is defined by the locus of end points of an error vector $\boldsymbol{\rho}$. This is given by the expression

$$\boldsymbol{\rho} = \mathbf{i}_r \Delta r + \mathbf{i}_\theta r \Delta\theta + \mathbf{i}_z \Delta z \qquad (3\text{-}62)$$

where

Δr, $\Delta\theta$, and Δz each represent the probability distributions appropriate to the various orbit parameters.

In using the expression of Equation (3-62), it is assumed that the errors in the orbit parameters are small and that the actual orbit which is followed is shifted only slightly from the reference conic. This is illustrated in the sketch of Figure 3.19. The probability distributions of $\boldsymbol{\rho}$ will depend upon the probability distributions of the various coordinates. For the present, we shall assume that the actual deviations in position which result from the navigation errors are small and that first-order error theory will be adequate. This assumption is considered to be reasonable since it is the mission of the navigation system and the navigator to assure that these errors are, in fact, maintained small.

The presence of the third component, ΔZ, of the error vector $\boldsymbol{\rho}$ makes allowance for the inclination of the actual (or erroneous) orbit plane with respect to the reference orbit. This inclination angle is defined so that a rotation of the orbit about the line of nodes of magnitude $\Delta\psi$ will bring it into coincidence with the reference orbit plane. The error component Δz will be given by

$$\Delta z = r\Delta\psi$$

as shown in Figure 3.19. The essentials of the error analysis may be most conveniently discussed in terms of an example. The error component Δr may be related to the errors in the various orbit parameters by differentiation of the orbit equation. If we take the reference orbit to be a Keplerian conic section, the orbit equation was developed in Chapter 2, Equation (2-21), and is

$$r = \frac{h^2/k}{1 + e \cos (\theta - \theta_p)}$$

Application of the chain rule for differentiation to the orbit equation gives rise to the expression

$$\Delta r = \frac{\partial r}{\partial h}\Delta h + \frac{\partial r}{\partial e}\Delta e + \frac{\partial r}{\partial k}\Delta k + \frac{\partial r}{\partial (\theta - \theta_p)}\Delta(\theta - \theta_p) \qquad (3\text{-}63)$$

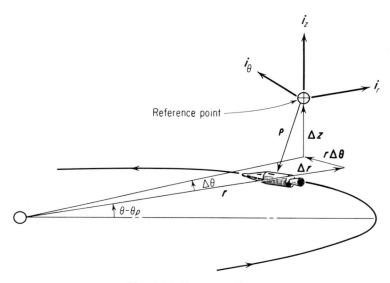

Fig. 3.19. Error coordinates.

In many cases which are of interest, the uncertainty which is present in the gravitational field will be so small as to cause errors which are negligible. When this is true, it would be proper to proceed under the assumption that the error in the gravitational field constant is negligible, for example, $\Delta k = 0$. However, on some important occasions, insufficient exploration data will exist and the uncertainty in this important constant will be of paramount significance. When this occurs, it will be necessary to evaluate the resulting error in position and velocity at various points in the orbit.

The partial derivatives which appear in Equation (3-63) may be calculated readily; they are tabulated below.

$$\frac{\partial r}{\partial h} = \frac{2r}{h} \qquad\qquad\qquad \frac{\partial r}{\partial e} = \frac{-r^2 k \cos(\theta - \theta_p)}{h^2}$$

$$\frac{\partial r}{\partial k} = \frac{-r}{k} \qquad\qquad \frac{\partial r}{\partial(\theta - \theta_p)} = \frac{er^2 k \sin(\theta - \theta_p)}{h^2}$$

The resulting error in r will be given by substitution of these partial derivatives into Equation (3-63), the resulting equation is

$$\Delta r = \frac{2r}{h}\Delta h - \frac{r^2 k \cos(\theta - \theta_p)}{h^2}\Delta e - \frac{r}{k}\Delta k + \frac{er^2 k}{h^2}\sin(\theta - \theta_p)\Delta(\theta - \theta_p) \quad (3\text{-}64)$$

An important alternative form of Equation (3-64) may be obtained which states Δr in terms of the deviation in orbit energy as a parameter rather than in terms of the deviation in the eccentricity. Recall the relation between energy and the eccentricity, it is [Equation (2-22)].

$$e^2 = 1 + \frac{2Eh^2}{k^2}$$

Differentiating, we obtain

$$\Delta e = \frac{h^2}{ek^2}\left(\Delta E + \frac{2E\Delta h}{h} + \frac{2E\Delta k}{k}\right) \qquad\qquad (3\text{-}65)$$

Making the appropriate substitutions, we obtain the expressions for Δr in terms of the deviation in energy rather than eccentricity.

$$\Delta r = \frac{2r}{h}\left[1 - \frac{Er}{ek}\cos(\theta - \theta_p)\right]\Delta h - \frac{r}{k}\left[1 + \frac{2rE}{ek}\cos(\theta - \theta_p)\right]\Delta k$$

$$- \frac{r^2 \cos(\theta - \theta_p)}{ek}\Delta E + \frac{er^2 k}{h^2}\sin(\theta - \theta_p)\Delta(\theta - \theta_p) \quad (3\text{-}66)$$

The other components of the error vector may be calculated in a manner similar to that shown above for Δr. However, this may not always be necessary since some of the components may be known directly as a result of guidance or navigation measurements. For example an on-board measurement of the true anomaly $(\theta - \theta_p)$ may be available as a result of celestial observations or a direct measurement from a gyroscopically stabilized reference. Under these circumstances the appropriate value for the uncertainty in the true anomaly will be the standard error in the celestial measurement or the accumulated drift error in the gyroscopes.

We can calculate the error component due to the error in the observation of the anomaly. Assume for the purpose that a navigation system is available in which the reference direction, θ_p, is indicated by a gyroscopic memory instrument and the radial direction is used to indicate θ and is observed through the use of telescopic sighting of the massive body at the focus of the orbit. Since the individual error contributions will not be known, a useful statistical evaluation of the error in the anomaly will be given by

$$\Delta(\theta - \theta_p) = \sqrt{(\Delta\theta)^2 + (\Delta\theta_p)^2} \qquad (3\text{-}67)$$

where

$\Delta\theta$ = the error in observation of the central body
$\Delta\theta_p$ = the accumulated error in the gyro reference

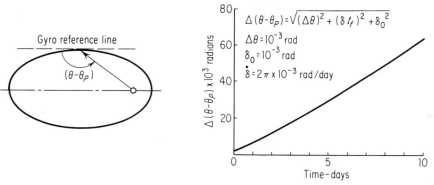

Fig. 3.20. Illustrating the measurement of true anomaly using a gyro reference.

These latter errors will be the result of an alignment error and a drift rate error, that is

$$\Delta\theta_p = \dot{\delta}t_f + \delta_0 \qquad (3\text{-}68)$$

Since we may reasonably assume that the initial alignment error is independant of the drift rate, and vice-versa, the deviation in the true anomaly will be given by an expression of the form

$$\Delta(\theta - \theta_p) = \sqrt{(\Delta\theta)^2 + (\dot{\delta}t_f)^2 + \delta_0^2} \qquad (3\text{-}69)$$

A graph showing the rate of growth of $\Delta(\theta - \theta_p)$ is shown in Figure 3.20. The graph is based on certain assumed error values which are shown in the graph. This is the value of $\Delta(\theta - \theta_p)$ which should be substituted into Equations (3-62) or (3-66) to obtain the error component Δr when a gyroscopic reference of the kind described is used.

The error expression for Δr (3-64) has been computed and stated in terms of the so-called "natural" parameters. Similar expressions may be calculated for the components $\Delta(\theta - \theta_p)$ and Δz for substitution into Equation (3-62). It will frequently be desirable or necessary to evaluate the errors in terms of the uncertainties which arise in the position and velocity determinations as a result of guidance or navigation operations. For example, we might wish to state the expected error at the destination in terms of the probable, or expected, error due to the guidance system at the shutdown (or burnout) of the thrust system or at some other navigational reference point. In the case of an ideal Keplerian orbit, this may be done readily since the natural orbit parameters are constant functions of the coordinates and their time derivatives; just such an analysis is presented for unperturbed orbits in Reference 3.12. Where perturbations act on the orbit of the spacecraft, these parameters are no longer constant and continuous navigational checks will be needed during the flight to establish corrections to be applied to the values of the orbit parameters.

To obtain the components of the error vector in terms of coordinates we consider the equations for the energy and the angular momentum of an orbiting spacecraft when given in terms of the coordinates at the reference point, these are

$$E = \tfrac{1}{2}(\dot{r}_0^2 + r_0^2\dot{\theta}_0^2) - \frac{k}{r_0}$$

and

$$h = r_0^2\dot{\theta}_0$$

The differentials may be calculated from these two expressions as follows

$$\Delta E = \dot{r}_0\Delta\dot{r}_0 + \left(r_0\dot{\theta}_0^2 + \frac{k}{r_0^2}\right)\Delta r_0 + r_0^2\dot{\theta}_0\Delta\dot{\theta}$$

and

$$\Delta h = 2r_0\dot{\theta}_0\Delta r_0 + r_0^2\Delta\dot{\theta}_0$$

These may be substituted into Equation (3-66) which yields

$$\Delta r = \left\{\frac{2r}{h}\left[1 - \frac{Er\cos(\theta - \theta_p)}{k}\right]2r_0\dot{\theta}_0 - \frac{r^2\cos(\theta - \theta_p)}{ek}\left(r_0\dot{\theta}_0^2 + \frac{k}{r_0^2}\right)\right\}\Delta r_0$$

$$- \frac{r_0\cos(\theta - \theta_p)}{ek}\dot{r}_0\Delta\dot{r}_0 - \frac{er^2k}{h^2}\sin(\theta - \theta_p)\Delta(\theta - \theta_p)$$

$$- \frac{r}{k}\left[1 + \frac{2rE\cos(\theta - \theta_p)}{ek}\right]\Delta k$$

$$+ \left\{\frac{2r}{h}\left[1 - \frac{Er\cos(\theta - \theta_p)}{k}\right]r_0^2 - \frac{r^2\cos(\theta - \theta_p)}{ek}r_0^2\dot{\theta}_0^2\right\}\Delta\dot{\theta}_0 \qquad (3\text{-}70)$$

A simplification occurs when the substitution $g = k/r^2$ is made.

$$\Delta r = \left\{ \left[\frac{r}{h} - \frac{E}{hg} \cos(\theta - \theta_p) \right] 4 r_0 \dot{\theta}_0 - \left(\frac{r_0 \dot{\theta}_0^2 - g_0}{eg} \right) \cos(\theta - \theta_p) \right\} \Delta r_0$$

$$- \frac{\dot{r}_0 \Delta \dot{r}_0}{eg} \cos(\theta - \theta_p) - \frac{eg}{\dot{\theta}^2} \sin(\theta - \theta_p) \Delta(\theta - \theta_p)$$

$$- \left[\frac{1}{r} + \frac{2E}{ek} \cos(\theta - \theta_p) \right] \frac{\Delta k}{g}$$

$$+ \left\{ \left[r - \frac{E}{g} \cos(\theta - \theta_p) \frac{2 r_0^2 r}{h} - \frac{r_0^2 \dot{\theta}_0^2}{eg} \cos(\theta - \theta_p) \right] \right\} \Delta \dot{\theta}_0 \qquad (3\text{-}71)$$

Now, by substitution back into Equation (3-62) we can evaluate the miss distance as an error vector.

This general analysis permits evaluation of a miss distance vector in many important examples. The formulation which has been given here will be recalled from time to time for special examples. Situations will arise from time to time which permit simplification of these expressions. The introduction of a moving destination will present complications requiring special treatment; these will be described in their turn in later chapters.

3.7 CORRECTIVE MANEUVERS

Space navigation problems will frequently lead to the determination of incremental velocity maneuvers which are designed to reduce the errors in the trajectory. The only errors which may be reduced in this way are those which have been observed or calculated as deviations from the intended trajectory. Errors arising from inaccurate or uncertain measurements by the guidance equipment can not be corrected. The method for calculation of these velocity corrections will be discussed in this section together with some considerations for the optimization of the maneuvers.

In those situations where it is required that a spacecraft in its orbit will pass through a specified destination point, (r_1, θ_1), the miss vector in the vicinity of the destination must be calculated in terms of the deviations from a specified trajectory which will be observed at a navigation reference point, (r_0, θ_0). The method for doing this was discussed in some detail in the previous section. This miss vector which is used for computation of guidance commands will be the result of calculations which are made on the deviations which are observed in the orbit coordinates when compared to those for an orbit which will effect the desired transfer. In the case of the miss vector computed at the reference point, it will be the result of the observed deviations in $\dot{r}_0$ and $\dot{\theta}_0$. First-order corrections to the trajectory may be made using error commands to the steering system which are calculated as follows

$$\Delta r_1 = S_1 \Delta \dot{r}_0 + S_2 \Delta \dot{\theta}_0 \qquad (3\text{-}72)$$

This may be expressed in terms of velocity components as

$$\Delta r_1 = \frac{\partial r_1}{\partial \dot{r}}\Delta \dot{r}_0 + \frac{1}{r_0}\frac{\partial r_1}{\partial \theta}r_0\Delta \dot{\theta}_0 \tag{3-73}$$

In order to reduce the predicted miss distance to a minimum, a maneuver should be commanded so that $\Delta r_1 = 0$; this will be true if

$$\frac{\partial r_1}{\partial \dot{r}}\Delta \dot{r}_c + \frac{1}{r_0}\frac{\partial r_1}{\partial \theta}r_0\Delta \dot{\theta}_c = -\Delta r_1 \tag{3-75}$$

Any velocity maneuver which has radial and tangential components as indicated in Equation (3-75) will cause the miss vector in the orbit plane to vanish within the limits of the navigation accuracy. Equation (3-75) is not specific in nature and an infinite combination of correction maneuvers may be calculated. It will become apparent that a special combination of $\Delta \dot{r}_c$ and $r_0\Delta \dot{\theta}_c$ may be found which will define the smallest velocity impulse to provide a given correction Δr_1. This combination of velocity components will define a direction in the orbit plane which will be called the *critical* direction.

Let a corrective maneuver be defined as consisting of a velocity impulse whose direction makes an angle ψ with the line of sight to the center of the gravity field. (See Figure 3.21.) The resulting change in the miss vector is then given by

$$\Delta r_1 = \left(S_{\dot{r}}\sin \psi + S_\theta \frac{\cos \psi}{r_0} \right)\Delta v_c \tag{3-76}$$

where

$$S_{\dot{r}} = \frac{\partial r_1}{\partial \dot{r}}$$

$$S_{\dot{\theta}} = \frac{\partial r_1}{\partial \theta}$$

$\Delta v_c =$ the magnitude of the commanded change in velocity.

To determine the value of ψ for which Δv_c will be a minimum for any given value of Δr_1, find the derivative

$$\frac{dv_c}{d\psi} = \Delta v_c \frac{S_{\dot{r}}\cos \psi - \dfrac{S_{\dot{\theta}}}{r_0}\sin \psi}{S_{\dot{r}}\sin \psi + \dfrac{S_{\dot{\theta}}}{r_0}\cos \psi} \tag{3-77}$$

A minimum correction velocity will be required if the numerator of this expression vanishes, that is if

$$\tan \psi = \frac{S_{\dot{\theta}}}{S_{\dot{r}} r_0} \tag{3-78}$$

Thus the minimum velocity impulse maneuver will be required for the correction
if the increment has components

$$\Delta \dot{r}_c = \Delta v_c \cos \psi = \frac{S_{\dot{r}} \Delta v_c}{(S_{\dot{r}}^2 + S_{\dot{\theta}}^2)^{1/2}} \tag{3-79}$$

$$\Delta r_0 \dot{\theta}_0 = \Delta v_c \sin \psi = \frac{S_{\dot{\theta}} \Delta v_c}{(S_{\dot{r}}^2 + S_{\dot{\theta}}^2)^{1/2}} \tag{3-80}$$

and the velocity magnitude is given by

$$\Delta v_c = r_1 \left(\frac{r_0}{S_{\dot{r}} S_{\dot{\theta}}} \right)^2 \tag{3-81}$$

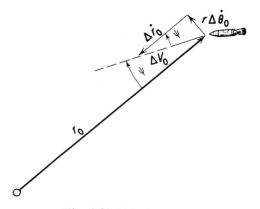

Fig. 3.21. Velocity errors.

The corrective maneuver will ordinarily be obtained through use of rocket
propulsion. The properties of this mode of propulsion have been discussed
briefly in Chapter 1.

PROBLEMS

1. A tracking system has determined that a satellite which is in orbit about the
   Earth has the following flight conditions at time $t = t_0$

   altitude $= 250$ statute miles
   tangential velocity $= 26{,}000$ ft/sec
   radial velocity $= +250$ ft/second

Calculate the orbit parameters

    angular momentum, h
    energy, E
    eccentricity, e
    time since passing perigee, t_p

2. Write the orbit equation which is applicable to the orbit described by the flight conditions which are given in Problem 1 above.

3. Develop the components of the acceleration vector as indicated in the expression of Equation (3-7).

4. Draw a graph, or contour plot, showing the iso-error lines for a spherical-polar tracking system. Select the ground elevation plane for the plot.

5. Calculate dx, dy, and dz for the three dimensional-spherical (range only) tracking system.

6. In a Doppler tracking system which radiates a 10 cm wavelength, a difference frequency in the returned signal of 27,500 cps is noted. What is the relative velocity of the spacecraft being observed with respect to the tracking station?

7. The spacecraft in the previous problem has a relative velocity at very great distance from the tracking station of 25,000 ft/sec; it will pass the tracking station at 150 miles distance. Compute the time history of the Doppler shift until the craft has passed out of the range of the station.

8. Using the equation for the orbit which was determined in Problem 2, above, compute the error coefficients which are shown in the expression of Equation (3-63).

REFERENCES

3.1. Goldstein, Herbert, *Classical Mechanics*. Addison-Wesley Press Inc., Cambridge, Mass., 1951.

3.2. McClure, Connie L., *Theory of Inertial Guidance*, Prentice-Hall Inc., Englewood Cliffs, New Jersey, 1960.

3.3. Pyne, Robert J., *Geometrical Dilution of Precision, Spherical-Polar System (SCR-584) Radar)*, AF Technical Report No. 26, Parsons-Aerojet Co., Cocoa Beach, Florida, 1951.

3.4. Holmes, Thomas, G. and Paul H. Reedy, *Geometrical Dilution of Precision, Three Dimensional Spherical (Range Only) System*, AF Technical Report No. 23, Parsons-Aerojet Co., Cocoa Beach, Florida, 1951.

3.5. Phillips, B. E., *Geometrical Dilution of Precision, Three Dimensional Hyper-bolic Systems*, AF Technical Report No. 21, Parsons-Aerojet Co., Cocoa Beach, Florida, 1951.

3.6. ———, *Doppler Shift Records Provide Satellite Range and Height Data*, Hewlett Packard Journal, Vol. 9, p. 5. Palo Alto, Calif., Nov.–Dec. 1957.

3.7. Mengel, J. J., *Tracking the Earth Satellite*, Proc. IRE, Vol. 44, No. 6, p. 755, June 1956.

3.8. Frye, W. E., *On the Use of Precision Frequency Signals in Space*, Proc. of the XIth Congress of the IAF, Stockholm, 1960.

3.9. Lyons, H., *Atomic Clocks*, Scientific American, Feb. 1957.

3.10. Synge, J. L., *Relativity: Special Theory*, Interscience Publishing Co., New York, 1956.

3.11. Berger, F. B., *The Design of Airborne Doppler Velocity Measuring Systems*, IRE Transactions, Vol. ANE–4, p. 157, Dec. 1957.

3.12. Frye, W. E., *On the Accuracy of the Long Range Ballistic Missile*, Journal of Applied Physics, Vol. 22, No. 5, pp. 585–589, May 1951.

3.13. Reedy, Paul H. and B. E. Phillips, *The Evaluation of Trajectory Measuring Systems*, AF Technical Report No. 20, Parsons-Aerojet Co., Cocoa Beach, Florida, 1951.

4

GUIDANCE OF THE BALLISTIC

MISSILE

Perhaps the earliest important application of the techniques of space navigation is the guidance of a ballistic missile. These missiles also represent the first historic example in which rocket power has been employed to place vehicles in trajectories about the Earth where the motion is approximately that of a particle in a Keplerian orbit. In this chapter, the rationale for ballistic missile guidance will be developed and some specific techniques will be analyzed. A brief discussion of the general characteristics of a ballistic missile trajectory will be presented. The validity of Kepler's laws as an approximation describing the greater portion of a missile flight will be justified. In addition, the properties of the three important segments (powered ascent, free-fall, and re-entry) are summarized.

In order to provide a theoretical basis for the study of missile guidance problems, a dynamical analysis of the free-fall flight will be given relating the point of impact of the missile to the flight conditions at an initial point. The mechanics of powered flight, and the effects which these have on the design of a guidance and control system are presented in Section 4.3. The principles of the design for a ballistic missile guidance computer will be discussed together with a simplified example and the performance of such a guidance computer will then be analyzed.

The design of any spacecraft will be concerned with the integrity of the craft as it travels through the atmosphere for entry, or re-entry, into the Earth or some other planet. This flight maneuver involves stresses which are capable of destroying the craft unless they are properly controlled through supervision of the trajectory. The practice of guidance immediately prior to, and during, the entry flight can do much to relieve these stresses which are due to the high rates of dissipation of energy in the atmosphere. Re-entry of a ballistic missile will be discussed in order to show the importance of the re-entry flight to the over-all flight of the missile.

4.1 TRAJECTORY CHARACTERISTICS

In the flight of a ballistic missile, rocket propulsion is employed to accelerate the missile to a position of high altitude and high speed. This places it on a trajectory which meets certain guidance specifications in order to carry a warhead, or other payload, to a preselected target. The missile payload travels along a free-fall trajectory to its destination; its motions follow, approximately, the laws of Keplerian motion. Kepler's laws are a special case of the three laws of Newton and may be stated as follows:

In a central gravity force field, the orbit of a body in motion is a conic whose focus is at the center of attraction of the force field.

The position vector of the orbiting body sweeps over equal areas in equal time intervals.

The ratio of the square of the periods of two orbiting bodies is equal to the ratio of the cubes of the semi-major axes of those orbits. (Closed orbits only.)

Small perturbations in the orbit of a ballistic missile will arise as a result of deviations from the ideal conditions of environment which were assumed by Kepler. Extremely small drag forces will result from residual atmospheric effects; also the Earth's gravitational field is known to depart from a true central force field since the Earth is non-spherical in shape and inhomogeneous in its mass distribution. These perturbations are most important in the effects they have on the portion of the missile trajectory which is closest to the Earth. The effects of atmospheric drag and those due to gravitational anomalies both diminish at increasing altitudes above the Earth. Experience shows that an adequate approximation of the trajectory will be obtained if these perturbations are neglected and the missile flight is treated as if it were in free fall in an ideal central force field.

In order to justify the use of the Kepler assumptions for a ballistic missile, consider an example of a six-thousand nautical mile flight. The geocentric range angle will be $100°$; a near minimum energy orbit for such a flight will have the properties that are shown in Figure 4.1 (neglecting the atmosphere of the Earth in the definition of the trajectory). Let us now estimate the forces which act on this vehicle as a result of atmospheric drag and non-spherical gravity moments. These will be calculated under the assumption that guidance cut-off occurs at 100 miles altitude.

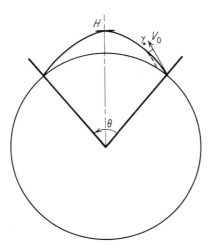

Coordinate	Value
Range, D	6000 m. mi
Max. alt., H	600 mi
Init. vel., V_0	24,100 ft/sec.
Init. flt. path, γ_0	20°
Time of flt, t_f	2000 sec.

Fig. 4.1. Typical ballistic missile trajectory.

Atmospheric Drag

Atmospheric drag acceleration will be a function of flight altitude, flight speed, and a ballistic parameter of the specific vehicle. The drag force will be given by the equation

$$F = (\tfrac{1}{2})C_D A \rho V^2 = \left(\frac{W}{g}\right)a \tag{4-1}$$

where

C_D = the drag coefficient
A = frontal area of the missile (ft^2)
ρ = density of the atmosphere (slugs/ft^3)
V = velocity of the missile (ft/sec)
W = weight of the missile (lbs)
a = drag acceleration (ft/sec^2)

The density of the atmosphere as a function of altitude is shown in the graph of Figure 4.2. Re-arranging the terms of Equation (4-1), the drag acceleration will be given by

$$a = (\tfrac{1}{2})\frac{C_D A}{W}V^2 \rho g$$

In the ballistic missile flight example, the time of flight is 2000 seconds. The air density at 100 miles altitude, and above, will be less than 10^{-10} lbs/ft³. The drag acceleration acting on a missile having a drag-weight parameter of 200 lb/ft² will experience a drag acceleration of not more than 14.5×10^{-4} ft/sec². If this acceleration were to act on the missile for the entire time of flight, the accumulated displacement would not exceed 290 ft. Actually the cumulative effect of air drag will be considerably less than indicated since the missile continues to climb to a higher altitude and exchanges its kinetic energy for potential energy thus reducing the effective velocity of the missile.

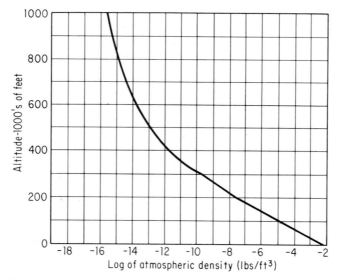

Fig. 4.2. Atmospheric density as a function of altitude (based or ARDC model of 1956).

Gravity Moments

One of the largest perturbing influences which will act on the orbit of a ballistic missile will be due to the gravitational accelerations caused by the Earth's oblateness. It is possible to represent the situation using the familiar central field terms with the addition of higher harmonic terms in the potential. This technique is well known to geodesists. Using standard methods of classical mechanics, it is possible to relate the coupling constants appearing in this potential to the departures from an orbit which has been predicted on the basis of a spherical gravity potential.

Missile flight will be described in a non-rotating spherical coordinate reference system (geocentric-equatorial), see Figure 4.3. The missile will be assumed to be at an altitude sufficiently high so that atmospheric drag may be neglected. It will also be assumed that the effects of gravitational anomalies and the extraterrestrial bodies (Sun, Moon, planets) may be disregarded.

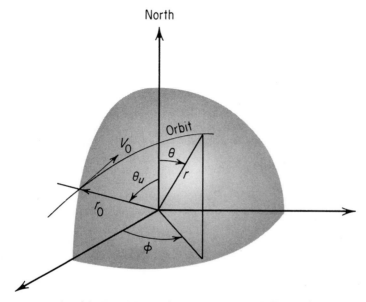

Fig. 4.3. Inertial coordinate to describe missile orbit.

The Earth's oblateness can be expressed in terms of a latitude-dependant potential function V. (Reference 4.2.)

$$V(r, \theta) = - \frac{GMm}{r}\left\{ \frac{R}{r} + J\frac{R^3}{r^3}[\tfrac{1}{3} - \cos^2\theta] + \ldots \right\} \tag{4-2}$$

where

G = the universal gravitational constant
M = the mass of the central body
m = the mass of the orbiting body
R = the radius of the Earth
r = orbital radius
J = a dimensionless coupling constant, approximately 1.6×10^{-3}.

The force of gravitational attraction and hence the acceleration due to gravity may be derived from the potential

$$\mathbf{g} = \left(\frac{1}{m}\right)[-\ \mathbf{grad}\ V(r,\theta)]$$

$$= -\frac{GM}{r^2}\left\{\mathbf{i}_r\left[1 + \frac{JR^2}{r^2}\left(\tfrac{1}{3} - \cos^2\theta\right) + \mathbf{i}_\theta\left(\frac{JR^2}{r^2}\sin 2\theta\right)\right]\right\} \quad (4\text{-}3)$$

For ballistic missile altitudes, the non-spherical acceleration terms shown will have magnitudes which are always less than a_1, as follows.

$$a_1 \leqslant \frac{4}{3}\frac{JR^2}{r^2}g = 0.068\ \text{ft/sec}^2$$

The resulting displacement which will not be accounted for if the non-spherical gravity moments are neglected will be bounded by

$$s = (\tfrac{1}{2})a_1 t^2$$

which, for our example trajectory will be less than 4200 ft. Thus it is noted that the effect of the gravity moments can be neglected only under special flight conditions or where extreme precision is not required. If these effects are taken into account, however, the assumption of a ballistic free-fall orbit may be valid.

Discussions of ballistic missile trajectories commonly make reference to three major sectors of the trajectory. These are defined below.

Powered Flight

This is flight through the atmosphere and extending into "free space" where the aerodynamic forces may be neglected. During this portion of the flight, the most important force acting on the vehicle is the thrust which is derived from a rocket engine, or cluster of engines. The acceleration of the missile from this thrust is usually in the neighborhood of 1.1 to 1.5 g ($g = 32.2\ \text{ft/sec}^2$) at lift-off, it increases as the mass of the vehicle decreases with fuel consumption and staging until a final value in the range of 5 to 10 g will be reached. At the time of thrust cut-off (burn-out), the vehicle will have attained an altitude such that aerodynamic forces are no longer of major importance to the trajectory. The velocity and position of the vehicle must be controlled along the trajectory so as to limit the aerodynamic loading of the structure and to place the vehicle on a free-fall trajectory which will carry it to its target, or destination.

Free-Fall

This is the flight through space which will be characterized by a free-fall orbit. The initial conditions of the free-fall flight determine the parameters of the orbit during this segment of flight; these parameters establish the trajectory to be followed.

Re-entry Flight

As the missile, in free-fall, approaches the Earth, it will penetrate the atmosphere where aerodynamic forces begin to exert major influence on the shape of the trajectory. The importance of this phase of flight to guidance and navigation arises from the high accelerations which are experienced by the missile on re-entry. The extremely high heating rates which are obtained during this flight severely limit the re-entry trajectories which are permissible for any given missile configuration. While the transition from powered flight to free-fall flight is abrupt, the transition from free-fall to re-entry flight is more gradual as a result of the build-up of air density as the missile penetrates the atmosphere.

4.2 THE BALLISTIC MISSILE IN FREE-FLIGHT

The flight conditions which obtain at the time of initiation of the free-fall portion of the flight have the greatest influence on the impact point of the missile. The powered flight is designed to place the vehicle in an appropriate trajectory so that upon thrust termination the missile will begin a free-fall orbit to the target. No guidance need be employed during this free-fall since the trajectory will be fully predictable. The re-entry trajectory is largely determined by the conditions of flight which obtain as the missile approaches the atmosphere of the Earth. Frequently, it is convenient to treat the re-entry flight as a terminal perturbation acting on the free-fall trajectory. Owing to its importance to the over-all flight, the free-fall trajectory will be discussed in some detail before treating the other segments of the trajectory.

The entry of a ballistic missile into its free-fall trajectory occurs abruptly upon the event of thrust cut-off but the termination of the free-fall trajectory is not similarly well defined. For the definition of free-fall, it will be convenient to adopt the convention of a *reference sphere*. The reference sphere is defined as the sphere with center at the center of the Earth having the thrust termination (burn-out) point on its surface. The free-flight will be assumed to terminate when the missile returns to the reference sphere. See Figure 4.4. This same convention may be employed to define the initial point for re-entry. In order to study the free-flight in mathematical terms, the flight will be described as planar with the plane of flight containing the center of the earth and the instantaneous velocity vector of the missile. When the plane of flight has been defined, the variable of greatest interest in an analysis will be the range of the missile to its impact point.

The important relations of the free-flight may be derived from the geometry of Figure 4.5. The range of the missile as it travels from reference sphere to apogee and back to the reference sphere is defined in terms of the geocentric angle between these two points of that sphere. This range angle will be given in terms of the true anomaly as follows

$$\sigma = 2(\pi - A_{\text{tref}}) \tag{4-4}$$

where

$A_{t\ ref}$ = the true anomaly at the point of intersection with the reference sphere.

The range may be related to the remaining orbit parameters through the orbit equation

$$r_{ref} = \frac{h^2/k}{1 + e \cos A_{tref}}$$

$$= \frac{h^2}{k[1 + e \cos(\pi - \tfrac{1}{2}\sigma)]} \tag{4-5}$$

From the above equation, it may be seen that for a given range and altitude of burn-out there is an infinite combination of parameters (momentum and

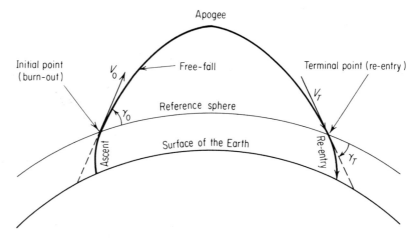

Fig. 4.4. The reference sphere.

eccentricity) which may be calculated. Each of these combinations will represent a different orbit. It will be shown that these may equally well be represented by a unique set of flight conditions—a velocity and a flight path angle passing through the burn-out point. The selection of a set of nominal burn-out flight conditions for any given mission may be made on the basis of minimum incremental energy required from launching to burn-out. This is equivalent to minimizing the required thrust energy. Another useful criterion might be the minimal sensitivity to guidance errors. In general the selection of the burn-out conditions will be the result of a complete analysis of the flight mechanics for an individual flight and will consider the missile configuration and the detailed mission requirements. Such an analysis is beyond the scope of this work and will not be discussed here.

The range traveled by a missile during its free-fall flight is given by the expression

$$\sigma = 2 \cos^{-1} \left[\frac{r_0 k - h^2}{r_0\, ek} \right] \qquad (4\text{-}6)$$

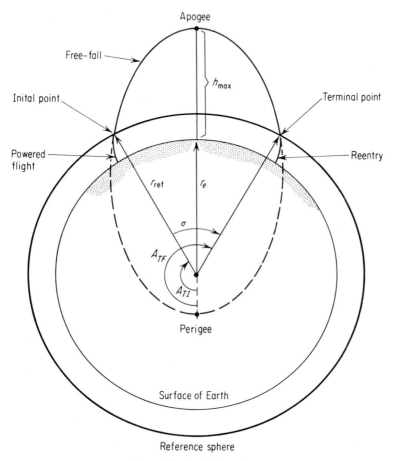

Fig. 4.5. Ballistic missile trajectory.

where

$$e = \sqrt{\left(1 + 2\frac{Eh^2}{k^2} \right)}$$

$$h = r^2 A_t$$

In terms of the flight conditions at burn-out, the range may then be stated as

$$\sigma = 2 \cos^{-1}\left[\frac{1 - (r_0/g)v_0^2 \cos^2 \gamma_0}{\sqrt{1+(v_0^2 - k/r_0)(v_0^2/g_0^2 \cos^2 \gamma_0)}} \right] \qquad (4\text{-}7)$$

Which may be rewritten in the alternative form (Reference 4.4):

$$\cot \frac{\sigma}{2} = \frac{v_e^2}{v_0^2 \sin^2 \gamma_0} - \cot \gamma_0 \qquad (4\text{-}8)$$

The time of flight for the missile is given by

$$t_f = \left(\frac{1}{n}\right)[A_{ef} - A_{e0} - e(\sin A_{ef} - \sin A_{e0})] \qquad (4\text{-}9)$$

$$= \left(\frac{2}{n}\right)\left(\frac{\cos \sigma/2}{1 + e \cos \sigma/2}\right)$$

where

$$A_{ef} = \sin^{-1}\frac{1 + e^2 \sin \sigma/2}{1 - e \cos \sigma/2}$$

The altitude at apogee will be given by

$$h_{\max} = r_a - r_e = \frac{h^2}{k}(1 - e) - r_e$$

These quantities are presented graphically in Figure 4.6 in the form of Universal Trajectory Curves. These curves may be used for graphic solutions of many ballistic missile design problems.

4.3 POWERED FLIGHT

The guidance of a ballistic missile occurs entirely during the powered portion of the flight, consequently its objective is to place the missile on a trajectory with flight conditions which are appropriate for the desired target. This is equivalent to steering the missile to a burn-out point which is uniquely related to the velocity and flight path angle for the specified target range. If there were no restrictions on the maneuvers which the missile can make during the powered flight, the guidance and control would be relatively simple and the only major problem would be that of precision in guidance.

Structural limitations and flight performance requirements will combine to restrict the ascent trajectory such that only limited correction maneuvers may be employed. These restrictions will be discussed briefly below and their influence on the guidance requirements will be treated in general terms before discussing the design of a guidance computer in some detail.

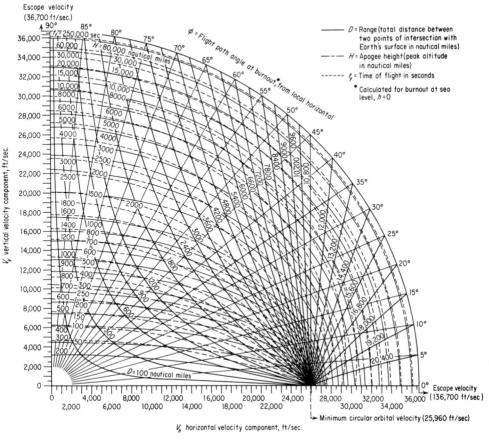

Fig. 4.6. Universal trajectory curve.

4.3.1 FLIGHT MECHANICS OF A POWERED FLIGHT

The profile of a typical ballistic missile ascent is shown in Figure 4.7. The range, velocity and altitude for the same missile are shown as functions of time in Figure 4.8. At the instant of lift-off, and for a brief period thereafter, the missile will lack sufficient velocity to provide aerodynamic stability. As the flight progresses, the dynamic pressure ($q = \rho v^2$) will increase due to increased velocity and the aerodynamic forces will tend to stabilize the missile in flight. (Provided, of course, that the missile possesses inherent dynamic stability.) At higher altitudes, the atmosphere will decrease in density until no further aerodynamic stability is imparted to the missile. The missile guidance and control system must be capable of operating through this entire range of environments. Steering is normally accomplished through directional control of the thrust vector; turning moments are impressed on the missile by directing the rocket engine so that the net thrust does not pass through the center of gravity of the body. This is done with the use of gimballed nozzles, jet vanes, jetavators, and so on. As the speed of the missile is increased, the aerodynamic moments and heating loads become important and the trajectory is dictated by the structural and heat limitations of the missile frame. During the staging interval, a brief period of instability will occur and it is necessary to reduce the upsetting moments which act on the vehicle by delaying the staging operation until it can be accomplished under conditions in which the dynamic pressure on the missile has been reduced to a level which limits the aerodynamic loading on the structure.

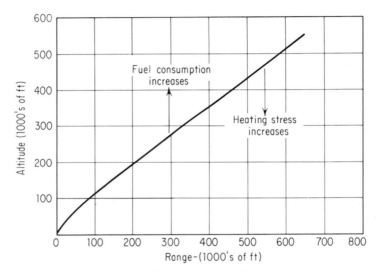

Fig. 4.7. Trajectory profile.

During the first stage of flight, the trajectory will be controlled by the flight control system which senses such parameters as aerodynamic loading, missile stability, and heating rate and modifies a programmed trajectory to account for variations in engine performance and to assure survival of the structure. Guidance (or navigation) does not ordinarily begin until the second stage flight has been initiated and the vehicle has left the atmosphere. At this time, the missile in its flight may have accumulated relatively large departures from the programmed trajectory. In the interest of efficiency of propulsion, it is desirable that the guidance system does not require the missile to return to the trajectory that was originally programmed. The discussions of Section 4.4. will describe a guidance computer that operates on the trajectory deviations that are observed and then uses these deviations to compute guidance commands. These commands are transmitted to the missile autopilot to bring the missile to a new trajectory leading to the specified target.

4.3.2 GUIDANCE REQUIREMENTS FOR POWERED FLIGHT

In order to guide a ballistic missile to its target, it will be necessary to select a combination of burn-out velocity and flight path angle which satisfy Equation (4-8) for the desired range. The selected flight conditions will place the missile on a trajectory passing through the appropriate point in the reference sphere.

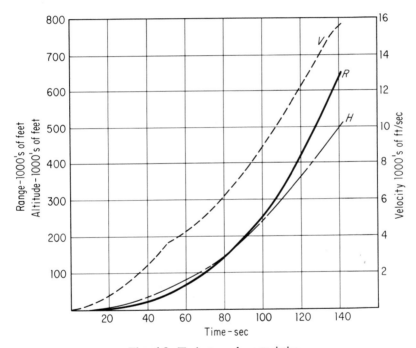

Fig. 4.8. Trajectory characteristics.

This point, sometimes known as the *aiming point*, will be chosen after making allowance for some systematic effects which displace the flight of the missile from its intended target. Among these are

Target motions due to the rotation of the Earth
Perturbations of the nominal trajectory due to non-spherical gravity fields, residual aero drag forces, and so on
Re-entry displacements.

Once the aiming point has been selected, the guidance and control system of the missile will be required to direct the thrust vector of the rocket in such a manner as to bring the vehicle to a burn-out point with velocity such that the missile in free-fall will reach an aiming point whose location has been selected so that the re-entry accelerations will just carry the missile to the actual target.

Guidance may be accomplished by any of a number of systems, the most promising of which are inertial, radio, and a mixture of these. Inertial systems have the advantage of fast in-flight response and they give good data on the short term changes in position and velocity, there is no need for long smoothing times with an inertial system. Radio systems, on the other hand, provide continuous measurements of position, and in some cases velocity. They do not experience drift errors such as those which are characteristic of gyroscopes. The radio systems are subject to errors, or uncertainties, due to noise in the individual measurements. In order to reduce the effects of these noise errors, radio guidance systems usually make use of relatively long smoothing, or averaging, times. This is particularly true when velocity data are to be derived from position measurements.

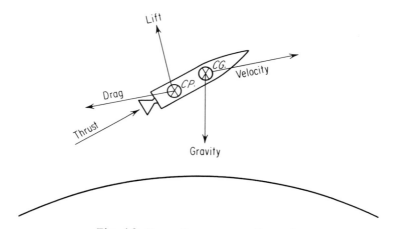

Fig. 4.9. Force diagram—ascending rocket.

The guidance and control of a ballistic missile are necessarily intimately related. The guidance is completed within the period of several seconds, or at most a few minutes after lift-off. During this brief interval, a loss of the guidance function would permit navigation errors to accumulate and grow so large that they could not be corrected within the limitations of the propulsion system or without requiring maneuvers which are so abrupt as to be structurally damaging to the missile. The dynamic forces which act on a rocket vehicle during its controlled ascent are indicated in Figure 4.9. In addition, aerodynamic coupling and thrust vector displacements lead to pitch, yaw, and roll moments which give rise to aerodynamic and inertia loading of the rocket structure. At the velocity with which these missiles travel, and with their optimized structures, loads of this kind must be carefully controlled or they will become destructive in magnitude. A complete discussion of the dynamics of a rocket in flight is beyond the scope of the present text. For a more complete discussion, the reader is referred to standard works on flight dynamics, cf. Reference 4.5.

The diagram of Figure 4.10 shows the relationship between the guidance system and a typical autopilot control system. The self-contained position and velocity indicator is a three axis accelerometer system. The theory of operation of such systems has been discussed in detail in Reference 4.6, where the equations of motion of a rocket vehicle which is influenced by gravitational and non-gravitational accelerations are discussed in detail.

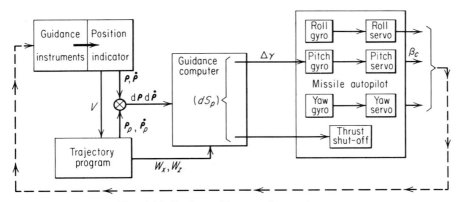

Fig. 4.10. Rocket guidance and control system.

4.4 THE GUIDANCE COMPUTER

A guidance computer which is suitable for the navigation of a ballistic missile must be capable of providing both steering commands and engine shut-off commands from data which are available on board the vehicle. The computation which is involved must be reduced to a minimum in the interest of airborne simplicity and reliability. The complete designation of a target involves ballistic computations to provide headings, corrections for Earth's rotation, and design values of the position and velocity vectors which should be obtained at the time of thrust cut-off. The corrections for Earth's rotation will require that the time of flight be approximately as predicted, but otherwise these corrections can be computed on the ground prior to flight and the indicated changes in range and heading may be applied to the computer program before launching. In-flight corrections to the program will be required as the missile deviates from the predicted trajectory but these may be calculated in flight and the necessary corrections to the program may be made as needed by means of biasing the autopilot reference. Ideally, the missile might be launched on a programmed course and, upon reaching the burn-out point, or after a predetermined time, the engines would be shut down. However, variations in missile performance and disturbances in the atmosphere make this impractical. The guidance computer to be discussed employs a programmed set of flight parameters which are designed to bring the missile to the vicinity of the desired flight path and burn-out conditions. Using position and velocity data from the position and velocity indicator, the deviations from the reference trajectory will be computed on-board the missile in terms of the total differential of an implicit function of the flight path parameters. This differential will be caused to vanish before the engine shut-off command will be given.

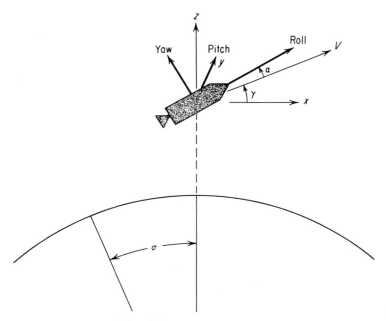

Fig. 4.11. Missile orientation.

The trajectory computer, operating in accordance with a preset program, will control the flight path angle as a function of a chosen independant variable, such as time after lift-off or velocity. The missile will be flown by the autopilot so as to maintain its trajectory in a plane containing the missile, the center of the Earth, and the aiming point. The geometry of the trajectory and the orientation of the missile are defined in the sketch of Figure 4.11. The missile pitch axis will be maintained parallel to the y axis; this flight restraint will serve to maintain the cross-range (y) coordinate and the cross-range velocity ($\dot{y}$) at null. This justifies the assumption which will be used in the following discussion that the missile motions are confined to a plane where $y = \dot{y} = 0$.

The missile in flight may be thought to be moving continuously from one state of position and velocity to another. At any time when thrust cut-off will be allowed to occur, the free-fall trajectory which ensues will be determined by the position and velocity state of the missile which obtains at cut-off. This state is identified by a function $f(x, z, v, \gamma)$. At the same time, and correlated with each possible burn-out point there are a variety of desirable states, $f(x, z, v^*, \gamma^*)$ each of which will bring the missile to the designated aiming point in a free-fall orbit. An explicit function of these variables,

$$S = S^*(x, z, v^*, \gamma^*)$$

may be defined in such a way that a missile for which $S = 0$ will proceed in a free-fall flight to its target if propulsion were to be cut-off at the instant that $S = 0$. This guidance function, S, expresses a definite relation between initial flight conditions for a free-fall orbit and the range to go. Using the example cited in a previous section, the guidance function for a central force field example will be

$$S = \sigma^* - 2 \cos^{-1}\left[\frac{1 - (r_0/g_0) V_0^2 \cos^2\gamma_0}{\sqrt{1 + (v_0^2 - k/v_0)(v_0^2/g_0^2 \cos^2\gamma_0)}}\right] \tag{4-10}$$

The missile, in its powered flight, will be programmed so as to approach the state where $S(x, z, v, \gamma) = 0$. However, due to disturbances from the atmosphere and other sources, the programmed trajectory will not be followed. It still provides a convenient aid to the control system by which the guidance function, S, may be driven to zero at the end of the powered flight. The programmed trajectory also provides a convenient reference trajectory for the calculation of small corrections when correction commands are necessary. The control system computer compares the value of S, computed on board the vehicle, with the precalculated value which is stored in the trajectory program. The computer directs the autopilot in such a way as to maintain these two quantities in coincidence. It is the purpose of the guidance computer to generate the commands which must be transmitted to the autopilot which will cause the missile to fly a trajectory where $S = 0$, at this time the command for thrust cut-off may be given. The programmed flight assures that speed and flight path angle will both develop along a path which is close to the predicted one. Consequently, linear approximations to S may be employed to define corrective commands and reduce the complexity which is required of the missile-borne computing equipment. This is equivalent to the expansion of the function S about the programmed trajectory in a Taylor's theorem expansion. The coefficients of the resulting series will not be constants but will be functions of position and velocity which may be stored in the tape programmer. This has the advantage that the programmer, which must be carried aboard the vehicle, may be used to reduce the amount of computing equipment which will be required.

The mathematics of the mechanization is discussed below. Let $(x_p, z_p, v_p, \gamma_p)$ be the programmed states, (x, z, v, γ) will be the actual states, and (x, z, v^*, γ^*) are the associated desired flight states. The basis for the steering and shut-off signals is the function $S(x, z, v, \gamma)$; when this quantity vanishes, the missile will have the correct velocity vector so that it will be on a free-fall trajectory to the target if thrust shut-down were to occur at the time. Neglecting powers of the trajectory deviations higher than the first, if follows that

$$S(x, z, v, \gamma) = S_p - \frac{\partial S_p}{\partial x}\Delta x_p - \frac{\partial S_p}{\partial z}\Delta z_p - \frac{\partial S_p}{\partial v}\Delta v_p$$

$$- \frac{\partial S_p}{\partial \gamma}\Delta \gamma_p \qquad (4\text{-}11)$$

where

$$S_p = S(x_p, z_p, v_p, \gamma_p)$$
$$\Delta q_p = (q_p - q).$$

The function which appears on the right hand side of Equation (4.11), S_p, and its derivatives are all evaluated along the programmed trajectory. These values may be stored in the memory of a trajectory programmer on board the vehicle.

Velocity supervision of the program may be used to insure that the programmed velocity will, at any time, be the actual velocity of the missile. Velocity supervision is accomplished by storing the trajectory parameters for control and guidance in a programmer which employs missile velocity as the independant variable. In this way $v(t) = v_p(t)$ and the differential Δv_p will vanish. The position of the craft, given by x and z, will be measured directly from the elements of the inertial or tracking systems. The sole variable which remains for control of the missile will be the flight path angle, γ. The guidance adjustments of the trajectory will, therefore, be made through commands which adjust the flight path angle. After a critical value of the velocity, $v = v_{\text{crit}}$, has been exceeded, and the value of S is made to vanish, a desired trajectory state will have been reached and the rocket engines may be shut-down.

The coefficient of Δx_p, Δz_p, and Δ_p, may all be computed on the ground in advance of the flight. Since they are functions of velocity along the trajectory, they may be coded and stored on the program tape for use at the time of need. An on-board computation of S may be written as

$$S = S_p - dS_p \qquad (4\text{-}12)$$

where

$$dS_p = W_x(v)\Delta x_p + W_z(v)\Delta z_p + W_\gamma(v)\Delta \gamma_p \qquad (4\text{-}13)$$

and the partial derivatives along the programmed trajectory are indicated by the weighting factors W_p.

The programmed trajectory must be chosen in such a manner that

$$S(x_p, z_p v, \gamma_p) = 0$$

when

$$\gamma_p = \gamma_p^* \text{ and } v_p = v_p^*$$

that is, the programmed trajectory is designed to hit the target. Consequently, if the missile is steered in such a manner as to maintain the differential expression of Equation (4-13) equal to zero for values of $v \leqslant v_p^*$, then the values of S will be in agreement along the actual and programmed trajectories and S will be made to vanish smoothly after the critical value of $v = v_{crit}$ has been exceeded. As has been shown, $S_p = 0$ when $v = v_p^*$, therefore $S = 0$ and the missile reaches a satisfactory state for thrust shut-off when the missile is at, or near, the programmed velocity although it may have departed considerably from the programmed trajectory.

The required guidance conditions will be met if the missile is steered under commands which maintain

$$dS_p = 0$$

Letting $\Delta\gamma_c$ be the commanded correction in the flight path angle which is necessary to reduce $dS_p = 0$, it may be shown that $\Delta\gamma_c$ is given by

$$\Delta\gamma_c = -\frac{dS_p}{(\partial S_p/\partial\gamma)} \tag{4-14}$$

Since the required correction, $\Delta\gamma_c$, is proportional to dS_p, the latter may be used directly, or with a suitable gain factor as a steering signal to be transmitted to the autopilot command receiver.

In summary, it has been shown that if the second-order differences from the programmed trajectories may be neglected in the expansion of the function S the guidance criteria $dS_p = 0$ will permit control of the missile steering to assure that engine shut-off commands may be given in the vicinity of the pre-established burn-out point. It is important to note, however, that a well chosen trajectory will have deviations in v which are greater in weight than the deviations in γ when these are evaluated as dispersions at the target. On this account, it is favorable for the actual signal for engine shut-off to be based on measurements of Δv and the function dS_p rather than to be based on measurements of the small angle $\Delta\gamma$ representing deviations in flight path orientation.

A functional block diagram of the guidance and control system for a ballistic missile which employs the computation system described here is shown in Figure 4.10. In this diagram, β is the angle between the engine and the longitudinal axis of the missile. β_c is the engine servo command signal which is generated from the guidance function deviations. dS_p. The velocity, v, derived from the computations made from inertial measurements serves to control the speed of the tape programmer thus assuring the equivalence of $v = v_p$.

4.5 ANALYSIS OF ERRORS IN BALLISTIC MISSILE GUIDANCE

It has been shown in previous sections of this chapter that the free-fall trajectory of a ballistic missile may be computed with a high level of precision if the position and velocity of the missile are known at the end of the propulsion, or exit, phase of the flight. Of course, a knowledge of the gravitational field and the velocity of rotation of the Earth will be required in this calculation. Throughout this text, a central gravity field will be assumed and the variations of the missile trajectory will be calculated assuming a non-rotating Earth. A major exception to this is that the effects of variations in the time of flight of a missile will require special treatment to account for Earth's rotation. However, these and other effects which are systematic are readily calculated. When the missile re-enters the atmosphere, it will experience air drag forces of high intensity. These may be computed, and their effect on the trajectory approximated by integration of the equations of motion of a body in a standard atmosphere. A precise calculation of the trajectory through the air will require that the actual conditions which are encountered in the atmosphere are known.

In this section, the errors in the missile impact point which arise due to errors in guidance during the exit phase of flight will be analyzed. In addition some methods which will permit the effect of Earth's rotation to be taken into account will be discussed. While the conditions of re-entry will not be discussed until the following section, the analytical means for estimating errors in the re-entry flight will be given.

4.5.1 DISPERSIONS DUE TO ERRORS IN EXIT GUIDANCE

The errors at impact will be analyzed under the assumption that errors in the initial position and velocity are small. This permits the application of linear approximations. The effects of variations in each of the initial position and velocity components on the range and deflection (cross-range) impact point dispersions are calculated separately. The calculation is made under the assumption that the separate sources of error are statistically independent. The individual errors found in this way may then be combined by adding their variances. The guidance errors will be calculated relative to an inertial coordinate reference frame which has its origin at the initial point of the free-fall flight and is oriented as shown in Figure 4.12. The z direction is vertically upward, and the x direction is horizontal in the plane of the trajectory. The positive direction is aligned downrange. The y axis is directed so as to make a right-handed set.

Effect of Errors in Initial Position

A variation in the range of the missile at burn-out, for example, due to an error in the powered guidance, will be propagated directly to impact to produce an error of the same size in the range at the terminal point. (The terminal point is the point of re-entry through the reference sphere.) To the degree of approximation which is made here, this may be stated as follows

$$\Delta\sigma(x_0) = \Delta x_0 \tag{4-15}$$

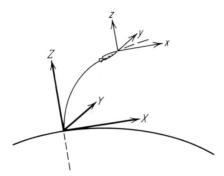

Fig. 4.12. Error reference frame.

The effect of a variation, Δz_0, in the initial altitude is to modify the radius of the reference sphere by an amount Δz_0. Owing to the symmetry of the trajectory, the velocity at the terminal point has the same magnitude as the velocity at the initial point, v_0; it has a flight path angle which is negative and of the same magnitude as the positive flight path angle which existed at burn-out. The resulting variation in range is

$$\Delta\sigma(z_0) = \Delta z_0 \cot\gamma_0$$

$$= \Delta z_0\left(\frac{x_0}{z_0}\right) \tag{4-16}$$

where

x_0 and z_0 are the x and z components of the velocity at the initial point, v_0.

An additional error arises due to the fact that the expression for the range of the missile, Equation (4-8), involves the altitude of burn-out through the sensitivity of the escape velocity to altitude, that is

$$\cot\frac{\sigma}{2} = \frac{k}{r_0\dot{x}_0\dot{z}_0} - \cot\gamma \tag{4-17}$$

differentiating Equation (4-17)

$$\Delta\left(\frac{\sigma}{2}\right) = \left[\frac{k\sin^2\sigma/2}{\dot{x}_0\dot{z}_0^2 r_0}\right]\Delta\dot{z}_0 \tag{4-18}$$

While the powered flight will be under the control of a guidance system which is designed to prevent the growth of deviations from the programmed trajectory in the lateral (y) direction, the drifts of the control system reference, cross winds and so on, will combine to produce an error in the y direction. This error will in turn be propagated to an error in the impact of the missile. To a first order of approximation, these errors may be considered to produce a rotation of the trajectory plane about an axis which is parallel to the initial velocity vector. This plane also contains the center of the Earth. The resulting error at the terminal point is a deflection error and may be calculated by the expression

$$\Delta d(y_0) = \Delta y_0 \cos \sigma \tag{4-19}$$

Effect of Errors in Initial Velocity

The semi-angular range, $\sigma/2$ may be expressed in terms of the x and z components of the initial velocity and the magnitude of the escape velocity, v_e, at the initial point (Equation 4-8)

$$\cot \frac{\sigma}{2} = \frac{v_e^2}{2\dot{x}_0 \dot{z}_0} - \cot \gamma$$

The variation in range angle due to variations in the x and z components of initial velocity are given by differentiation of the above expression

$$d \cot \frac{\sigma}{2} = - \csc^2 \frac{\sigma}{2} d\frac{\sigma}{2}$$

$$= \frac{\partial \cot \sigma/2}{\partial \dot{x}_0} d\dot{x}_0 + \frac{\partial \cot \sigma/2}{\partial \dot{z}_0} d\dot{z}_0 \tag{4-20}$$

which may be reduced to

$$d\sigma = (A\, d\dot{x}_0 + B\, d\dot{z}_0) \tag{4-21}$$

where

$$A = \left(\frac{v_e^2}{\dot{x}_0 \dot{z}_0} + \frac{2}{\dot{z}_0} \right) \sin^2 \frac{\sigma}{2} \tag{4-22}$$

$$B = \left(\frac{v_e^2}{\dot{x}_0 \dot{z}_0^2} - \frac{2x_0}{\dot{z}_0^2} \right) \sin^2 \frac{\sigma}{2} \tag{4-23}$$

The variation in range is related to the variation in the semi-angular range by the equation

$$\Delta X = 2r_{\text{ref}} \Delta \left(\frac{\sigma}{2} \right) \tag{4-24}$$

A variation in the initial velocity which is in the lateral direction, $\Delta \dot{y}_0$, results in a rotation of the plane of the missile trajectory. The change in the azimuth of the plane is given by

$$\Delta\varphi = \frac{\Delta\dot{y}_0}{\dot{x}_0} \tag{4-25}$$

hence the error at impact due to the lateral velocity error is expressed as

$$\Delta y = r_{\text{ref}} \sin\left(\frac{\Delta\dot{y}_0}{\dot{x}_0}\right) \tag{4-26}$$

The magnitude of the accumulated errors at impact may be estimated by calculating the root mean square (rms) of the expressions which were developed above. Assuming that the separate contributions to the errors are statistically independant, the rms errors in range and deflection will be given by the square root of the sum of the squares of the individual errors. Thus, to a first order of approximation, the total errors which are accumulated at the terminal point, that is, at the point where the missile descends through the reference sphere, may be calculated from the expressions

$$\Delta X = \left[\Delta x_0^2 + \left(\frac{\dot{x}_0}{\dot{z}_0}\right)^2 \Delta z_0^2 + 4 r_{\text{ref}}^2 (A^2 \Delta \dot{x}_0^2 + B^2 \Delta \dot{z}_0^2)\right]^{1/2} \tag{4-27}$$

$$\Delta d = \left[(\cos\sigma - \tan\gamma \sin\sigma)^2 \Delta y_0^2 + \frac{r_{\text{ref}}^2 \sin^2\sigma}{\dot{x}_0^2} \Delta \dot{y}_0^2\right]^{1/2} \tag{4-28}$$

Effect of the Rotation of the Earth

The rotation of the Earth will introduce a dependance on the time of flight into the errors which will appear at the terminal point of the flight. This dependance may be calculated from analysis of the equation for the time of flight of the ballistic missile, Equation (4-9)

$$t_f = \left(\frac{2}{n}\right)\frac{\cos\sigma/2}{1 + e\cos\sigma/2}$$

When the variation of the time of flight which results from the variations in initial position and velocity is known, the contribution to the error at the terminal point due to the rotation of the Earth may be calculated. It will be in the longitude direction and will be given by the product of the velocity of the re-entry point, which is due to the rotation of the Earth, times the variation in the time of flight.

$$\Delta_l = (\Omega r_{\text{ref}} \cos\lambda)\Delta t_f \tag{4-29}$$

The sensitivity of the time of flight to errors in position and velocity in the horizontal directions is such that they will not introduce errors which must be considered in a first-order error analysis.

4.5.2 ERRORS ACCUMULATED DURING RE-ENTRY FLIGHT

Re-entry considerations will be the subject of the following section; the means for estimating the errors in this portion of the trajectory as a function of the uncertainties in the effective acceleration will be discussed here.

The errors occurring at the terminal point on the reference sphere may be translated down to the point of impact on the surface of the Earth by the consideration of the equation of motion for a particle in flight. These equations may be stated in vector form as follows

$$\frac{d^2\mathbf{r}}{dt^2} + g\frac{r_0^2}{r^3}\mathbf{r} = b(t) \tag{4-30}$$

A linearized approximation may be applied for the gravitational force (Reference 4.6) to provide the differential equations for the variations of the trajectory from a standard re-entry trajectory which has been chosen in advance. (See Figure 4.13.) These variations are given in terms of Δd, and ΔX in the deflection and range direction, respectively. As the missile traverses the atmosphere, these components will be governed by the differential equations for the increments

$$\Delta d + \omega^2 \Delta d = \beta_d(t) \tag{4-31}$$

$$\Delta X + \omega^2 \Delta X = \beta_\chi(t) \tag{4-32}$$

where

$$\omega^2 = \frac{g}{r}$$

$\beta_d(t)$ = the component of the perturbing acceleration in the deflection direction

$\beta_\chi(t)$ = the component of the perturbing acceleration in the range direction.

The perturbing accelerations are non-gravitational accelerations which are not accounted for in the standard trajectory and its integration. Examples of such perturbing accelerations are

Non-standard winds
Variations in the physical properties of the re-entry body
Deviations of the atmosphere from the assumed standard.

The solutions to Equations (4-31) and (4-32) may be written at once in terms of the Faltung (folding) integrals, they are

$$\Delta d_e = \Delta d_t \cos \omega t + \frac{\Delta \dot{d}_t}{\omega} \sin \omega t + \frac{1}{\omega} \int_0^t \beta_d(\tau) \sin \omega(t - \tau)\, d\tau \tag{4-33}$$

$$\Delta X_e = \Delta X_t \cos \omega t + \frac{\Delta \dot{X}_t}{\omega} \sin \omega t + \frac{1}{\omega} \int_0^t \beta_\chi(\tau) \sin \omega(t - \tau)\, d\tau \tag{4-34}$$

The solutions to these error equations, when presented in this form, permit numerical evaluation of the integrals from experimental data. This has, perhaps, certain advantages over more precise analytical expressions.

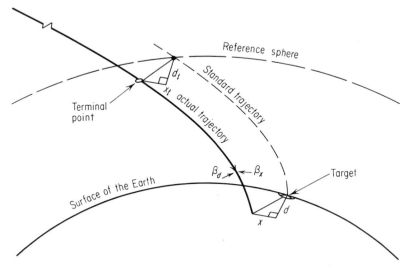

Fig. 4.13. Re-entry error analysis.

4.6 RE-ENTRY CONSIDERATIONS

A major problem in the development of a ballistic missile is that of re-entry. Indeed, the over-all problem of atmospheric entry is important to the design of any spacecraft. Re-entry flight is characterized by the dissipation of great quantities of kinetic and potential energy by the spacecraft. While a large fraction of this energy is transferred to the atmosphere, relatively large quantities of it will be deposited in the craft as heat. *Re-entry* has become a generic term for a broad function which may be accomplished by a variety of vehicle configurations in a variety of environments. Several distinct parameters of approach and entry may be considered; some of these are listed below.

Environment

1. Earth
2. Planetary
3. Lunar (no atmosphere)

Velocity

1. Hyperbolic
2. Parabolic

3. Super-circular
4. Circular
5. Sub-circular

Approach Angle

1. Grazing
2. Shallow entry
3. Deep entry
4. Vertical entry

Vehicle Configuration

1. Ballistic: $L/D < 0.1$
2. Lifting body: $0.1 \leqslant L/D \leqslant 1.0$
3. Winged re-entry: $L/D > 1.0$

Provision for Dissipation of Energy

1. Radiation cooling
2. Evaporation (or sublimation)
3. Ablation[1]

The specific energy levels, measured in watt-hrs/lb, for several different spacecraft are shown on the graph of Figure 4.14. This energy must be dissipated prior to impact with the surface of the Earth. While several mechanisms are available for the dissipation of this energy (that is, Rocket braking, Drag braking, Direct impact), the most practical solution is to dissipate this energy through exchange with the atmosphere. The duration of the energy exchange will, of course, determine the average and peak power rates which are involved in this exchange of energy.

It is estimated that only about 5 per cent of a vehicle's energy is absorbed by the body in re-entry (Reference 4.7). The rest of the energy is handled by the air in the shock envelope which surrounds the vehicle. At an entry angle of 3 deg there is a total heat input at the stagnation point of about 9000 Btu/ft²/sec. This must be compared with similar figures for a steam plant (10 Btu/ft²/sec) and an atomic reactor (400 Btu/ft²/sec).

The atmosphere of the Earth is a thin shell of gas which envelops the planet in much the same proportions as the skin of an apple. The greatest part of the atmosphere (approximately 99 per cent) is below an altitude of 100,000 ft. The significant aerodynamic limit is generally considered to be between 300,000 and 350,000 ft. The range of entry velocities will be from 600 mph (vertical drop from 400 miles altitude) to as high as 25,000 mph (entering spacecraft);

---

[1] *Ablation* (*n*) A process of removal by carrying away. Ablation cooling is accomplished by removal of a plastic coating after the heat energy has been deposited in the ablating surface.

some of these are noted in the graph of Figure 4.14. The range of re-entry angles applicable to several kinds of vehicles is shown in the diagram of Figure 4.15.

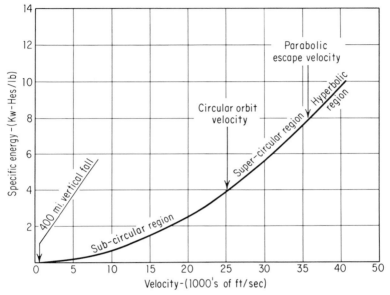

Fig. 4.14. Specific re-entry energy of a body approaching earth ($h = 300,000$ ft).

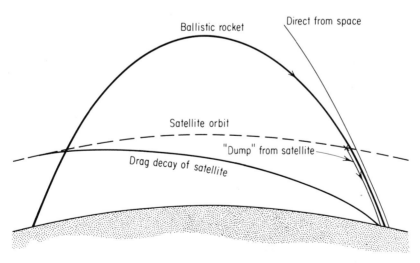

Fig. 4.15. Various types of entry.

The motion of a craft prior to entry into an atmosphere is governed by the principles of celestial mechanics. This motion will subsequently be modified when the vehicle begins to pass through the upper atmosphere. Initially, the body will pass through a region of free molecular flow when gas-dynamic drag forces begin to act to slow the vehicle. In the denser atmosphere (say below 300,000 ft), the flow of air is of the continuum type and both lift and drag forces act on the entering body as shown in Figure 4.16.

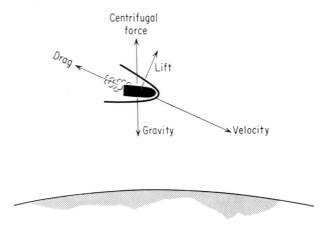

Fig. 4.16. Forces acting during entry.

The general effect which the vehicle configuration has on the trajectory which will be followed by the entering body is illustrated in Figure 4.17. Typical examples of re-entry trajectories are shown in Figure 4.18.

Spacecraft entry trajectories will be similar to those for ballistic missiles. The physical laws which apply are the same for both cases except that the velocity range for spacecraft which enter the atmosphere from orbits will be from 25,000 to 37,000 ft/sec and higher on Earth entry. A similar velocity range (70–115 per cent of escape velocity) will apply to entry into the atmosphere of other planets. The atmospheric properties are different for the different planets; the approximate variation of atmospheric density with altitude on Earth and its neighbor planets is shown on the graph of Figure 4.19. Two important parameters which are related to the properties of the atmosphere are

$$\text{Deceleration} \quad \sim \rho v^2$$
$$\text{Heating rate} \quad \sim \rho v^3$$

The trajectories of spacecraft on entry into planetary atmospheres are discussed in considerable detail in References 4.8 and 4.9. Some general properties of these trajectories are illustrated in Figures 4.20 and 4.21.

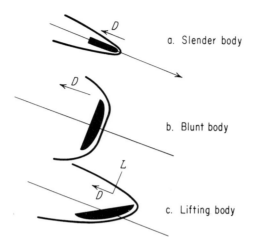

Fig. 4.17. Aerodynamic forces on various bodies.

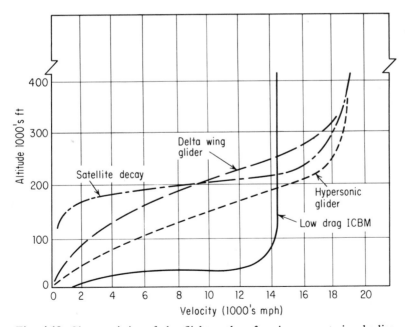

Fig. 4.18. Characteristics of the flight paths of various re-entering bodies.

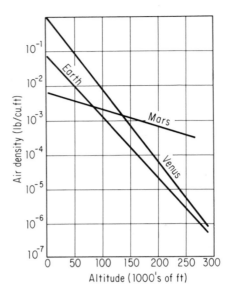

Fig. 4.19. Density distribution of planetary atmospheres.

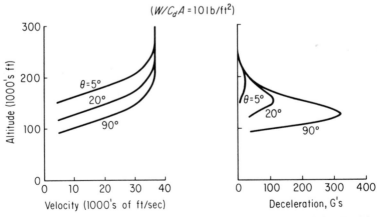

Fig. 4.20. Velocity and deceleration during direct entry into the Earth's atmosphere from space at various angles.

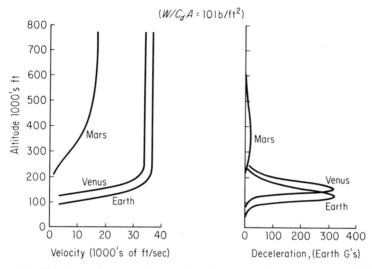

Fig. 4.21. Velocity and deceleration during direct entry from space at $\alpha = 90°$ into three planetary atmospheres.

PROBLEMS

1. The circular satellite velocity is given as a function of altitude by the equation

$$v_{\text{circ}} = \sqrt{\frac{k}{r}}$$

Estimate and graph the acceleration that will be required to overcome the drag acting on the satellite for circular orbits over the range of 50 to 175 nautical miles. Assume $C_d A/W = 100$ lb/ft². Prepare a similar graph showing the drag acceleration that acts on ballistic missiles in the same range of altitudes, choose velocity magnitudes of 10,000; 15,000 and 18,000 ft/sec.

2. Using the chart that appears in Figure 4.6, determine graphical solutions for the burn-out conditions of missiles on the following flights,

Range (nautical miles)	Flight Path Angle at b.o. (degrees)
500	60
1500	55
5000	45
8500	40

3. Estimate the flight path angle that corresponds to minimum burn out velocity in each range, problem 2. Show the following parameters for each of these examples

>   Vertical velocity at burn-out
>   Horizontal velocity component at burn-out
>   Maximum altitude
>   Time of flight.

4. Plot a graph showing the total velocity of the missile at burn-out for a 5000 mile flight having flight path angles in the range of 20 deg to 65 deg. What value gives the minimum time of flight, the minimum burn-out velocity?

5. Develop an analytical expression showing the flight path angle and velocity as a function of range. Show the flight path angle, as function of range, that corresponds to minimum velocity.

6. Using the minimum velocity condition that was developed in the previous example, calculate the differential showing the sensitivity of range to flight path angle.

7. Assuming the guidance function that was given in Equation (4-10) find the weighting function W_x, W_z, and W_γ.

8. Find the numerical values of the weighting functions for the minimum velocity trajectories that were found in problem 3 above. Plot these in graphical form.

9. Estimate the weighting functions as a function of time for the trajectory that is given in Figures 4.7 and 4.8. Use time intervals of 20 seconds.

10. Graph W_x, W_z, and W_γ as a function of burn-out flight path angle for a 5000 mile flight.

11. Find the error coefficients for a 5000 nautical mile flight. Tabulate these for flight path angle values of 30, 40, and 50 deg at burn-out.

REFERENCES

4.1. Blitzer, Leon, Morris Westerfield and Albert D. Wheelon, *Perturbations of a Satellite's Orbit Due to the Earth's Oblateness*. J. Appl. Physics, **27**, 10, p. 1141, Oct. 1956.

4.2. Jeffreys, H., *The Earth, Its Origin, History, and Physical Constitution*. University Press, Cambridge, England. Third Edition, p. 129, 1952.

4.3. Reece, J. William, R. David Joseph and Dorothy Shaffer, *Ballistic Missile Performance*, Proc. of the 24th IAS Annual Meeting, New York, Jan. 24, 1956.

4.4. Frye, W. E., *On the Accuracy of the Long Range Ballistic Rocket*. J. Appl. Physics, **22**, No. 5, pp. 585–589.

4.5. Kolk, W. Richard, *Modern Flight Dynamics*, Prentice-Hall, Inc., Englewood Cliffs, N. J., 1961.

4.6. Gilvarry, J. J., S. H. Browne and I. A. Williams, *The Theory of Blind Navigation by Dynamical Measurements*. J. Appl. Physics, **21**, p. 753, 1950.

4.7. Judge, John F., *Reseach Focuses on Re-Entry Problems*. Missiles and Rockets, May 30, 1960.

4.8. Gazley, Carl, Jr., *Deceleration and Heating of a Body Entering a Planetary Atmosphere from Space*. The RAND Corp., P–955, Santa Monica, Calif., Feb. 1957.

4.9. Gazley, Carl, Jr., *The Penetration of Planetary Atmospheres*. The RAND Corp., P–1322, Santa Monica, Calif., Feb. 1958.

4.10. Miele, Angelo, *Optimum Burning Programs as Related to Aerodynamic Heating for a Missile Traversing the Earth's Atmosphere*, Advances in Astronautical Sciences, Vol. 2, Plenum Press Inc., New York, 1957.

4.11. Foy, W. H., Jr., *Steering of an Ascent Rocket for Maximum Cut-off*. Advances in Astronautical Sciences, Vol. 2, Prenum Press Inc., New York, 1957.

5

NAVIGATION FOR SATELLITES

The significance of the artificial satellite has been the subject of many recent studies and demonstrations. We have seen that the artificial Earth satellite will make important contributions to many military and civilian missions. While the significance of the artificial satellite as a weapons carrier is perhaps in doubt, its application to such military missions as reconnaisance and surveillance is well recognized. Several important non-military missions for the near-Earth satellite have been established. Among these are communications, navigation, weather observation and prediction, and the collection of scientific data regarding the Earth and its environment. The advent of manned satellites has perhaps introduced a new dimension for their application. The very existence of a manned space flight capability will doubtless introduce many new applications of these vehicles including rescue, repair and maintenance, inspection, and the military mission of interception. The potential importance of satellites is largely dependant on guidance to place them in prescribed orbits and subsequently to predict their positions accurately over some extended time interval in the future. Each of the many applications mentioned above will require that guidance and navigational control be exercised over the satellite vehicle. This chapter will discuss the means for doing this and the general nature of satellite orbits.

Satellite operations call for two distinct kinds of navigation. The first of these deals with the ascent trajectory and terminates with the injection of the satellite into its stable orbit. A second navigation problem is concerned with the determination of current position of the satellite and with directing the maneuvers which may be necessary to permit the satellite to complete its mission. Both of these problems will be discussed in this chapter. Although it is not a navigation problem in the strict sense of the word, satellite attitude control will be discussed briefly; this study derives its significance from the fact that it is intimately related to the application of maneuvers as commanded by a navigator. No detailed discussion will be included here regarding the means for determining the orbit parameters when measurements are made from the ground; this has been discussed in Chapter 3. In a final section of the chapter, the means for effecting satellite rendezvous will be treated. It will be shown that the problems of on-orbit rendezvous are affected by the environment in which the rendezvous is to occur.

The term *satellite* refers to a smaller body which orbits about another, generally reference is made to a planet. For purposes of the present discussion, it will be convenient to restrict this definition further to include only Earth-centered orbiting bodies. Although Earth satellites may travel in stable periodic orbits over a range of altitudes from 150 miles out to lunar distance and beyond, most artificial Earth satellites will be confined to altitudes such that the orbit period is less than 24 hours. This restricts the satellites to average altitudes of about 22,000 miles and less. The orbit characteristics of several early satellites have been listed in Table 5.1 for example. To list all of the many satellites that have been launched more recently would not be fruitful. The list given shows the full range of orbital parameters that is applicable.

While an extensive discussion of the flight mechanics of the satellite is beyond the scope of the present book, it should be noted here that the inclination of the orbit of an artificial satellite is directly related to the heading of the vehicle occurring at the time of injection into its orbit. The minimum possible inclination will be equal to the latitude of the injection point and this will be realized only if the satellite is injected into orbit with an east–west heading. The satellite orbit will, in general, follow a closed path about the center of the Earth. Its ground path, however, will not be closed but will appear to precess as a result of the Earth's rotation. Two important perturbations are known to act on the orbit of a near Earth satellite. The deceleration which results from aerodynamic drag will be small, as shown in a calculation in Chapter 4, but its effect cannot be neglected over the relatively long life which may be required of these vehicles. The oblate shape of the Earth is known to give rise to a non-spherical gravitational field which exerts disturbing torques and forces on the satellite in its motion. The effect of this dipole in the gravity function was discussed briefly in the previous chapter. It introduces a regression of the nodes at a rate which is a function of the orbit altitude and its inclination. For more detail regarding these orbital characteristics the reader is referred to a standard text on orbit mechanics; cf. Reference 5.1.

Solar storms will, on occasion, disturb the orbit of an Earth satellite. For example a great solar storm occurred November 12, 1960 and produced a

Table 5.1. TYPICAL SATELLITE PARAMETERS

Satellite	Code Name	Launch Date	Period Mins	Apogee Alt. Statute Miles	Perigee Alt.
1957 ALPHA I	Rocket Body	4 October 57			
1957 ALPHA II	Sputnik I	4 October 57			
1957 BETA	Sputnik II	3 November 57			
1958 ALPHA	Explorer I	31 January 58	109.0	1257	218
1958 BETA I	Rocket Body	17 March 58	138.3	2687	402
1958 BETA II	Vanguard I	17 March 58	133.9	2450	404
1958 GAMMA	Explorer III	26 March 58			
1958 DELTA I	Rocket Body	15 May 58			
1958 DELTA II	Sputnik III	15 May 58	92.9	421	111
1958 EPSILON	Explorer IV	26 July 58			
1958 ZETA	Atlas	18 December 58			
1959 ALPHA I	Vanguard II	17 February 59	125.6	2051	347
1959 ALPHA II	Rocket Body	17 February 59	129.7	2281	347
1959 BETA	Discoverer I	28 February 59			
1959 GAMMA	Discoverer II	13 April 59			
1959 DELTA	Explorer VI	7 August 59	686.2	23980	117
1959 EPSILON	Discoverer V	13 August 59			
1959 ZETA	Discoverer VI	19 August 59			
1959 ETA	Vanguard III	18 September 59	130.0	2325	316
1959 IOTA I	Explorer VII	13 October 59	101.2	673	346
1959 IOTA II	Rocket Body	13 October 59	101.2	673	343
1959 KAPPA	Discoverer VII	7 November 59	95.6	590	125
1959 LAMBDA	Discoverer VIII	20 November 59	159	1049	945
1960	Echo	12 August 60			

This report reflects data computed and compiled by the National Space Surveillance Control Center, Bedford, Massachusetts.

substantial change in the orbit of the Echo I balloon satellite. When launched, Echo I had a perigee of 945 statute miles and an apogee of 1049 miles. At the time of the storm it had a perigee of 619 miles and an apogee of 1334 miles. Even though the atmospheric drag is extremely small at those altitudes, the effect was measurable on an object with the characteristics of Echo ($W/C_dA \approx 0.0235$ lb/ft^2). Calculations by NASA's Goddard Space Flight Center indicate that the atmospheric drag acting on the satellite increased by a factor of two for several days. During this time the orbital period increased two seconds each day; following this, the drag fell back to its previous level. This increase in drag is believed to have been caused by an increase in air density which resulted from the expansion of the air at lower levels in the atmosphere.

5.1 ASCENT GUIDANCE

Guidance for an ascending satellite vehicle is concerned with the control of a booster to assure that the satellite payload attains a suitable orbit at the end of its powered flight. In the event that the only requirement for this orbit is that it be stable and that it have a specified shape, three parameters will be sufficient to define the orbit. On the other hand, it has been shown in Chapter 2 that a space orbit requires six parameters to define it completely where the ideal Keplerian situation applies, consequently all six flight coordinates must be subject to control. When these parameters are expressed in terms of measurable flight conditions, they will involve three components of a position vector and a like number of components of a velocity vector; both vectors may be observed at the time of orbit injection. These parameters may be related to the following coordinates which can be observed directly:

1. Location of the sub-satellite point[1] at injection (latitude-longitude)
2. Heading at injection
3. Altitude of orbit injection
4. Velocity magnitude (speed) at injection
5. Flight path angle at injection.

In order to establish a forecast of future positions, another parameter will be needed; the time of injection.

Because of the general nature of rocket booster trajectories as discussed in Chapter 4, the heading, sub-satellite point, and time of injection are all largely determined at the time of launching the boost vehicle. Thus, the ascent variables which are formally placed under the close control of a satellite guidance system are the last three mentioned,

Altitude at injection
Velocity at injection
Flight path angle at injection.

[1] The *sub-satellite point* is defined to be that point on the surface of the Earth which is directly below the satellite.

5.1.1 TRAJECTORY REQUIREMENTS

A satellite orbit will be stable if injection occurs at an altitude so high that drag deceleration does not decrease the energy of the orbiting body at an excessive rate. In addition, the velocity at injection must be high enough that the orbit will remain above the sensible atmosphere and its drag effects. The curves which are given in Figure 5.1 show the way in which the atmosphere acts to decrease the life of a satellite.

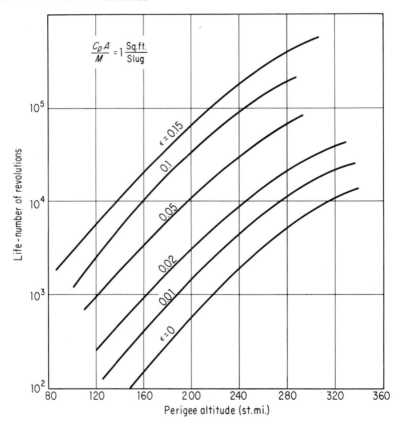

Fig. 5.1. Drag-life curves for earth satellites.

The velocity which is required for a satellite orbit about the Earth is a function of the altitude at which injection occurs. It may be derived from the orbit Equation (2-24)

$$r = \frac{h^2}{k(1 + e \cos A_t)}$$

where

$$h = r\dot{x}$$

$$e = 1 + \frac{2Eh^2}{k^2}$$

$$E = (\tfrac{1}{2})(\dot{x}^2 + \dot{z}^2) - \frac{k}{r}$$

A convenient parameter which may be used for computation of useful data is the circular orbit velocity, that is, the orbiting velocity for which $e = 0$. This parameter is

$$\dot{x}_c = v_c = \sqrt{\frac{k}{r}} \tag{5-1}$$

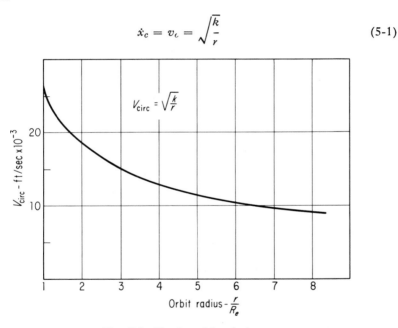

Fig. 5.2. Circular orbit velocity.

The circular orbit velocity is shown as a function of distance from the center of the Earth in Figure 5.2. For non-circular orbits, the horizontal component of velocity will depend on the phase of the injection point relative to the orbital apogee. When the velocity is observed as a function of true anomaly it will be given by the relation

$$v_{\text{orb}}^2 = \left(\frac{k}{r}\right)(1 + e \cos A.) \tag{5-2}$$

This may be normalized as follows

$$\frac{v_{orb}}{\sqrt{k/r}} = \dot{\xi}_{orb} = \sqrt{1 + e \cos A_t} \tag{5-3}$$

This expression has been shown in the graph of Figure 5.3.

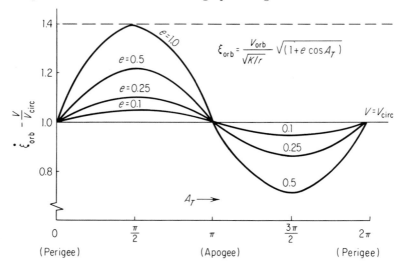

Fig. 5.3. Normalized orbit velocity—eccentric orbit.

The flight path angle for the orbiting vehicle is defined as the angle between the vehicle velocity vector and the local horizontal plane. This angle will be given by the expression

$$\sin \gamma = \frac{ek}{Vh} \sin A_t \tag{5-4}$$

The variation of the flight path angle which occurs as the satellite travels around its elliptic orbit is shown in Figure 5.4.

The eccentricity of the orbit measures the shape of the orbit. It is a property of the conic which describes its shape; it also provides a useful means to define the relation of the apogee and perigee of elliptical orbits. The apsidal radii have been graphed as a function of eccentricity, these are shown in Figure 5.5.

A satellite ascent flight may be considered as an example to show the influence the injection flight conditions have on the orbit. The mission will be chosen to be one requiring an orbit 400 miles above the surface of the Earth and with eccentricity less than 0.01. The flight conditions at injection must lie within the following envelope:

Altitude: 400 miles ± 40 miles

Velocity: 24,700 ± 1200 ft/sec
Flight path angle: 0° ± 5.5°.

A typical ascent flight for this mission is shown in the sketch of Figure 5.6.
A powered boost flight places the satellite vehicle on a ballistic trajectory with a
maximum altitude (apogee of the ascent ellipse) of 400 miles. When the satellite
vehicle reaches this altitude, an additional velocity impulse will boost the
satellite into its stable orbit. This is accomplished by increasing the orbit energy
in such a way as to bring the perigee of the ascent ellipse to an altitude which is
above the atmosphere of the Earth. The velocity increment required for this
boost will be determined as the deficit between the horizontal velocity at apogee
and the velocity required for circular orbit at this altitude, that is

$$\Delta v = \frac{k}{r} - v_{\text{apogee}} \qquad (5\text{-}4)$$

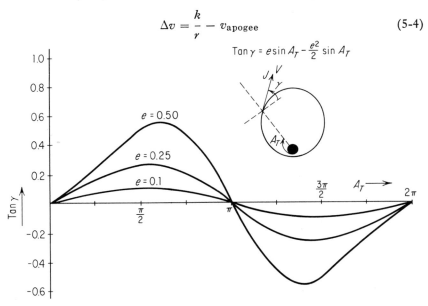

Fig. 5.4. Tangent of flight path angle vs. true anomaly.

The orbit injection impulse, Δv, must be directed in the plane of the orbit and
the horizontal plane within the ±5.5 degree tolerance. Upon achieving the
necessary orbiting velocity, the satellite vehicle rocket engines are shut down
and the satellite continues in its stable orbit indefinitely until energy losses
from external causes reduce its velocity and it falls to Earth.

The apogee of the ascent trajectory will be related to the flight parameters of
that orbit by the equation

$$r_{\max} = \frac{h^2}{k(1 - e)} \qquad (5\text{-}5)$$

which may be written in terms of the flight parameters as

$$r_{max} = r_i \left[\frac{\dot{\xi}_2^2}{1 - \sqrt{(1 - \dot{\xi}_i^2)^2 - \dot{\xi}_i^2 \dot{\zeta}_i^2}} \right] \qquad (5\text{-}6)$$

where

r_i = the geocentric radius of the injection point

$$\dot{\xi}_i = \frac{\dot{x}_i}{\sqrt{k/r_i}}$$

$$\dot{\zeta}_i = \frac{\dot{z}_i}{\sqrt{k/r_i}}$$

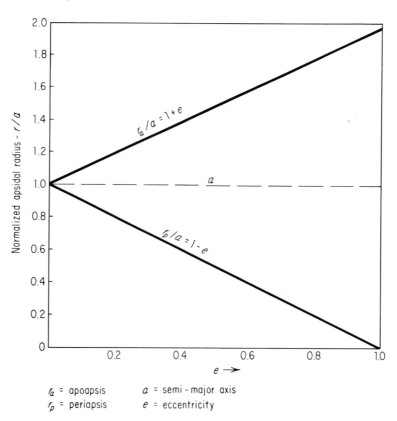

Fig. 5.5. Apsidal radii for elliptical orbits.

The time to apogee measured from the time of booster burn-out will be given in terms of the eccentric anomaly, A_e, by

$$t_a = \frac{1}{n}(\pi - A_{ei} - e \sin A_{ei}) \tag{5-7}$$

where

$$A_{ei} = \sin^{-1}\left[\frac{\sqrt{1 + e_a^2}\, \sin \alpha}{1 - e_a \cos \alpha}\right]$$

$$= \cot^{-1}\left[\frac{1}{\dot{\xi}_{B0}\dot{\zeta}_{B0}} - \frac{\dot{\xi}_{B0}}{\dot{\zeta}_{B0}}\right]$$

e_a = the eccentricity of the ascent ellipse

$$= \sqrt{(1 - \dot{\xi}_a^2)^2 - \dot{\xi}_a^2 \dot{\zeta}_a^2}$$

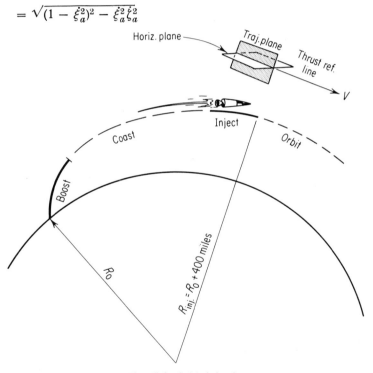

Fig. 5.6. Orbit injection.

A useful approximation for the time to apogee will be given by the more familiar expression

$$t_a = \frac{\dot{z}_{B0}}{g_{\text{eff}}} \tag{5-8}$$

where g_{eff} represents an *effective* value of the acceleration due to gravity. It is computed to represent the gravity over the coast trajectory by a single constant parameter. This will be approximated as follows

$$g_{eff} = g_i - \frac{\dot{x}_a^2}{r_a} = \frac{k - \dot{x}_i^2 r_i}{r_i^2}$$

(5-9)

5.1.2 ACCURACY REQUIRED FOR ORBITS

The accuracy of guidance which is required may be indicated by calculation of the error coefficients which show the sensitivity of the orbit parameters as a function of the deviations of the flight conditions that are monitored by the guidance system. These deviations are reckoned from nominal, or precalculated values; they usually represent errors in the function of the guidance and control system. This section presents the error coefficients for the orbit parameters of a circular satellite of the Earth.

The so-called natural parameters were developed in Chapter 2. They are usually listed as

1. Orbit energy
2. Orbit angular momentum (3 vector components)
3. Eccentricity
4. Argument to perigee.

In addition, the orbit period is frequently used as a parameter interchangeable with the orbit energy. It is related to the orbit energy through the relations

$$T = 2\pi \sqrt{\frac{|a|^3}{k}}$$

(5-10)

and

$$a = - \frac{k}{2E}$$

(5-11)

Thus,

$$T = 2\pi \sqrt{\frac{k^2}{8E^3}}$$

(5-12)

The orbit parameters listed above may be stated in terms of the vehicle flight coordinates and the guidance error coefficients will be obtained by calculation of the differentials of the individual parameters with respect to each of the coordinates which measure the flight conditions. The partial differentials of the parameters which are significant for near circular orbits have been calculated; they are shown in Table 5.2. The range of the orbit velocity and period are shown for circular orbits about the Earth in Figure 5.7.

Table 5.2. VARIATION OF ORBIT PARAMETERS WITH VARIATIONS IN FLIGHT COORDINATES

Parameter	f	$\dfrac{\partial f}{\partial r}$	$\dfrac{\partial f}{\partial v}$	$\dfrac{\partial f}{\partial \gamma}$
Angular Momentum	$h = rv \cos \gamma$	$v \cos \gamma$	$r \cos \gamma$	$-rv \sin \gamma$
Energy	$E = \dfrac{v^2}{2} - \dfrac{k}{r}$	$\dfrac{k}{r^2}$	v	—
Eccentricity	$e = \dfrac{r^2 v^2 \cos^2 \gamma}{r_p k} - 1$	$\dfrac{2}{r_p}$	$\dfrac{2r}{r_p \cos \gamma}$	$-\dfrac{r \sin 2\gamma}{r_p}$
Period	$T = 2\pi \sqrt{\dfrac{a^3}{k}}$	$\dfrac{3\pi}{E^2}\sqrt{\dfrac{a}{k}}\,\dfrac{\partial E}{\partial r}$	$\dfrac{3\pi}{E^2}\sqrt{\dfrac{a}{k}}\,\dfrac{\partial E}{\partial v}$	—

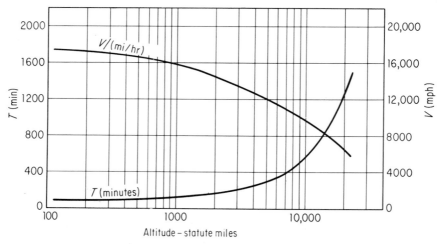

Fig. 5.7. Circular orbit parameters.

5.1.3 EXTRAPOLATION OF BOOSTER GUIDANCE

In mechanizing a satellite guidance system it may be convenient to employ a system which relies upon guidance equipment that is installed in the booster. Such a system functions as an extrapolation device to provide an open loop extension of the solution derived by the more accurate equipment carried in the booster. The guidance of the earlier stages serves to place the satellite in an ascent ellipse which is controlled with precision to provide the desired orbit properties. Differential corrections may be transmitted to the satellite stage to make minor adjustments in the pre-programmed guidance (or control) system. After an accurately timed coasting period, the guidance system must provide the commands to the torquing devices which will re-align the vehicle so that thrust will be applied in a direction such as to increase the horizontal component of the velocity vector without contribution to the vertical or cross course components. This means that the satellite guidance system must include the means for indication (or sensing) the attitude of the vehicle and that the control system must include the means for applying torques to the body of the craft. The design of suitable torquing devices and their control will be discussed briefly in Section 5.5 in this chapter.

The thrust at apogee will nominally be applied in a direction which is defined by a vector in the plane of the ascent orbit and which is horizontal at the time of injection. For brief thrusting periods, such as those with which we are concerned here, the flight near apogee may be approximated by a horizontal straight line segment. For thrust reference purposes, the curvature during this short interval may be neglected. The horizontal plane may conveniently be defined using a horizon scanner that provides an electrical reference to the horizon. No such convenient indicator may be employed to define the orientation of the reference plane. Gyroscopic memories will, however, provide an acceptable reference to the trajectory.

An indication of the trajectory plane may, under certain circumstances, be obtained using a single axis gyro in a mode that is analogous to a classical gyro-compass. A single axis gyro is mounted in the vehicle with its gimbal axis constrained to the horizontal plane. It is assumed that this plane has been determined with the aid of the horizon scanner.

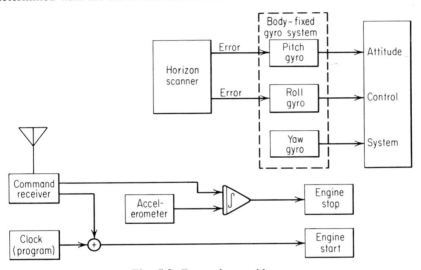

Fig. 5.8. Extrapolater guidance.

An example of the extrapolator type of guidance system is illustrated in Figure 5.8. This system might be described as a stable autopilot. Attitude of the spacecraft is controlled with reference to the gyro package which is, in turn, supervised by the horizon scanner. Engine start signals are derived from the timer and engine shut-down commands are derived from the integrating accelerometer. The clock setting and the integrator initial bias may be adjusted by commands that are transmitted to the satellite from the booster guidance. These commands will be computed on the basis of the final guidance conditions that are sensed by the booster guidance system at the time of separation.

The accuracy of an extrapolation system can usually be less than that which is required for guidance of the satellite itself. In the comments which follow, the errors in the booster guidance system will be assumed to be statistically in-dependant of those of the satellite system; consequently, resultant errors will be found by the familiar RSS method. Consider an example in which a circular orbit at three hundred miles altitude is required. Errors will be of three general classes. These are listed below together with the permissible errors for an eccentricity less than 0.01.

Errors in position $\Delta r = \pm 40$ miles
Errors in velocity $\Delta v = \pm 125$ ft/sec
Errors in attitude reference $\Delta \gamma = \pm 1°$.

In a typical booster-satellite system, the booster guidance is considered to have guidance of an ICBM quality. The booster will be assumed to carry the satellite vehicle to an altitude of, say, 100 miles; the precision guidance system will establish the orbit at burn-out to be the desired ascent trajectory with the following error magnitudes as an upper limit

Errors in position $\Delta r = \pm 1$ mile
Errors in velocity $\Delta v = \pm 1.0$ ft/sec.
Errors in attitude reference $\Delta \gamma = \pm 0.1°$

After burn-out, the satellite vehicle will coast to an apogee where the self-contained satellite guidance acts to monitor the application of a velocity increment of about 3500 ft/sec in the horizontal direction.

The net errors which can be permitted in the extrapolation type of satellite guidance system may be calculated for the case of the 0.01 eccentricity orbit as

$$\Delta q_{total} = (\Delta q_{boost}^2 + \Delta q_{sat}^2)^{1/2}$$

Consequently

$$\Delta q_{sat} = (\Delta q_{total}^2 - \Delta q_{boost}^2)^{1/2}$$

and, after making the appropriate substitutions

$$\Delta r_{sat} = (40^2 - 1^2)^{1/2} \approx 40 \text{ miles}$$

$$\Delta v_{sat} = (125^2 - 1^2)^{1/2} \approx 125 \text{ ft/sec}$$

$$\Delta \gamma_{sat} = (1^2 - 0.1^2) \approx 1 \text{ deg}$$

It may be seen that the precision of the booster guidance may be used to permit the guidance carried into orbit to be of minimum precision; the full latitude of the tolerances for the over-all flight are allowed for the extrapolation system. These error allowances may be calculated in terms of fractions of the total values over which the satellite guidance has supervision. Thus,

$$\frac{\Delta r}{r} = \frac{40}{400} = 0.1$$

$$\frac{\Delta v}{v} = \frac{125}{12,000} = 0.01$$

The total error in the flight path angle at injection into orbit is also strongly influenced by the accuracy of the booster guidance. The total error in the flight path angle will be limited by the following expression (See Figure 5.9)

$$\Delta\gamma = \frac{\delta v_{eff}}{v_{total}} = \frac{\sqrt{\delta v_{boost}^2 + \delta v_{sat}^2}}{v_{total}}$$

$$\Delta\gamma_{total} = \frac{\sqrt{(v_{boost}\Delta\gamma_{boost})^2 + (v_{sat}\Delta\gamma_{sat})^2}}{v_{total}}$$

$$\Delta\gamma_{sat} = \frac{\sqrt{(v_{total}\Delta\gamma_{total})^2 - (v_{boost}\Delta\gamma_{boost})^2}}{v_{sat}}$$

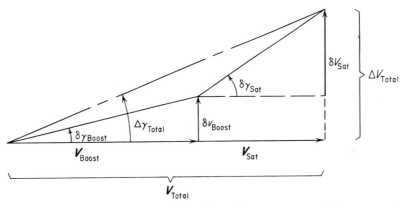

Fig. 5.9. The evaluation of flight path angle errors—extrapolation system.

5.2 SATELLITE ATTITUDE CONTROL

Control of the attitude of a satellite vehicle is perhaps not a direct part of its guidance or navigation. However, the attitude of a satellite during its propulsion determines the velocity change which is attained. Further, the attitude will affect the field of view of the telescopes and antennae which it carries in orbit. In some missions, the control of satellite attitude will be essential to the satisfactory completion of its mission.

During the ascent of a satellite to its orbit there may be one or more extended coasting intervals where the ascending vehicle is in a free fall orbit. During these intervals, an attitude reference must be retained to permit the control system to maintain alignment or to realign the vehicle prior to thrust reapplication. If this is not done prior to ignition of the thrust engines, the thrust axis of the satellite will be misaligned relative to the trajectory and a transient maneuver will result. In general this is inefficient use of the limited propulsion energy. The vehicle dynamics during these coast intervals are similar to those of a vehicle in orbit; it is in free fall with no convenient means for rapid on-board determination of the vertical. Aerodynamic and dynamic torques acting on the vehicle are small and, consequently, whatever stable attitudes may exist will have long oscillatory periods associated with them.

Orbiting vehicles will frequently be assigned to missions requiring that the payload be oriented in some special attitude in order to align the sensors. Examples are astronomical observation satellites, reconnaissance vehicles, communication satellites, and many other scientific vehicles. These will require orientation within a few degrees for a communication satellite to a few seconds of arc, or less, for an astronomical observatory satellite. In missions where high resolution images of the Earth are to be recorded, for example in a reconnaissance satellite, the attitude rate may be more critical than the actual attitude. The attitude rates must be so low as not to degrade the images beyond tolerable limits during the photographic exposure time.

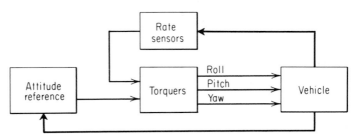

Fig. 5.10. Attitude control system.

Satellite rendezvous and refuelling missions will be discussed briefly later in this chapter. The rendezvous phase of these missions will terminate with a coupling, or docking operation. In order to accomplish this, the attitude of one satellite must be stabilized, that is the vehicle can not be permitted to tumble. The attitude of the other satellite must be under precise control of an operator or automatic docking control device. This control of attitude permits the alignment and joining of couplers without structural damage to either vehicle.

A schematic diagram of a generalized attitude control system is shown in Figure 5.10. The attitude reference may be supplied in a number of specific ways. For example, a gyro stabilized platform, an angle of attack indicator, a horizon sensor, or a celestial body tracker may each be used and programmed to provide the attitude reference which is required in satellite missions. Gyros will, in general, be subject to excessive drifts when boost accelerations are applied and also during extended coast (orbit) periods. While some work has been reported on a satellite attitude control device based on the use of an angle of attack indicator (Reference 5.2), their application appears to be limited in altitude. Celestial body trackers and horizon scanners appear to be the most interesting of the devices mentioned for use in many satellite applications. Those missions in which payload orientation relative to the ground and to ground stations is important will find the horizon scanner more convenient. Celestial body trackers will provide a useful reference for inertial space and astronomical orientations where these are required by the mission at hand.

Attitude controlling torques may be applied to the orbiting vehicle in a number of ways, among these are the acceleration of flywheels and masses which are retained in the vehicle system for this purpose, the application of small reaction jets, and the use of residual aerodynamic forces. Flywheel methods of torquing and the acceleration of internal masses are, in effect, momentum exchange techniques in which the flywheel or other control mass is required to absorb the momentum which has been given to the vehicle by the action of the various external torques which are applied to it. If these external torques are indeed random in character (direction and magnitude), the average angular momentum of a set of flywheels used for attitude control will vanish over a

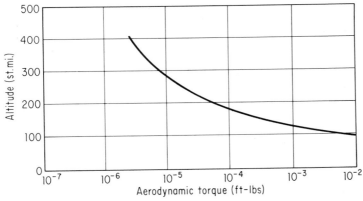

Fig. 5.11. Aerodynamic torque on a cylindrical satellite (axis of cylinder normal to direction of flow, aerodynamic moment—2ft² ft).

long time interval. However, the design of a control system will frequently require that provisions be made for the desaturation of these flywheels. Saturation is a result of the action of long term biases in the disturbing torques. Reaction jet systems function by the ejection of mass from the vehicle and are naturally limited by the quantity of fuel or gas which is carried. Aerodynamic torques will be small in magnitude as shown in Figure 5.11. An advantage arises with the use of aerodynamic torques in that their use does not require continuous application of power. Aerodynamic torques will frequently be useful for trim purposes to reduce bias torques to a level where wheel saturation will be retained within tolerances.

Attitude disturbances may arise from several sources and torques which appear as disturbances in one context may be used as the basis for control in another system. Among the many important sources of torques which may be applied to a satellite affecting its attitude are the following:

Gravity gradient torque
Aerodynamic torque
Radiation pressure
Earth's magnetic field
Meteorite impacts
Cosmic ray impacts
Internal moving parts.

The relative magnitude of these various torques will depend largely on the altitude of the satellite and its particular configuration and desired attitude. They will not be discussed in further detail here; a summary of the important effects is contained in Reference 5.3.

The horizon scanner and the celestial body tracker are each very important instruments for application to satellite attitude control. In addition, these instruments will be discussed in their context as navigation instruments. Detailed functional descriptions of their operation will be deferred until those subjects are treated. The horizon scanner will be discussed in Section 5.3 of this chapter while celestial body trackers will be discussed in Chapter 6.

5.3 ON-ORBIT NAVIGATION

As in the case of the terrestrial forms of the art of navigation, navigation of a satellite requires that certain data be observed which will permit the vehicle's position to be calculated. In addition, it is necessary to make observations which permit the course and speed of the vehicle to be determined. These data are then used for subsequent calculation of the changes in heading and speed which are required in order to execute the maneuvers indicated by the mission of the satellite. The techniques for the calculation of orbit maneuvers have been discussed in general terms in Chapter 2, Section 2.3. Consequently, attention will be centered here on the means for observing position, course, and speed of the satellite and the application of these data to the determination of orbit parameters. The orbit of a satellite about an ideal (spherical) Earth is fully specified by its six fundamental parameters, consequently navigational observations will be selected with the determination of these parameters in mind. Certainly the most satisfactory method for defining these parameters is through the use of ground tracking stations; this technique has been discussed in some detail in Chapter 3. While it may be presumed that tracking techniques will be employed so far as practical, an interesting problem arises when one considers the means which are available to the occupant of a satellite vehicle by which he may make navigation observations and determine the parameters of his own orbit. Under certain conditions of loss of ground communication, such a self-contained navigation system may prove necessary for survival. The following discussions will deal with the navigation of a satellite using only those observations which may be made from on-board the vehicle.

5.3.1 NAVIGATION USING GROUND OBSERVATIONS

An instrument which permits the continuous observation of the ground position of the sub-satellite point from on board an orbiting vehicle will be capable of providing all of the data which are required to calculate the parameters of the orbit in question. An instrument of this kind will aslo require an indication of the time of observation to correlate position and velocity observations. The record of measurements will provide a ground track similar to the one shown in Figure 5.12. From such a record, the satellite navigator will be able to derive directly the following information regarding the orbit parameters:

The Energy of the Orbit

The orbit energy is derived from the orbit period using the relation

$$E = -\left(\frac{\pi k}{2T}\right)^{2/3}$$

The period is measured as the time between successive crossings of the same parallel of latitude.

The Orbit Inclination

The orbit inclination relative to the equatorial plane of the Earth will be given by the maximum latitude observed

$$A_i = \lambda_{max}$$

The Line of Nodes

The line of nodes, together with the orbit inclination, will define the orientation of the orbit in space. The line of nodes will be a line in the plane of the equator which is common to that plane and to the satellite orbit plane. It cuts the surface of the Earth at points where the orbit plane crosses the equator. Since the orbit is fixed in space, or at least precessing at a relatively slow rate, the terminal points of the line of nodes will appear to precess relative to a point on the Earth. These nodal points will have a ground speed which is given by

$$V_{1.o.n.} = R_e \Omega_e$$

The Location of Perigee

The longitude and latitude of the sub-satellite point for perigee will be those values for which the ground speed of the satellite is observed to be

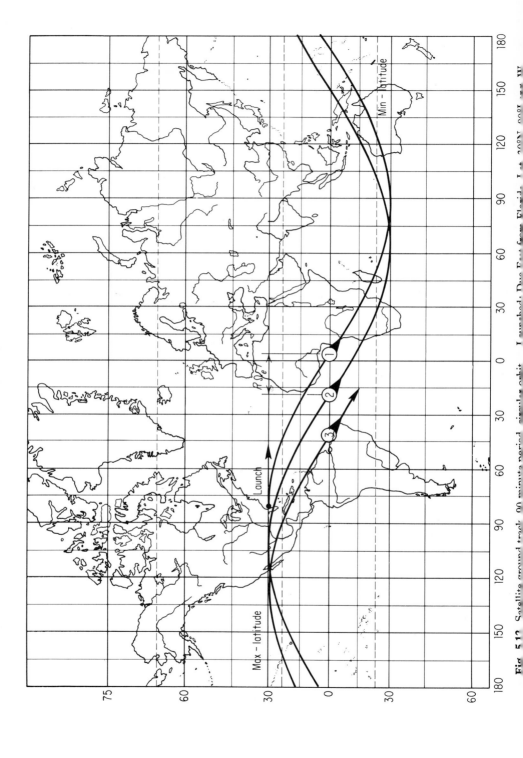

Fig. 5.12 Satellite ground track, 90-minute period, circular orbit. Launched: Due East from Florida. Lat. 30°N; 90°W. Inclination W.

maximum. In reckoning the ground speed for this purpose, it will be necessary to make allowance for the rotation of the Earth. The vector relations which permit the equivalent ground speed to be determined are illustrated in Figure 5.13.

The Time of Passing Perigee

The time which is correllated with the observation of perigee will be t_p. This will, of course, be repeated at intervals of $t_p + T$; the apogee will occur at times of $t_p + (2n + 1)T/2$.

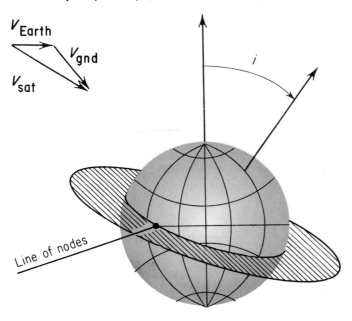

Fig. 5.13. Orbit ground track.

The Eccentricity of The Orbit

The eccentricity may be computed from the observed values of the satellite inertial velocity at perigee and apogee respectively.

$$e = \frac{1/v_p - 1/v_a}{1/v_p + 1/v_a}$$

where the inertial, or satellite, velocity terms are calculated as shown in Figure 5.13.

The Angular Momentum of the Orbit

The orbit angular momentum may be calculated from the parameters listed above, it is

$$h = k\left(\frac{e^2 - 1}{2E}\right)^{1/2}$$

These relations will permit the occupant of a satellite to calculate the first-order parameters of the satellite orbit in which he is traveling. The effects of residual atmospheric drag, gravity dipole moments and other perturbing influences will be detected by the way in which these parameters change with time.

The ground track of a satellite may be determined by observation of passing landmarks whose positions are known in terms of latitude and longitude in advance. Prominent surface features such as the tip of a peninsula, the mouth of a river, or a characteristic light pattern or beacon aid to navigation may be employed as landmarks. The observations may be made in a number of ways, for example, photographically, with TV, and by direct vision. We will discuss, as an example, a device to aid the astronaut in making these visual observations. This device will be called a *Satellite Nadir Sextant.*

The mission which has been outlined for the Satellite Nadir Sextant can be accomplished by a simple telescope with its axis aligned to the local vertical permitting observation of a ground swath directly below the satellite. A graduated reticle is supplied to permit the estimation of the angle between the optical axis and the landmark under observation. It is stabilized to the local vertical by a pair of gyros which receive error commands for the platform alignment servos from an automatic horizon scanning device, the principles of the horizon scanner will not be discussed here but will be treated in a later section. The likelihood that a satellite will pass directly over a specified landmark in any brief period, for example one day, is extremely small. Consequently it will be necessary to provide the sextant telescope with as broad a field of view as possible, consistent with accuracy requirements. The telescope must also provide the means to determine satellite position from observations of landmarks over as broad a ground swath as possible. The operating features of the sextant are illustrated in Figure 5.14.

The relationship between the geocentric angle from the local vertical to the landmark under observation and the angle observed from the satellite are related as follows (see Figure 5.15)

$$\sin A_c = \left(\frac{h}{R_e} + 1 - \cos A_c\right)\tan A_0 \qquad (5\text{-}17)$$

Now, making the assumption that the field of view is small, the following substitutions may be made

$$\sin A_c = A_c; \quad \cos A_c = 1 - \frac{A_c^2}{2} + \ldots$$

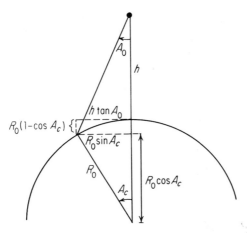

Fig. 5.14. Satellite nadir sextant.

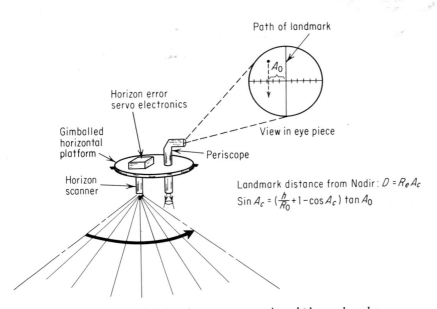

Path of landmark

A_0

View in eye piece

Horizon error
servo electronics

Gimballed
horizontal
platform

Periscope

Horizon
scanner

Landmark distance from Nadir: $D = R_e A_c$

$\sin A_c = (\frac{h}{R_0} + 1 - \cos A_c) \tan A_0$

Fig. 5.15. The relations between geocentric and observed angles.

After simplification and solving the resulting quadratic equation, it follows that

$$A_c = \frac{1}{\tan A_0}\left(1 \pm \sqrt{1 - \frac{2h\tan^2 A_0}{R_e}}\right) \tag{5-18}$$

This angle has been graphed as a function of the observed angle and the satellite altitude; it is shown in Figure 5.16a.

The field of view of the sextant telescope is illustrated in the inset of Figure 5.14. A calibrated reticle is oriented by the operator to align it at right angles to the apparent motion of the ground points. The observation of one ground point of known position will fix the position of the satellite on a circle having radius ρ, where

$$\rho = R_e A_c$$

$$\rho = \frac{R_e}{\tan A_0}\left[1 \pm \sqrt{1 - \frac{2h\tan^2 A_0}{R_e}}\right] \tag{5-19}$$

The simultaneous observation of two landmarks which have been noted in this manner will permit an accurate position fix to be established. In order to estimate the orbit parameters, the time must be recorded along with the observations of position. Data reduction may be accomplished either by graphical means in which the time of observation is plotted on a map or precalculated stripchart or by the use of specifically programmed digital computers. The selection of these methods will depend primarily on the desired accuracy.

The accuracy of this means of navigation may be estimated in terms of the accuracy of the instrument that is used for observing the ground. The error in the radius of the circle of position may be used to measure the error in a determination of position; the circle of position is the locus of points where the satellite may be located on the basis of the observation of a single landmark. The error in the radius of the circle of position will be related to the error in the observed angle as follows

$$d\rho = R_e \, dA_c \tag{5-20}$$

where A_c is related to A_0 as shown in Equation (5-18). The error in geocentric angle, A_c, that results from an error in estimating the observed angle will be given by the error coefficient

$$\frac{\partial A_c}{\partial A_0} = -\csc^2 A_0 \mp \frac{1}{2}\left[\frac{\csc^2 A_0 + \left(\frac{2h}{R_e}\right)\sec^2 A_0}{\sqrt{\cot A_0 - \left(\frac{2h}{R_e}\right)\tan A_0}}\right] \tag{5-21}$$

Similarly, the error in geocentric angle may be estimated in terms of the error

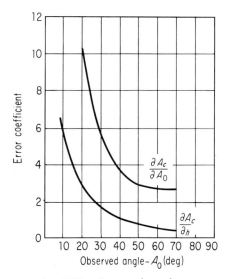

Fig. 5.16a. Geocentric angle vs observed angle.

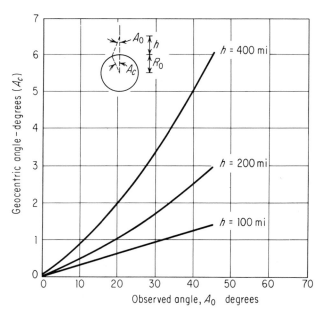

Fig. 5.16b. Error coefficients for determination of geocentric angles to observed landmarks. Orbit altitude = 200 miles.

in the measurement of altitude

$$\frac{\partial A_c}{\partial h} = \cot A_0 \pm \cfrac{1}{R_e \sqrt{1 - \left(\dfrac{2h}{R_e}\right) \tan^2 A_0}} \tag{5-22}$$

The error in estimating the position of the satellite that is due to an error in the observations will be determined from the relation

$$d\rho = R_e \frac{\partial A_c}{\partial A_0} dA_0 + R_e \frac{\partial A_c}{\partial h} dh \tag{5-23}$$

The magnitude of these error coefficients are shown as functions of the observed angle from the nadir to a landmark in the graph of Figure 5.16b.

Errors in the observed angle can probably be held to within 0.1–1.0 deg (0.02–0.002 radians), however it is apparent that altitude must be known with precision in order to hold the errors in position within a reasonable tolerance. For example, if the observed angle is 30°, then altitude must be known within ± 2 ft in order to provide position error less than 10 miles for a 200 mile altitude satellite. Accuracy of this kind will certainly require that an altimeter of some kind, perhaps radar, will be present on board the spacecraft.

5.3.2 On-Orbit Applications of Celestial Navigation

Celestial navigation has been practiced for centuries as a means for determining positions and steering ships at sea; more recently, it has been adopted as a means to navigate aircraft. One of the earliest known navigation techniques is that of estimating position from sightings that are made on the stars. The navigator at sea determines his position from calculations based on the measurement of the angle of elevation of the line of sight to three, or more, stars. This section will deal with the application of similar techniques for the determination of position of a satellite.

In the practice of celestial navigation, a star sight consists of a measurement of the angle of elevation between the horizontal plane and the line of sight to a star. The arc distance (in angular units) on the surface of the Earth from the navigator to the substellar point of the star which is observed is equal to the complement of the observed angle of elevation. This defines a locus of points on the Earth which are equidistant from the substellar point; this locus describes a *circle of position* on the surface of the Earth. Two such circles provide two intersections on the Earth while a third sight (derived from a third separate star) will permit the resolution of ambiguity in position together with a check of the methods used. The techniques described may also be used in navigating an orbiting vehicle. Since the stars are at a great distance from the Solar System, their parallax is less than a second of arc when observed from any point within the Earth's orbit. Consequently, the stars may be considered to be fixed in inertial space. The geocentric angle between the vertical at an observer's position and the vertical at the substellar point is equal to the angle which is observed between the local vertical at the observer and the line of sight to the star. As a matter of convenience, the complement of this angle is frequently measured, this complement is the angle of elevation of the line of sight to the star. The positions of the substellar points may be determined as a function of time through reference to a *Nautical Almanac*. The observer's position will be at a point on the circle which is centered at the substellar point and which has a radius equal to a ground distance of

$$\rho = \left(\frac{\pi}{2} - A_{el}\right) R_e$$

see Figure 5.17.

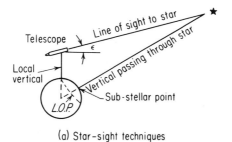

(a) Star-sight techniques

(b) Intersection showing how sub-satellite point is found at the union of three cicles of position

Fig. 5.17. Application of star sighting to satellite navigation.

As mentioned above, star parallax noted on the Earth is negligible; the same applies to observations from satellites confined to cis-lunar space. The celestial navigation techniques that have been described above may therefore be employed to determine the position of the sub-satellite point from an observation point on board the satellite. The specification of the orbit parameters may then proceed in the manner described in the previous section. The details of the calculations that are required for this computation and the aids to computation which are available are described in various Hydrographic Office publications (Reference 5.5).

In a satellite vehicle, as in an aircraft, direct observation of the horizon is not satisfactory for the determination of star elevations. For the case of observations made from a satellite, the line of sight to the horizon will be depressed relative to the horizontal plane. The angle of depression will depend on the altitude of the satellite (see Figure 5.18). However, the horizontal plane may be defined through use of a device called a *horizon scanner*. This consists of an optical, or infra-red sensitive telescope which is moved so that its field of view scans about an axis which has been set at an angle from the optical axis of the telescope.

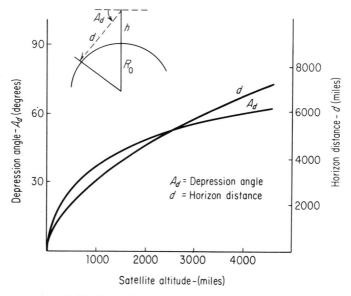

Fig. 5.18. Line of sight to the horizon from a satellite.

When this angle is equal to the depression of the horizon, the light intensity that is sensed by the telescope will be approximately constant during each revolution of the scanner if the rotary axis is aligned with the local vertical. The horizontal plane is then defined as the plane which is normal to the rotary axis of the telescope when a null error signal is obtained.

An instrument which will provide the measurements needed to perform celestial navigation from an orbiting satellite will consist of a telescope with a calibrated mounting which permits the angles of elevation to be measured. This telescope must be coupled to a reference which permits the angles measured to be referred to the local horizontal. The operating features of a horizon scanner are illustrated in the sketch of Figure 5.19. The navigation instrument that has been described is shown in the sketch of Figure 5.20. It will consist of a telescope mounted to a platform which is stabilized to the horizontal through application of a set of gyros that are supervised by the horizon scanner. The telescope may be manually operated permitting an occasional "fix" to be made as desired. The telescope may also be programmed or operated as an automatic star tracker making input to a digital computer to calculate a continuous record of position and velocity as well as the important orbit parameters.

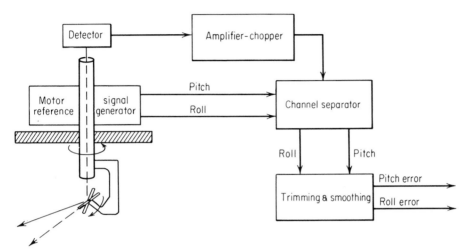

Fig. 5.19. Horizon scanner.

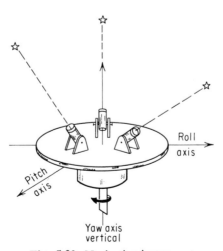

Fig. 5.20. Navigation instrument.

The accuracy of navigation by this means is directly related to the accuracy with which the angles are measured and to the accuracy of the horizontal reference. The ground positions which are determined will be in error by one nautical mile for each minute of angle error in the measurement. The errors in the horizontal reference are, presumably, independent of the errors in the measurement of star positions and the two errors should be added as the root sum square.

5.3.3 THE ORBIT GYRO COMPASS

The terrestrial application of a single axis gyroscope to form a North-seeking gyro compass is described in most standard texts on the dynamics of the gyroscope, cf. Reference 5.6. This same mode of operation may be employed on orbit to provide an indication of the direction of the orbit angular velocity. (See Figure 5.21.) The angle between this vector and the line of sight to the pole star will be approximately constant for an unperturbed orbit and will represent the inclination of the orbit as it would be observed on Earth.[2]

A single axis gyroscope may be placed in an orbit with its gimbal axis constrained to a vertical axis, for example, it might be mounted on a platform that is oriented to the horizontal by error commands generated by an horizon scanner. When observed relative to inertial space, this gyro will appear to tumble about an axis which is perpendicular to its gimbal axis and parallel to the orbit angular velocity vector, Ω. The gyro will experience a torque about its gimbal axis which is equal to

$$\mathbf{L} = \frac{d\mathbf{H}}{dt} = \mathbf{H} \times \Omega_{\text{orbit}} \tag{5-24}$$

$$= I_g(\omega_g \times \Omega_{\text{orbit}})$$

where

I_g = the moment of inertia of the gyro gimbal
ω_g = the angular velocity of the gyro wheel
Ω_{orbit} = the orbit angular velocity of the satellite.

As a result of the special way in which the gyro has been oriented in space, this torque will be felt about the gimbal axis only and it will be equal to the following

$$L_{\text{gim}} = I_g\omega_g\Omega \sin A_{\text{gim}} \tag{5-25}$$

For small angles about the gimbal axis, this will reduce to

$$L = H_g\Omega A_{\text{gim}} \tag{5-26}$$

[2] Precision observations of the pole star reveal that it is not fixed over the pole. Due to motions of the Earth, it appears to describe a small ellipse about 1° in diameter above the pole. This figure grows and diminishes on a cycle having a period of about 25,000 years.

This torque will cause the gyro to precess about its one free axis until it reaches a position where $A_{\text{gim}} = 0$. The gyro will tend to overshoot and oscillate as a result of the gimbal inertia. The period of this oscillation may be found from the theory of simple harmonic motion; it is

$$T = 2\pi\left(\frac{I_{\text{gim}}}{H_g}\Omega_{\text{orbit}}\right)^{1/2} \tag{5-27}$$

The orientation where $A_{\text{gim}} = (2n + 1)\pi$ is one of unstable equilibrium and will not be discussed further here.

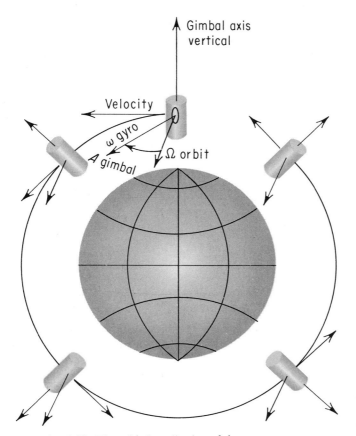

Fig. 5.21. The orbital application of the gyro-compass.

In a navigation instrument version, the gyro case will be driven about the gyro gimbal axis until the displacement angle about that axis vanishes. This will have the effect of reducing the period of the oscillatory motion and will permit a reference line on the gyro case to indicate the direction of the gimbal axis. This reference line will be the nominal indicator of the orbit angular velocity vector; the satellite attitude control torquers being used to align the satellite until the error signal is null.

5.3.4 SATELLITE ORBIT NAVIGATOR

Following the discussions of the previous sections, it may be seen that an extremely useful instrument for use as an orbit navigator may be constructed using a combination of the instruments which have been described. A gyro-stabilized platform which is controlled about the pitch and roll axes by the error signals from an horizon scanner and about the yaw axis by a gyro orbit indicator provides the base on which the instrument is mounted. See Figure 5.22. Star

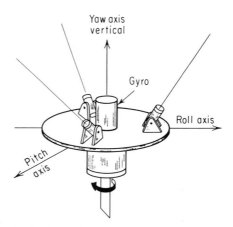

Fig. 5.22. Satellite sextant with gyro-compass.

telescopes will determine present position using the platform as a reference for the measurement. In addition, the torquing signal to the pitch gyro provides a measure of the orbit angular rate. The depression angles noted when the stars are occulted in the shadow of the Earth will provide an estimate of the altitude of the satellite, this altitude is

$$y = R'_e(\sec A_d - 1) \qquad (5\text{-}26)$$

where

y = altitude of the satellite
A_d = the depression angle noted by the telescope
R'_e = the radius of the Earth increased by the altitude at which the atmosphere obscures the star from view, approximately 4100 miles.

5.4 SATELLITE RENDEZVOUS

Space flight missions which require rendezvous between two or more satellites may arise in a variety of operational situations. Certain military missions will require inspection or interception of one satellite vehicle by another and the importance of rescue missions will become apparent with the advent of manned space flight. Indeed, the anti-ballistic missile missile and the orbital bomber are each special cases of orbital rendezvous vehicles. More peaceful applications of rendezvous will arise in the performance of modification and maintenance of operating satellites and the refuelling of orbiting vehicles. As the performance of manned missions on orbit becomes more common, many occasions will arise requiring inter-station shuttle and re-supply vehicles. The economic need for the rendezvous mission is apparent where small maintenance and supply vehicles are employed to extend the useful life of a large and expensive station after the initial depletion of some item of critical supply or fuel for its engine or power source. More subtle advantages may be derived from the use of rendezvous and refuelling missions which extend the range of vehicles. In this extension, the operating capability of smaller vehicles will be greater than without refuelling, in this way missions can be carried out which would not be feasible if they depended upon a single launch.

In principle, orbit rendezvous may be considered to refer to any inter-orbital transfer operation. For purposes of the following discussions, the rendezvous vehicle will be assumed to be required to accomplish orbit changes and then to match orbit parameters with its objective in order to maintain an on-station position with relation to it. Some special missions will require that actual contact or *docking* of one vehicle with the other be accomplished. These requirements imply that the rendezvous vehicle must be navigated and controlled so that its position and velocity vectors relative to the objective will vanish simultaneously. Unless this is accomplished with precision, a destructive collision will result aborting the mission. In our discussions of satellite rendezvous, we shall limit attention to manned satellite vehicles in orbit about the Earth. This choice has the effect of limiting the orbits to be considered. At altitudes of less than about 130 miles, the satellite will de-orbit after only a few orbit periods (Reference 5.9); while at altitudes in excess of about 400 miles, the Van Allen radiation will create a need for shielding which is assumed to be in excess of vehicle performance capability. Under these restrictions the orbit eccentricity will be limited by the maximum value calculated below

$$e = \frac{4400 - 4130}{4400 + 4130} = 0.032$$

In cases where the orbits are so nearly circular, see Figure 5.23, it will be convenient to study rendezvous problems as though they were represented by transfer from one circular orbit to another. This class of transfer has been discussed in general terms in Chapter 2 (Section 2.3), in that discussion it was shown that the general problem of orbit transfer can not be solved but that certain constraints may be applied to the problem that will simplify its analysis.

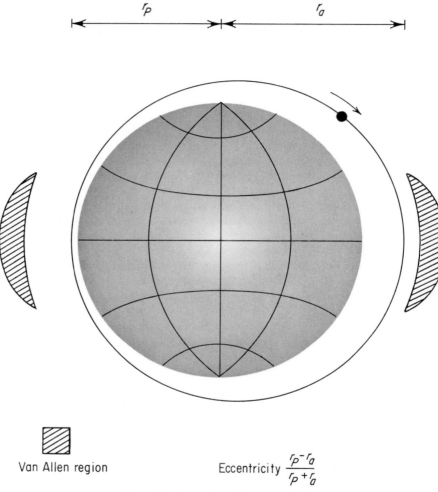

Van Allen region   Eccentricity $\dfrac{r_p - r_a}{r_p + r_a}$

Fig. 5.23. Eccentric orbits about Earth.

The discussion also outlined a series of steps, or maneuvers, which may be applied in sequence to permit a practical solution of the problem. These steps are

1. Change of orbit plane
2. Transfer of orbits within the plane
3. Advance or retard position within the orbit
4. Final closure.

A sequence of these steps will effect rendezvous between two satellite vehicles. The exact sequence which is employed will depend largely on the initial conditions for the rendezvous. Frequently these will be determined by the conditions of ascent and injection of the rendezvous vehicle into its orbit. For example, an intercepting vehicle which is injected into a circular orbit in the plane of the orbit of the reference satellite will require only the last two or perhaps three steps.

To each of the maneuvers listed above there will correspond a characteristic velocity and hence a fuel requirement. Whenever it is convenient, these maneuvers will be reduced through use of the ascent guidance or through judicious timing of the maneuver. The ascending rendezvous vehicle will be launched in to an orbit where the total rendezvous maneuver will be as small as possible. Theoretically, of course, it should be possible to place an orbiting vehicle on any desired trajectory thus to effect rendezvous entirely by means of the ascent guidance system. A rendezvous system of this kind is described in Reference 5.7. Operational limitations may, however make the use of this kind of guidance system extremely limited and some increased flexibility will be required. We shall discuss some examples of guidance to rendezvous and then make some comments regarding the general case of rendezvous where it is not considered feasible to reduce the maneuver by application of the ascent guidance to the rendezvous.

5.4.1 Rendezvous by Direct Ascent

The simplest form which a satellite rendezvous operation may take is that of rendezvous by direct ascent. This mode of rendezvous depends largely upon the use of the booster guidance which, if desired, may be effected from the launch site or from a complex of down range stations. The technique is roughly analogous to that of shooting at a moving target; aiming lead angles are used to compensate for the time of flight. In order to take account of guidance errors which may be expected to occur in the operation of the booster system, it will usually be necessary to include terminal maneuvers in the guidance system. For the direct rendezvous, it will be convenient to discuss the vehicle trajectory in sectors. These sectors are defined as follows.

Launch

The first period of powered flight through completion of the transfer ellipse. During the launch phase, the vehicle is given most of the characteristic velocity.

Adaptation

A short period of powered flight which occurs near apogee of the transfer ellipse and which adjusts the trajectory for errors which occurred in the launch phase.

Search and Acquisition

A period during which the rendezvous vehicle searches for and acquires the reference satellite with its guidance radar.

Homing

A period of active terminal guidance which culminates in rendezvous.

These trajectory regions are illustrated in the sketch of Figure 5.24. Rendezvous maneuvers of this kind are described in considerable detail in the literature (cf. Reference 5.7).

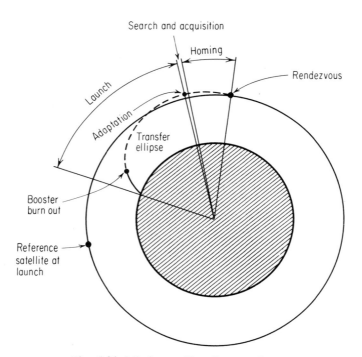

Fig. 5.24. Mission profile—direct rendezvous.

An example of direct ascent rendezvous will be used to illustrate the technique. The satellite for rendezvous will be known as the *reference satellite*, the *chaser* or *interceptor* will be launched to meet it. The reference satellite is assumed to be initially on an orbit and to have been tracked so that the reference satellite orbit parameters are known and have been stored in the interceptor satellite guidance system. At an appropriate time prior to launch, the reference satellite will be in a trajectory which carries it directly over the chaser launch site. The launch time is selected with precise relation to this passage; the interceptor is launched on a trajectory that is programmed to produce an interception of the reference satellite by the chaser after an adaptation maneuver is effected (see Figure 5.25). The particular interception geometry which is shown in the figure is favorable to rendezvous with minimum propulsion since it assures that the encounter between the two vehicles will be one in which the reference satellite overtakes the chaser vehicle. An over-all performance advantage is obtained in this mode since the major velocity increments are all applied in the same sense; none are subtractive. This has the effect of minimizing the characteristic velocity for the flight.

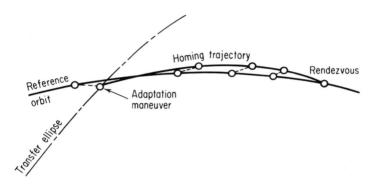

Fig. 5.25. Geometry of direct ascent rendezvous.

As the two vehicles approach coincidence, a doppler radar system monitors their relative velocity and their separation; it commands the chaser to apply propulsion in such a way as to cause the velocity and separation vectors to vanish simultaneously. The discussions in a later section (Section 5.4.3) will show that this rendezvous homing may be treated as though it were occurring in a field free space environment.

It will be interesting to consider the errors which may occur in a guidance system that supervises a rendezvous of this kind. The following listing of error sources are those which are considered to be of importance.

1. Errors due to inaccuracies in the ascent guidance. (It should be noted that while position errors are transposed to the reference point directly, velocity errors are propagated in such a way that they grow with time.)
2. Errors in determination of the orbit parameters of the reference satellite.
3. Errors in the operational timing.

The closed loop homing guidance system acts at the close of the rendezvous series of maneuvers. It provides the means to minimize the effect of these errors and to correct for them. A block diagram of such a homing guidance and control system has been shown in Figure 5.26. The acquisition and the range requirements for the homing guidance radar system will be determined largely as a result of a design trade-off with the accuracy and weight of the ascent guidance system.

The primary advantage of this direct ascent rendezvous system is that it requires minimum dependance on the satellite guidance equipment; it relies on the booster guidance for its operational accuracy. This reduces the amount of precision equipment which must be carried in the satellite. Direct ascent is also designed to require minimum vehicle propulsion on orbit. The major

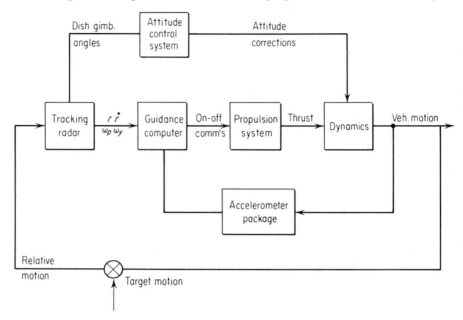

Fig. 5.26. Homing guidance system.

disadvantage is that the operational application of the direct ascent rendezvous is limited as the result of the inability of the system to provide for orbit plane changes other than minor adjustments. The reference satellite must also have orbit inclination in excess of the chaser launch latitude. The launch "window" is open infrequently for rendezvous of this kind, and when it is opened it remains open for only a very brief interval of time.

5.4.2 COPLANAR ASCENT

A more general example of satellite rendezvous is one in which the interceptor vehicle is launched into an orbit which is in the same plane as the orbit of the reference satellite. The subsequent maneuvers will require the maneuvers of a general orbit transfer with the exception of the plane change maneuver; the plane change maneuver is usually the greatest requirement for propulsion. In missions of this kind, a reference satellite is assumed to have been placed on a stable orbit with an altitude of more than 130 miles but less than 400 miles. A second satellite is to be launched for the rendezvous; it is placed in an orbit which is nearly circular and matches the orbit of the first within the accuracy which is available from the guidance system. This section will deal with the restrictions which are placed on an ascent trajectory for missions of this kind.

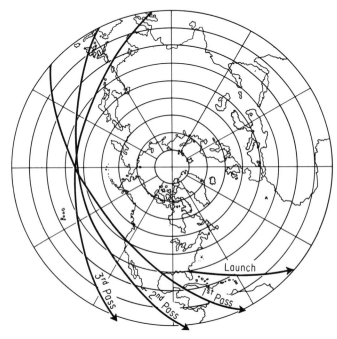

Fig. 5.27. Polar plots of orbit tracks ($T = 90$ min.).

The inclination of the reference orbit must be at least as great as the latitude of the site for the launch of the chaser vehicle. Further restrictions may be imposed on the launching azimuth as the result of range safety and booster disposal regulations. These latter are, however, matters of legal and administrative concern and they will not be discussed further here. It will be assumed that the launching site is adequate to perform the mission at hand.

As an example for purposes of discussion, we shall take the reference satellite to be one which has previously been launched into orbit and the rendezvous satellite will be fired from the same launch base into an orbit which is designed to be identical with that of the reference satellite. As a result of the rotation of the

Earth, the orbit of the reference satellite will trace an open figure on the surface of the Earth, see Figure 5.27. The launch base will be in the plane of the reference orbit once every 12 hours unless the satellite is launched from an equatorial base into a zero inclination orbit. The reference satellite will be at the latitude of the launch site twice every orbit period. In the special case where the orbit inclination angle is numerically equal to the latitude of the launch site, the orbit trace will meet the small circle of the launch site latitude in osculation; this special case will be characterized by a launching azimuth of $\pi/2$ from true

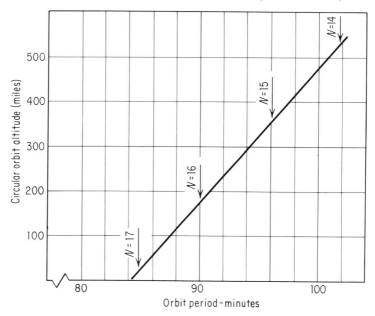

Fig. 5.28. Orbit period vs altitude.

North. The chaser satellite can be launched in the same direction to a matching orbit only every second 12 hour interval, that is at 24 hour intervals. The coplanar launch may be obtained only at 24 hour intervals and the direct ascent to rendezvous can only be accomplished as described in the previous section when the reference satellite latitude has a prescribed offset from the launch site to permit the chaser to be boosted to apogee as the reference satellite overtakes it. In this section, we shall deal with the problems of coplanar ascent. The on-orbit rendezvous will provide for the phase matching that is required to complete the rendezvous.

The reference satellite will pass through its injection point at 24 hour intervals only if the orbit may be considered to be stationary in space and if the period is commensurate with the 24 hour diurnal period. A listing of commensurate orbit periods is given in Table 5.3. The orbit period of Earth satellites in the altitude range of interest is shown in Figure 5.28. The altitudes corresponding to the periods which give an integral number of cycles in a 24 hour period are also shown on the figure. From these data, it is apparent that a suitable orbit for rendezvous at 24 hour intervals occurs at 357 miles altitude ($T = 96$ min) where the satellite closes its figure on the surface of the Earth every 15 cycles. Longer periods between rendezvous attempts will occur for satellites orbiting at other altitudes; these may be found in the same manner as the values shown in Table 5.3 using two, three, and more days as the basic time interval.

Table 5.3. ORBIT PERIODS AND ALTITUDES GIVING AN INTEGRAL NUMBER OF PERIODS IN ONE 24 HOUR DAY

N	T (min)	T (hrs:min)	Altitude (statute miles)
1	1440	24:00	22,289
2	720	12:00	12,576
3	480	8:00	8,660
4	360	6:00	6,458
5	288	4:48	5,050
6	240	4:00	3,994
7	206	3:26	3,195
8	180	3:00	2,603
9	160	2:40	2,108
10	144	2:24	1,696
11	131	2:11	1,350
12	120	2:00	1,049
13	111	1:51	795
14	102	1:42	535
15	96	1:36	357
16	90	1:30	175
17	84.7	1:24.7	20

The discussions of the next section deal with the mechanics of a rendezvous operation, a reference orbit of 357 statute miles has been chosen for that discussion since this orbit is compatible with a 24 hour rendezvous. This orbit has the following nominal properties:

Altitude (st. mi)	357
Radius (st. mi)	4357
Orbit Period (min)	96
Velocity (ft/sec)	24820
Velocity (mi/hr)	4.7
Energy (mi^2/sec^2)	-11
Angular Momentum (mi^2/sec)	0.0205
Eccentricity	0

5.4.3 Rendezvous Orbit Mechanics

A mathematical description of rendezvous operations may be given in terms of the relative motions of two orbiting bodies. The geometry of the situation is shown in Figure 5.29. One body, the reference satellite is in free-fall orbit under the influence of gravity accelerations only; its motion will be represented by an integral of the following differential equation

$$\ddot{\mathbf{R}}_{ref} = \mathbf{g}_{ref} \tag{5-27}$$

The intercepting satellite will be subject to gravitational accelerations but in addition it will also be acted upon by the non-gravitational accelerations of its own thrust engine; its motion will be described by an integral of the equation

$$\ddot{\mathbf{R}}_{int} = \mathbf{g}_{int} + \mathbf{b}(t) \tag{5-28}$$

where $\mathbf{b}(t)$ represents the non-gravitational accelerations which are applied to the intercepting satellite as it maneuvers to effect the rendezvous. The relative position of the two satellites will be given by a relative position vector which is defined as the difference of the respective position vectors.

$$\boldsymbol{\rho} = \mathbf{R}_{ref} - \mathbf{R}_{int} \tag{5-29}$$

The vector differential equation of relative motion will be obtained by application of Equation (5-29)

$$\ddot{\boldsymbol{\rho}} + (\mathbf{g}_{int} - \mathbf{g}_{ref}) = -\mathbf{b}(t) \tag{5-30}$$

The two gravity terms appearing in Equation (5-30) will be given by the expressions

$$\mathbf{g}_{int} = \left[\frac{k}{R_{int}^3}\right]\mathbf{R}_{int}$$

$$\mathbf{g}_{ref} = \left[\frac{k}{R_{ref}^3}\right]\mathbf{R}_{ref} \tag{5-31}$$

The gravity difference vector may be written as the difference of the gravity vectors as seen by both vehicles

$$\Delta\mathbf{g} = (\mathbf{g}_{int} - \mathbf{g}_{ref})$$

$$= k\left[\left(\frac{\mathbf{R}}{R^3}\right)_{int} - \left(\frac{\mathbf{R}}{R^3}\right)_{ref}\right] \tag{5-32}$$

When the above expression, Equation (5-32), is substituted into the equation for the relative motion, the resulting differential equation will be non-linear and can not be integrated directly. However, some useful information may be derived from considering the motion of the two satellites in a restricted example which involves some linearizing assumptions.

If the two satellites are both assumed to be operating at approximately the same altitude, the magnitude of the two position vectors will be identical, that is

$$|\mathbf{R}_{ref}| = |\mathbf{R}_{int}|$$

and the Equation (5-32) may be rewritten as

$$\Delta \mathbf{g} = \left(\frac{k}{R^3}\right)(\mathbf{R}_{int} - \mathbf{R}_{ref})$$

Making the indicated substitution, Equation (5-30) becomes

$$\ddot{\boldsymbol{\rho}} - \left(\frac{k}{R^3}\right)\boldsymbol{\rho} = -\mathbf{b}(t) \qquad (5\text{-}33)$$

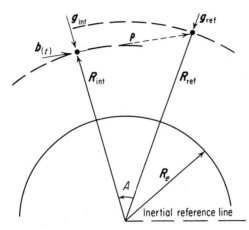

Fig. 5.29. The geometry of the rendezvous in relative motion.

The above equation describes an approximation to the relative motion of the two satellites. This relative motion is that of the interceptor satellite orbiting about the reference satellite (or vice-versa) with the orbit being perturbed by the effects of the accelerations which are applied to the chaser satellite. The period of this relative motion may be determined in the same manner as for conventional satellites (See Chapter 2). The relative period is, of course related to the relative gravity vector and is derived from the cyclic frequency term

$$T = \frac{2\pi}{\omega} = 2\pi \left(\frac{R^3}{k}\right)^{1/2}$$

The vector differential equation which describes the relative motion, Equation (5-33), may be written as a set of scalar differential equations which relate the vector components and their time derivatives to the thrust accelerations that are applied to the interceptor. When this is done, the resulting differential equations may be solved individually. The solutions to the equations of relative motion will be discussed in terms of a two dimensional example. For this purpose, consider the relative position of the two satellites as defined by a position vector that is measured from the interceptor to the reference satellite. The form of the equations of motion will depend upon the coordinate reference used for the measurements. A convenient reference will be defined as follows:

axis $\hat{1}$: Directed upward along the vertical at the interceptor satellite

axis $\hat{2}$: Directed forward along the line that is defined by the intersection of the orbit plane and the horizontal plane at the origin

axis $\hat{3}$: Directed along the orbit angular velocity vector with the sense making a right handed coordinate set.

This coordinate reference frame is illustrated in Figure 5.30.

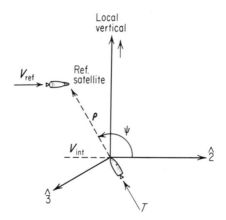

Fig. 5.30. Local vertical coordinate reference.

In the chosen reference frame, the relative acceleration will be represented by a vector which is a function of position and time

$$\ddot{\boldsymbol{\rho}} = \ddot{\boldsymbol{\rho}}(\rho, \theta, \psi, t) \tag{5-34}$$

The acceleration vector may be calculated from the position vector as follows

$$\frac{d^2\boldsymbol{\rho}}{dt^2} = \ddot{\boldsymbol{\rho}} + \ddot{\boldsymbol{\theta}} \times \boldsymbol{\rho} + 2\dot{\boldsymbol{\theta}} \times \dot{\boldsymbol{\rho}} + \dot{\boldsymbol{\theta}} \times \dot{\boldsymbol{\theta}} \times \dot{\rho} \tag{5-35}$$

where

$\dot{\theta}$ = the local angular velocity of the satellite relative to the center of the Earth.

Recalling, now, that the two satellites are initially injected into the same plane, obviating the need for change of plane maneuvers, the relative acceleration components may be written as

$$\frac{d^2\rho}{dt^2} = [\hat{\mathbf{u}}_1](\ddot{\rho} - \dot{\theta}^2\rho) + [\hat{\mathbf{u}}_2](\ddot{\theta}\rho - 2\dot{\theta}\dot{\rho}) \tag{5-36}$$

The component equations of motion may then be written as

$$\ddot{\rho} - \dot{\theta}^2\rho = \Delta g_1 - b_1(t) \tag{5-37}$$

$$2\dot{\theta}\dot{\rho} + \ddot{\theta}\rho = \Delta g_2 - b_2(t) \tag{5-38}$$

When the two satellites are close enough that the gravity difference vector may be neglected, the latter equation may be rewritten yielding the familiar angular momentum equation

$$\frac{d}{dt}(\rho^2\dot{\theta}) = -\rho b_2(t) \tag{5-39}$$

Before proceeding with the solution of Equations (5.37) and (5.38), consider the conditions under which the gravity difference terms (Δg_1, and Δg_2) may be neglected. The gravity difference terms are

$$\Delta g_1 = \left(\frac{k}{R^3}\right)\rho \cdot [\hat{\mathbf{u}}_1] = \left(\frac{k}{R^3}\right)\rho \sin\theta \tag{5-40}$$

$$\Delta g_2 = \left(\frac{k}{R^3}\right)\rho \cdot [\hat{\mathbf{u}}_2] = \left(\frac{k}{R^3}\right)\rho \cos\theta \tag{5-41}$$

The gravity difference vector is illustrated in Figure 5-31; its dimensionless magnitude is given by

$$\left|\frac{\Delta g}{g}\right| = \sqrt{1 + \left(\frac{R_{int}}{R_{ref}}\right)^4 - 2\left(\frac{R_{int}}{R_{ref}}\right)^2 \cos A} \tag{5-42}$$

If the approximation is made that the interceptor altitude is incrementally different from the altitude of the reference satellite, that is

$$|R_{int}| = |R_{ref}| + |\delta R|$$

and then neglecting the second-order terms in δR, the magnitude of the gravity difference will be expressed as

$$\frac{\Delta g}{g} = \sqrt{1 + \left(\frac{1}{1 + \delta R/R}\right)^4 - \left(\frac{1}{1 + \delta R/R}\right)^2 \cos A} \tag{5-43}$$

Equation (5-43) has been evaluated and a graph is shown in Figure 5.32. From the Figure, it may be seen that the gravity difference has a magnitude that is less than one per cent of the total gravity acceleration in the reference orbit when the satellites are within $\pm$ 30 miles of each other. This difference vector

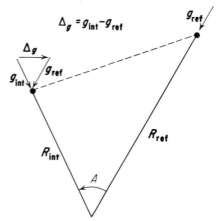

Fig. 5.31. Relative gravity.

$$\frac{\Delta g}{g_{int}} = \sqrt{1 + \left(\frac{1}{1 + \frac{\delta R}{R_{int}}}\right)^2 - 2\left(\frac{1}{1 + \frac{\delta R}{R_{int}}}\right)^4 \cos A}$$

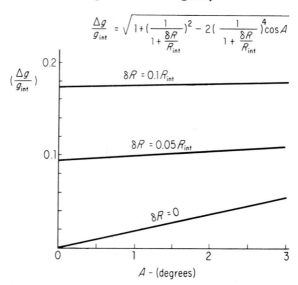

Fig. 5.32. The magnitude of the gravity difference vector.

will vanish as the distance between the two satellites decreases. It will be useful, then, to require that the guidance for ascent to orbit will be adequate to place the two satellites within this range of each other. Thereafter, the encounter may be considered to be taking place in field free space since the gravity that acts on both is the same within a useful measure of approximation.

The properties of an adequate guidance system for supervision of the ascent trajectory will depend, to a degree, on the characteristics of that trajectory. For purposes of an example, consider the ascent trajectory that is illustrated in Figure 5.33. The guidance accuracy requirements that would be associated with this trajectory are shown in Table 5.7; the numbers that are shown in the table have been chosen as adequate to permit the execution of a rendezvous under the restrictions of a field-free encounter as described in the previous paragraph. While this guidance accuracy would be adequate to monitor the

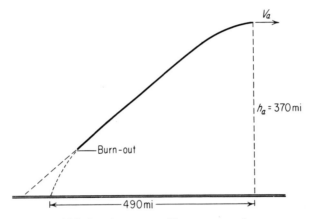

Fig. 5.33. Rendezvous satellite—ascent trajectory.

Altitude at apogee	370 st. miles
Flight path angle at burn-out	30°
Range to apogee	490 st. miles
Distance, launcher to apogee	565 st. miles
Velocity at burn-out	14,500 ft/sec
Horizontal velocity at burn-out	11,100 ft/sec
Vertical velocity at burn-out	9000 ft/sec
Horizontal velocity at apogee	11,100 ft/sec
Time of boost	250 sec
Average acceleration during boost	1.8 g
Time from burn-out to apogee	176 sec

ascent flight and to place the intercepting satellite in the vicinity of the reference satellite so that the effects of gravity on their relative motion may be neglected, the error velocity of this guidance is such that the two satellites will drift apart in time unless the rendezvous operations are initiated immediately. An error of only 5.0 ft/sec in the total velocity of the interceptor at injection will cause the separation of the two satellites to grow at a steady rate of about 5.5 miles during each orbit period. The error in azimuth reference at the time of injection may cause an error in the orbit inclination of about 1 deg. This will introduce an oscillation of the interceptor, when seen from the reference satellite, which has a period equal to the orbit period and an amplitude of about 75 miles; the oscillation will appear to occur in the local horizontal plane.

Table 5.4. GUIDANCE REQUIREMENTS FOR ASCENT TO RENDEZVOUS

Error source	Error	Resultant errors	
		Position	Velocity
Range error	25 st.mi	$(\Delta q_2) = 25$ mi	—
Altitude error	30 st.mi	$(\Delta q_1) = 30$ mi	—
Cross–range Errors (injection)	0.3 deg	$(\Delta q_3) = 25$ mi	—
Azimuth errors (injection)	1.0 deg	—	$(\Delta \dot{q}_3) = 240$ ft/sec
Flight path angle Error (injection)	0.3 deg	—	$(\Delta \dot{q}_1) = 72$ ft/sec
Total velocity Error	5.0 ft/sec	$(\Delta q) = 1.6$ mi	$(\Delta \dot{q}) = 5.0$ ft/sec
Time of ascent	3 sec	$(\Delta \dot{q}_2) = 15$ mi	

q_1 = vertical; q_2 = range; q_3 = cross range.

Returning, now, to the rendezvous and the solution of Equations (5.37) and (5-38), the satellites will be within the vicinity of one another upon entry into the orbit. Within an adequate level of accuracy, the rendezvous may be analyzed while neglecting the gravity difference vector. The equations of relative motion may then be written

$$\ddot{\rho} - \dot{\theta}^2 \rho = - b_1(t) \qquad (5-44)$$

$$\frac{d}{dt}(\rho^2 \dot{\theta}) = - \rho b_2(t) \qquad (5-45)$$

The solution to these equations may be obtained directly for circular orbits, that is

$$\dot{\theta} = \text{const} = \Omega_{\text{int}}(t = 0) = \dot{\theta}_0$$

Under this constraint, the angular momentum equation yields a direct integral

$$\dot{\theta}_0 \frac{d}{dt} \rho^2 = - \rho b_2(t) \qquad (5-46)$$

$$b_2(t) = - 2\dot{\theta}_0 \dot{\rho} \qquad (5-47)$$

The equation describing the radial motion is linear when the assumption of constant angular velocity is made, it becomes

$$\ddot{\rho} - \dot{\theta}_0^2 \rho = b_1(t) \qquad (5\text{-}48)$$

The rendezvous requires that both the position and the velocity vectors vanish simultaneously; this will occur if the radial acceleration is controlled according to the following relation.

$$b_1(t) = 2\dot{\theta}_0^2 \rho + 2\zeta\dot{\rho} \qquad (5\text{-}49)$$

The resulting differential equation is

$$\ddot{\rho} + 2\zeta\dot{\rho} + \dot{\theta}_0^2 \rho = 0 \qquad (5\text{-}50)$$

The solution to Equation (5-50) may be written directly, it is as follows.

$$\rho = e^{-\zeta t}\left[\rho_0 \cos \dot{\theta}_i t - \frac{(\zeta\rho_0 - \dot{\rho}_0)}{\dot{\theta}_0} \sin \dot{\theta}_i t\right] \qquad (5\text{-}51)$$

where

$$\dot{\theta}_i = \sqrt{\dot{\theta}_0^2 - \zeta^2}$$

By direct differentiation of (5-51), the radial velocity (the velocity along the line of sight between the reference satellite and the chaser), will be computed to be

$$\dot{\rho} = e^{-\zeta t}\left\{\dot{\rho}\ \cos \dot{\theta}_i t + \left[\left(\frac{\zeta^2}{\dot{\theta}_i} + \dot{\rho}_i\right)\rho_0 + \frac{\zeta}{\dot{\theta}_i}\dot{\rho}_0\right] \sin \dot{\theta}_i t\right\} \qquad (5\text{-}52)$$

Equations (5-47) and (5-49) imply certain acceleration programs for the chaser vehicle. These programs may be approximated using several thrust level rocket nozzles or they may be obtained through the use of a fully throttleable rocket engine. The acceleration vs time profiles may be computed from the following relations

$$b_1 = 2\dot{\theta}_0^2 \rho + 2\zeta\dot{\rho}$$

$$= 2\ e^{\zeta t}\left\{(\dot{\theta}_0^2 \rho_0 + \zeta\dot{\rho}_0) \cos \dot{\theta}_i t\right.$$

$$\left. + \left(\zeta\left[\left(\frac{\zeta^2}{\dot{\theta}_i} + \dot{\theta}_i\right)\rho_0 + \frac{\zeta\dot{\rho}_0}{\dot{\theta}_i}\right] - \frac{\dot{\theta}_0^2(\dot{\rho}_0 - \zeta\rho_0)}{\dot{\theta}_i}\right) \sin \dot{\theta}_i t\right\} \qquad (5\text{-}53)$$

and

$$b_2 = -2\dot{\theta}_0\dot{\rho}$$

$$= 2\dot{\theta}_0\ e^{-\zeta t}\left\{\rho_0 \cos \dot{\theta}_i t + \left[\left(\frac{\zeta^2}{\dot{\theta}_i} + \dot{\theta}_i\right)\rho_0 + \left(\frac{\zeta}{\dot{\theta}_i}\right)\dot{\rho}_0\right] \sin \dot{\theta}_i t\right\} \qquad (5\text{-}54)$$

The time history of the rendezvous will be non-oscillatory and the position and velocity vectors will vanish simultaneously if the damping factor, ζ, is chosen to provide critical damping for the system. This will obtain if

$$\zeta = \dot{\theta}_0 \tag{5-55}$$

When the system damping has been adjusted in this manner the relative motion of the two vehicles will be described by the simplified equations

$$\rho = \rho_0\, e^{-\zeta t} \tag{5-56}$$

and

$$\dot{\rho} = \dot{\rho}_0\, e^{-\zeta t} \tag{5-57}$$

The acceleration programs will be controlled in magnitude by the following equations

$$b_1 = 2(\dot{\theta}_0^2 \rho_0 + \dot{\theta}_0 \dot{\rho}_0)\, e^{-\zeta t} \tag{5-58}$$

and

$$b_2 = 2\dot{\theta}_0 \dot{\rho}_0\, e^{-\zeta t} \tag{5-59}$$

The direction of the thrust will be referenced to the chaser coordinate reference frame as illustrated in Figure 5.30.

The time varying properties of the quantities which are described by Equations (5-56) through (5-59) are shown graphically in Figure 5.34. The graphs shown in the figure are based on the 370 mile circular orbit, initial position separation was taken to be 25 miles (132,000 feet), and the initial closing velocity was assumed to be 10 feet/sec. The rendezvous is effective in about one orbit period or about 5760 sec. It will be noted that the total velocity and acceleration is never so great as to represent a major perturbation to the chaser orbit.

The block diagram shown in Figure 5.35 shows a mechanization of a rendezvous control system of the type which has just been described. The offset of the line of sight for the radar seeker which tracks the reference satellite will be established from the relation

$$A_{\text{offset}} = \tan^{-1}\frac{b_2}{b_1} \tag{5-60}$$

The system will call for a variable thrust vector; the total propulsion energy required may be estimated from the integral of the curves shown in Figure 5.34. The instantaneous magnitude of the thrust vector will be given by the relation

$$T = (b_1^2 + b_2^2)^{1/2} \tag{5-61}$$

When the appropriate substitutions have been made, Equation (5-61) will be given by

$$T = 2\dot{\theta}_0 e^{-\zeta t}\sqrt{\dot{\theta}_0^2 \rho_o^2 + 2(\dot{\theta}_0 \rho_o \dot{\rho}_o + \dot{\rho}_o^2)} \tag{5-62}$$

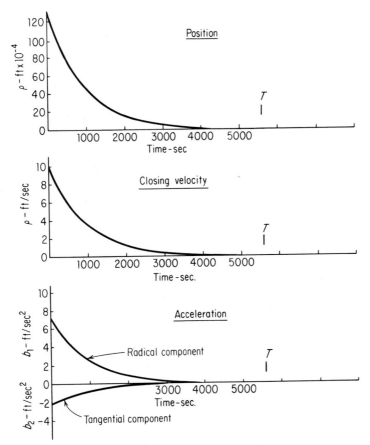

Fig. 5.34. Dynamic analysis of a rendezvous.

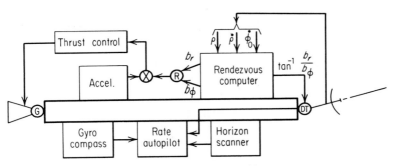

Fig. 5.35. Rendezvous guidance.

5.4.4 GENERAL APPLICATIONS OF SATELLITE RENDEZVOUS

The preceding discussions have dealt with restricted examples of satellite rendezvous. Under the circumstances of an urgent mission such as rescue, maintenance, or inspection of an unknown or hostile satellite no restrictions are likely to be placed on the two orbits. The rendezvous will involve transfers which are similar to those of a general inter-orbital transfer. Maneuvers such as orbit inclination changes and rotations of the line of nodes may be necessary. In addition, maneuvers which change the orbit altitude, eccentricity, and the orientation of the line of apsides may be required. The orbit mechanics of these situations have been discussed briefly in Chapter 2 and will be discussed with reference to some specific problems of interplanetary travel in Chapter 6.

The application of an intermediate parking orbit will alleviate the problems which are associated with an unfavorable launch window. Plane change maneuvers can be made when urgency requires them at the expense of propulsion and fuel. Two satellites which are orbiting in the same plane will be capable of matching their orbits using a modification of the classical Hohmann transfer (see Section 2.3.2).

While techniques of this kind are indeed important to the methods of satellite rendezvous, the reader will recognize that the required guidance and navigation methods are quite similar to those which have been discussed in Chapter 2 and that will be discussed in Chapter 6. Consequently we shall not discuss orbit transfers of this kind in this chapter.

At the conclusion of the gross stage of rendezvous, it may be necessary to effect a final closure to the point of actual contact or docking of the interceptor satellite with the reference vehicle. Unless this is done promptly, a small residual velocity of the interceptor relative to the reference vehicle will lead to excessive drifts. A residual velocity of 1 foot per second will result in a separation of approximately one mile in each orbit cycle or about 18 miles per day. The final closure will be accomplished under supervision of a closed loop control system that employs doppler radar and direct visual means for sensing. The control of this maneuver will require an intricate combination of thrust control and attitude control systems. The mechanization of such a system is a matter of control system, or autopilot, design and will not be discussed further here. A control system of this kind is discussed with reference to the characteristics of the vehicle propulsion system in Reference 5.12.

PROBLEMS

1. Compute the orbit energy of a satellite as a function of eccentricity for Earth orbits with perigee at 100, 1000 and 10,000 miles respectively. Let eccentricity vary over a range of 0 to 0.5.

2. Estimate the orbit life of a satellite that has $C_D A/M = 1$ ft^2/slug if the satellite is initially at 280 n.mi with eccentricity $e = 0$. Consider a satellite at 160 miles, $e = 0.15$; 160 miles, $e = 0.01$. Give orbit lifetimes in units of days.

3. At the completion of the booster burn, a space vehicle is at 100,000 feet altitude and has a horizontal velocity component $\dot{x}_i = 8600$ feet per second and a vertical velocity component $y_i = 5000$ feet per second. Find the apogee and the eccentricity of the ascent ellipse; determine the time from burn-out to apogee.

4. Plot a graph that shows the orbit period as a function of orbit energy for orbits that have eccentricity in the range of 0 to 1.0 where perigee altitude is 100 miles, 1000 miles, 10,000 miles.

5. Compute the boost velocity that is required to inject the space vehicle described in Problem 3 into a circular orbit when it arrives at apogee.

6. Consider an orbital gyro compass in which the gyroscope has wheel angular momentum of 10^4 cgs units and the gimbal has moment of inertia of 0.30 gm cm^{2}sec. Determine the period of the gyro compass as a pendulum oscillating about the vertical when the unit is installed in a satellite in a circular orbit, 300 miles altitude. Find the period at 3000 miles, at 30,000 miles.

7. Given Earth satellites having orbit periods of 2 hours, 4 hours, 8 hours and 12 hours respectively; compute and graph the corresponding energy levels.

8. A satellite is in a circular orbit at 300 miles altitude, its orbit inclination is 40 deg; plot a graph that shows the satellite ground speed as function of latitude. Let the latitude vary from the equator north and south to 40 deg.

9. Repeat the calculations of Problem 8 for a satellite that has perigee at 300 miles and an eccentricity of 0.5, let the latitude of the perigee vary as a parameter.

10. Given two satellites at 400 miles altitude, determine the displacement, velocity, and acceleration profiles for a "dead beat" closure assuming initial separation of 20 miles and a relative velocity of 35 feet per second, closing. Repeat the problem with a -35 foot per second initial velocity, separating.

11. Determine the characteristic velocity of a closing maneuver as discussed in each case of Problem 10. Assuming a satellite that weighs 2000 lbs, determine the fuel required and the time-thrust profile. Assume a 10 per cent fuel reserve at the completion of the maneuver.

REFERENCES

5.1. Moulton, F. R., *Periodic Orbits*, 1920.

5.2. Dessler, A. J. *et al.*, *A New Instrument for Measuring Atmospheric Density and Temperatures at Satellite Altitudes*, Jet Propulsion, Dec. 1958, p. 87.

5.3. Frye, W. E. and E. V. Stearns, *Stabilization and Attitude Control of Satellite Vehicles*, ARS Journal, December 1957, p. 927.

5.4. De Bra, D. B. and E. V. Stearns, *Problems of Attitude Control of Satellites and Interplanetary Vehicles*, Electr. Eng., Vol. 77, 1958, p. 1088.

5.5. Hydrographic Office, H. O. 217 (Aids to Navigational Computation), U.S. Government Printing Office.

5.6. Deimel, Richard F., *Mechanics of the Gyroscope*, Dover Publication, Inc. 1950.

5.7. Duke, W. M., E. A. Goldberg and I. Pfeiffer, *Error Analysis Considerations for a Satellite Rendezvous*, ARS Journal *31*, No. 4, April 1961, p. 505.

5.8. Satyendra, K. N. and R. E. Bradford, *Self-Contained Navigational System for Determination of Orbital Elements of a Satellite*, ARS Journal *31*, No. 7, p. 949, July 1961.

5.9. Breakwell, J. and L. Koehler, *Elliptical Orbit Lifetimes*, Advances in Astronautical Sciences, Vol. 3, Plenum Press Inc., New York, 1958.

5.10. De Bra, D. B. and R. H. Delp, *Rigid Body Attitude Stability and Natural Frequencies in a Circular Orbit*, J. of the Astro Sciences, *3*, No. 1, Spring 1961.

5.11. Mueller, Rudy R., *Investigation of Possible Satellite Position-Sensing Methods*, ARS Paper No. 913–59 Proceedings of the ARS 14th Annual Meeting, Sheraton Park Hotel, Washington, D.C., November 16–20, 1959.

5.12. Felleman, Phillip G., *Analysis of Guidance Techniques for Achieving Orbital Rendezvous*, AAS Paper No. 62–9, Proceedings of the 8th Annual Meeting of the AAS, Sheraton Park Hotel, Washington, D.C., January 16–18, 1962.

5.13. Swanson, Robert S. and P. W. Soule, *Rendezvous Guidance Technology*, Proceedings of the National Meeting on Manned Space Flight. IAS, 30 April to 2 May, 1962. St. Louis, Mo.

6

INTERPLANETARY NAVIGATION

From the point of view of general interest, the conquest of space seems to imply the ability to operate a transportation system linking the Earth to its sister planets. There are, of course, many technological barriers which must be cleared from the road to the other planets. Not the least of these is the development of adequate propulsion systems and the means for supplying the needs of the occupants of such a craft for the duration of a journey of several million miles. The environment which exists on the various planets is an important consideration.

This chapter will describe interplanetary transfer orbits and some of the basis for their selection. The dependance of the transfer orbits on the spacecraft mechanics and the initial configuration of the Solar System will be discussed. With reference to interplanetary transfer, the principles of navigation from ascent through injection into the transfer orbit, midcourse correction, and re-entry and landing will be presented. Some suggestions are made regarding the mechanization of the guidance and navigation systems for these functions. Some special problems which are associated with the return flight will be the subject of the concluding section.

Regardless of the evaluation which we might assign to the prospects for manned interplanetary flight, it will be possible to consider the navigational aspects of such a flight and to outline the solution to some of the problems. Indeed, we may progress to the conception and definition of mechanizations of systems which may be applied to the various tasks. Interplanetary navigation

Table 6.1. ACTIVITY SPHERES OF THE PLANETS

Planet	Radius of the Activity Sphere		
	astronomical units*	statute miles	r/r_{planet}
Mercury	0.000746	69,500	46
Venus	0.00412	386,000	102
Earth	0.00618	575,000	142
Mars	0.00378	351,000	190
Jupiter	0.3216	29,800,000	706
Saturn	0.3246	30,220,000	848
Uranus	0.346	32,200,000	2,180
Neptune	0.5805	54,000,000	4,000
Pluto	0.2366	22,000,000	~ 12,000

* 1 Astronomical unit = 149.4 × 10⁶ Km = 92.84 statute miles.

will be strongly influenced by the general properties of the Solar System. These were discussed in Chapter 1. Briefly, the planets lie in, or near, a plane which is defined by the plane of the orbit of the Earth (the plane of the *ecliptic*). They are in orbits which are nearly circular, that is with eccentricity approximately equal to zero. Except in the close vicinity of the planets, the gravitational force of the Sun exerts the greatest influence on the spacecraft. The strength of the solar gravity field is indicated by Figure 6.1. An activity sphere has been defined by La Place, it specifies the space in which the planets, rather than the Sun, should be considered as the central body in the analysis of the encounter between a planet and a small body such as a spacecraft. The radius of this sphere is given by (Reference 6.2)

$$r_{crit} = R_1 \left(\frac{m_1}{M}\right)^{2/5} \tag{6-1}$$

where

R_1 is the distance of the disturbing body, planet, from the Sun
m_1 = the mass of the disturbing body
M = the mass of the Sun.

The radii of the activity spheres for the various planets have been tabulated in Table 6.1.

Man's initial interplanetary operations will doubtless employ minimum energy orbits in which the force due to the Sun's gravity plays an important part in the motion of the spacecraft. In a transfer between two circular orbits in the same plane, the minimum energy transfer follows a trajectory which is tangent to both orbits along a diameter. These trajectories are known as *Hohmann Orbits* (Reference 6.2). As the relative inclination of the planetary orbits is increased, the minimum energy path will depart from the Hohmann orbit due to the large energy requirement associated with the plane change maneuvers. The actual minimal energy transfer will depend upon the initial configuration of the two planets, in the inclined orbit example the minimum will be a Hohmann orbit if the departure and arrival is adjusted to occur at the nodal line. Vertregt (Reference 6.3) has shown that while the minimum energy orbits require the least fuel, they require maximum time in transit. The navigation problem for Hohmann orbits involves control of the thrust to obtain sufficient velocity in the plane of the orbit and normal to the line of sight to the Sun. The thrust is cut off when these conditions are precisely obtained.

An interesting problem in interplanetary navigation arises under the assumption that the fuel is not an operating limitation. This will be the case when propulsion means (for example solar, ionic, or nuclear jets) can be made so efficient as to allow application of continuous thrust levels which are not negligible with respect to the solar gravity acceleration over a major portion of the flight. This situation is obtained when the acceleration of the craft is maintained at about $10^{-4} g$ or more. Under these conditions, the trajectory of the spacecraft is computed by an integration of all of the accelerations acting on the craft. The Keplerian equations of motion in a central force field will not apply to this special case.

In planning the navigation of an interplanetary spacecraft, it becomes apparent that the flight is made up of several distinct elements each of which requires a different approach for its analysis and solution. These elements will be discussed separately; the first segment is the ascent from the surface of the Earth leading to a *transfer orbit* which has been selected to place the spacecraft on its way in an orbit which will cause the spacecraft to pass in the vicinity of the destination planet. The second portion of the flight will be termed *mid-course flight*; it is the period during which the craft traverses the great distance between the planets in a free fall or low thrust path. Navigation during this interval of time will be concerned with the act of confirming that the craft will pass suitably close to the planet at the appointed time in the mission. Corrective maneuvers will be computed and applied to the craft during the mid-course flight.

The third portion of the flight will be termed *homing*. This is concerned with the conditions which are necessary to convert the transfer orbit into one which brings the spacecraft along a path which is suitable for entry into the atmosphere of the planet. Chapman has shown that this condition may be satisfied if the craft is navigated along an entry corridor which he defines in terms of a set of parameters which are characteristic of the planet and the spacecraft. (Reference 6.4.) A fourth segment of the flight deals with the guidance and control of the *return flight*. We shall discuss each of these in its proper turn.

It is not possible to discuss the problems of navigation in the Solar System without first describing the Solar System in sufficient detail to permit the locations of the planets and the spacecraft to be defined in an unambiguous fashion. A brief and qualitative description of the Solar System was presented in Chapter 1 where the arrangement of the planets and the parameters of their individual orbits were discussed in nominal terms. The standard reference direction in Solar System space is the Sun-Earth line at the time of the Vernal Equinox. The Vernal Equinox occurs about 21 March; it is the time when the Earth's solar orbit and the Sun-Earth line are coplanar. Approximately six months later, 21 September, and in opposition to the Vernal Equinox, is the Autumnal Equinox.

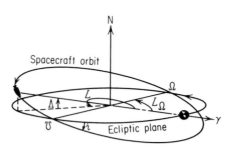

Fig. 6.1. Solar gravity field.

This reference line, the Sun-Earth line at the Vernal Equinox, is directed toward a point in the constellation of *Aries*. This point is designated by the symbol ♈; it is slowly moving on the celestial sphere as a result of the precession of the polar axis of the Earth. The direction of motion or of *revolution* of bodies in the Solar System is conventionally given as seen from the north pole of the ecliptic plane which is located in the same celestial hemisphere as the projection of the terrestrial north pole, that is, the *northern celestial hemisphere.* When seen from this direction, all planets and most satellites and other bodies in the Solar System move counterclockwise in so-called *direct orbits.* A body which is moving in a clockwise direction when seen from the north celestial poles is said to be in *retrograde* motion. Orbital inclinations are measured with respect to the ecliptic plane. The angle of inclination is measured counterclockwise from the ecliptic at the *ascending node.* The ascending node is the point where the orbiting body crosses through the ecliptic on its way from the southern celestial hemisphere to the northern. If the inclination is more than 90 deg, the orbit will be retrograde. (See Figure 6.2.)

In addition to the orbit inclination, the *longitude* of the ascending node (☊) of an orbit is of particular importance. This is the angle subtended at the Sun between the vernal equinox and the ascending node. Thus, 0 *deg longitude of the ascending node* indicates the point at which the orbit coincides with the reference direction to the Vernal Equinox and the orbit is passing from south to north. In an elliptic orbit about the Sun, the point of closest approach, or periapsis, is called the *perihelion,* and the point of farthest distance is called the *aphelion.* The line connecting these two points is the major axis of the ellipse. The perihelion of an unperturbed orbit is invariant in space; but the gravitational fields of the planets disturb one another and the planetary perihelions are not

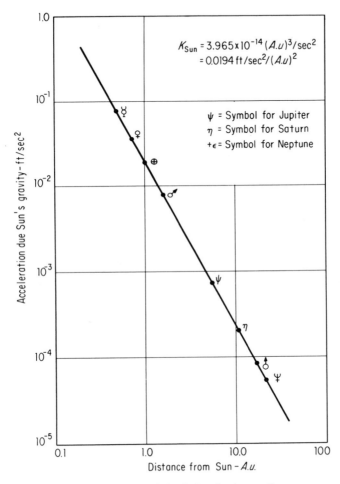

Fig. 6.2. Solar system latitude-longitude coordinates.

constant. This position is defined by the longitude of the perihelion, $\pi = \omega + \Omega$, for the orbits of planets and planetoids. The angle ω is the angle between the two lines Sun-Vernal Equinox and the Sun-perihelion. The reference time for which this angle is given is called the *epoch.*

6.1 INTERPLANETARY ORBITS

The selection of an interplanetary orbit involves more than the simple orbit to orbit transfer. It is necessary to select an orbit which will carry the spacecraft from a specific point or body moving in one orbit to another specific body which is moving in its own orbit. The relative positions of the two planets (origin and destination) will be changing with time before initiation of the transfer as well as after. The selection of an orbit for the transfer will, or course, be related to this initial configuration of the planets. The classical Hohmann orbit, for example, depends upon waiting until a certain planetary configuration is obtained so that at the end of one half period for the transfer orbit, the destination planet will be at a position with longitude $\pi/2$ different from the longitude of the original planet at the time of initiation of the transfer. Transfer between inclined orbits is even more sensitive to the starting point. If the transfer is to be accomplished from a point on the line of nodes to another point on the same line, there will be no requirement for maneuvers which change the orbital plane.

Situations may arise where the interplanetary mission at hand can not tolerate the delays which would be required in waiting for planetary configurations of the kind involved if transfers like those described above are to be used. Similarly the mission may require transfer times which are less than those which are indicated by the minimum energy examples. The characteristics of reduced flight time trajectories will be discussed in the following section.

Before proceeding to discuss the factors which influence the selection of a transfer orbit, it seems to be appropriate to discuss the meaning of the term *minimum energy transfer orbit*. Such an orbit is one which demands the expenditure of least energy from the propulsion system in order to transfer from the orbit in which a body is traveling, to place it in a transfer orbit, and then to match its orbit with that of a destination body. Depending on the nature of the specific transfer, the orbit which requires the least characteristic velocity may, or may not, be the transfer orbit with the least energy in the sense that energy is defined by Equation (2-13) and implicitly by Equation (2-22). A minimum energy transfer orbit is generally considered to be the one that involves the least characteristic velocity for the over-all maneuver.

Transfers are established by the definition of a series of velocity maneuvers; it is also necessary to define the direction in which these velocity increments should be added to the initial velocity of the craft in order to place it in the desired orbit. This requires the solution of an orbit which passes through two definite points in space and which has a transfer time which is appropriate to the specific situation at hand. While this problem can not be solved in general terms we shall discuss some practical applications of its resolution which will be useful in the practice of space navigation.

6.1.1 Selecting an Orbit

A major consideration in planning for interplanetary flights is the tremendous energy which is required from the propulsion system to effect the transfer of a spacecraft from the vicinity of one planet to that of another. If possible, then, it would be desirable to make such a transfer using the minimum energy in the maneuvers. For the special case of transfer between coplanar circular orbits, the minimum energy transfer defines a class of paths known as *Hohmann orbits* (Reference 6.2). These orbits are illustrated in Figure 6.3. A summary of the properties of these orbits is shown in Table 6.2. When the initial and final orbits are not coplanar and eccentricities are introduced, the minimum energy

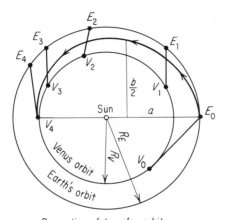

Properties of transfer orbit

Major axis, $a = R_E - R_V$

Minor axis, $b = \sqrt{R_E R_V}$

Transfer time $= \pi \sqrt{\dfrac{K}{a^3}}$

Fig. 6.3. The Hohmann orbit.

maneuver will depart from that which is described by the Hohmann orbit. The theory of minimum energy orbits is beyond the scope of this text and represents an area of specialized study in itself. For the details of this special problem, the reader is referred to works of analysts of celestial mechanics, for example Reference 6.5. It will provide some useful insight into the navigation problems of interplanetary space to consider the following generalization of the problem.

The studies reported by Hohmann demonstrated that the application of tangential impulses at the apsides of a cotangential transfer orbit will require minimum expenditure of rocket fuel in order to transfer between coplanar circular orbits. Since that time, it has been recognized that the same maneuvers

Table 6.2. HOHMANN ORBIT PROPERTIES FOR INTERPLANETARY FLIGHT

Planet	Hohmann launch vel.	Hyperbolic excess vel.	Transfer time
Mercury	44,000 ft/sec	26,600 ft/sec	100 days
Venus	38,000	10,900	150
Mars	38,000	10,900	260
Jupiter	46,000	29,800	2·7 years
Saturn	49,000	34,300	6·0
Uranus	51,000	37,100	16·0
Neptune	52,000	38,000	31·0
Pluto	53,000	39,800	46·0

will minimize fuel consumption for transfer between certain other coplanar orbits where the departure and arrival both occur at the apsides of the two orbits. The considerations leading to the Hohmann orbit customarily consider only one or two impulse maneuvers. When three or more impulses are considered, some special examples may be found in which transfer may be accomplished for less total transfer energy than with two impulse maneuvers. For example, in transfers where the final orbit is many times larger, or smaller, than the initial orbit, fuel can be saved by transferring beyond the final orbit, applying retro-thrust at the apogee of this ellipse and entering the final orbit at the perigee of a second transfer ellipse. See Figure 6.4. The absolute minimum fuel consumption in this case would necessitate escape from the original orbit along a parabola followed by an infinitesimal impulse which is applied after escape and which causes the vehicle to return along a new parabola. The maximum possible savings in this maneuver is about 8 per cent of the total characteristic velocity. (Reference 6.6.) This saving would probably not justify the added time and complexity involved in the use of such a maneuver.

Although the study of Hohmann orbits and coplanar transfers has proved useful in order to estimate the magnitude of the propulsion required for space travel, a realistic evaluation of the maneuvers required makes it necessary that the effects of orbit inclination and the eccentricity be taken into account. The flight mechanics of such a transfer have been discussed in Reference 6.7 where the maneuver has been evaluated in terms of the *hyperbolic excess velocity* required to obtain interplanetary transfer. The hyperbolic excess velocity, v_∞, can be obtained from the energy equation as expressed in Equation (2-14); it is

$$v_\infty = \sqrt{v^2 - \frac{2k}{r}} = \sqrt{v^2 - v^2_{esc}} \qquad (6\text{-}2)$$

The contour chart of Figure 6.5 shows a contour map that indicates the hyperbolic excess velocity required for trips to Mars ($\male$) from the Earth ($\oplus$). The contours have been drawn in a plane where the abscissa represents the dates of departure from and arrival at the Earth (shown as the Julian calendar date). The ordinates show the dates of arrival and departure when reckoned from Mars. The departure speeds (as indicated by hyperbolic excess velocity) from the Earth are shown by the solid contour lines at the left of the chart and the speed of arrival at Mars is shown by the corresponding dotted contour. To the right of the chart, Mars departures are indicated by the solid contours and the arrival speeds at the Earth are shown by the dotted lines. The velocity values shown have been normalized using one tenth of the Earth's mean orbital speed as a unit. (1 EMOS = 29.77 km/sec = 18.5 mi/sec, 0.1 EMOS = 1.85 mi/sec.)

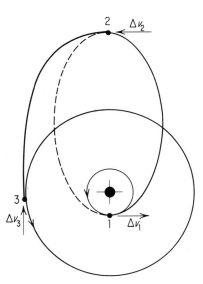

Fig. 6.4. Transfer by three impulses: (1) escape from inner orbit to first transfer orbit, (2) transfer at apoapsis of first transfer orbit to second transfer orbit, (3) transfer to final orbit.

Flight durations are shown in days and are indicated by the difference between the Julian dates that are shown on the ordinate and the abscissa. A one-way transfer is represented by a point that has convenient values for the departure and arrival speeds. The dates for nodal transfer are indicated on the reference axes. The calculations leading to these charts has been described in the literature, Reference 6.7; the calculations include the effects of planetary orbit inclinations as well as the eccentricity of the orbits. Charts such as those shown in Figure 6.5 may be used to plan a complete journey. An example has been indicated on the chart.

Departure from a node, for example Julian date 244 0903, *and* arrival at a node, for example J–244 1083, are both required in order for the flight to be in the ecliptic plane. No ecliptic plane flights are possible when the initial or terminal points are not on the nodes. Hohmann transfer requires ecliptic plane flight, *and* the appropriate initial configuration for 180 deg transfer between the two planets; no such flight opportunity occurs in the time period that is shown in the chart of Figure 6.5. An example of the use of the chart is shown on the face of the Figure. The key points of the example are as follows:

	Jul. Date	*Cal. Date*	*Duration*	*Speed*
Leave ⊕	244 0880	10/21/70	—	0.3470 EMO's
Arrive ♂	1100	5/29/71	220 da	0.2828
Leave ♂	2130	6/28/71	30	0.1965
Arrive ⊕	1260	11/5/71	130	0.1361

Duration of journey: 380 days

6.1.2 CHARACTERISTIC VELOCITY AND THE ENERGY OF TRANSFER

The principles of rocket propulsion were discussed briefly in Section 1.7 where the relations between fuel consumption and velocity increments were developed. Since the fuel for propulsion of a rocket frequently represents a major fraction of its total mass, it is customary to discuss the maneuvers of a rocket system in terms of its *characteristic velocity*, which may be related to fuel requirements. This term refers to the sum total of all the velocity increments that a rocket must develop, or dissipate, by fuel consumption in the course of a given maneuver or journey. The characteristic velocity is useful in evaluation of interplanetary flight plans and in estimation of the capability of a given rocket system to meet the indicated flight plan. Let us assume that a spacecraft is to be launched from the Earth to a landing on a distant planet. The complete sequence of maneuvers will be defined by a series of steps as follows:

1. Escape from the Earth: v_{e0}
2. Orbit plane change to the plane of the selected transfer orbit: v_{i0}
3. Change of hyperbolic velocity relative to the Earth, placing the craft in transfer orbit: v_{t0}
4. Deceleration in the vicinity of the destination reducing the hyperbolic excess velocity relative to the destination planet: v_{tf}
5. Change in plane to that of the orbit of the destination from that of the transfer orbit: v_{if}
6. Reduction of velocity gained in falling through the gravity field of the destination planet: v_{ef}.

The characteristic velocity for the journey may be calculated on a one-way or a round trip basis. For a one-way journey the characteristic velocity will be given by the sum of each of the individual terms listed above.

$$v_c = v_{e0} + v_{i0} + v_{t0} + v_{tf} + v_{if} + v_{ef} \qquad (6\text{-}3)$$

Depending upon the manner in which these individual increments of velocity are introduced into the system the total energy which is required of the propulsion system may be reduced. In any case of practical interest, the transfer may be resolved into two periods of maneuvers. The first maneuvers will be at the point of origin and the second group of maneuvers will occur in the vicinity of the destination. The first three velocity increments may then be combined in some convenient fashion and the final three maneuvers may be similarly grouped. If this is done, a reduced *characteristic velocity* will be obtained which reflects the vector summation of the groups of velocity increments. The fuel consumed and the equivalent kinetic energy of the transfer must be calculated on the basis of this reduced characteristic velocity which will depend upon the specific program of maneuvers which is elected for the mission at hand.

As the spacecraft approaches the atmosphere and the gravitational field of a planet, accelerations may be applied to the craft which perturb and distort its trajectory. These accelerations may be used to introduce, in part, the maneuvers indicated in the second group of velocity increments. Similarly, there are effects of gravity loss and drag loss which act to increase the total velocity required in the vicinity of the originating planet.

Inter-orbital maneuvers will involve one, or more of the following orthogonal components:

Maneuvers involving a change in the tangential velocity; $\Delta v = v_{\text{tangential}}$

Maneuvers in the orbit plane, but which involve changes in the radial component of the velocity. These are related to the orbital flight path angle $\Delta \varphi = \Delta v_{\text{radial}}/v_c$

Maneuvers which involve changes in the orbit plane. An orbit plane change of angle $\Delta \psi$ will result from a velocity increment which is applied normal to the orbit plane; $\Delta \psi = \Delta v_{\text{normal}}/v_c$

The point at which a plane change maneuver is made will always be the node of the former orbit and the new orbit. This point and the point at the center of the force field for the orbit will define the line of nodes and hence the relative orientation of the new orbit. Plane change maneuvers which are commanded at a point other than one on the desired line of nodes will require two successive plane change maneuvers, each of which will be larger than the single plane change which would be required if the maneuver had been executed at the node.

The characteristic velocity for the maneuver may be calculated from the expression

$$v_c = \sqrt{\Delta v^2_{\text{tang.}} + \Delta v^2_{\text{rad.}} + \Delta v^2_{\text{norm.}}} \qquad (6\text{-}4)$$

This may also be calculated from the values of the velocity vector of the craft before and after the maneuver, that is

$$\mathbf{v}_c = \mathbf{v}_f - \mathbf{v}_0 \tag{6-5}$$

where

$\mathbf{v}_f$ = the final velocity vector
$\mathbf{v}_0$ = the velocity vector before the maneuver.

From the geometry shown in Figure 1.6, it will be seen that the characteristic velocity is given by

$$v_c^2 = v_0^2 + v_f^2 - 2v_0 v_f \cos \Delta \varphi \tag{6-6}$$

The angle between the initial velocity vector and the direction of the thrust axis during the maneuver will be called the *thrust angle*, α, it is given by

$$\alpha = \sin^{-1}\left(\frac{v_f}{v_c}\right) \sin \Delta \varphi \tag{6-7}$$

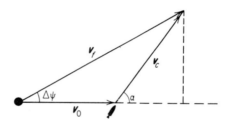

Fig. 6.6. Departure maneuver.

As a general rule, great flexibility will be available to navigators of spacecraft in the selection of their maneuvers. If no limitations were placed on the transfer, it would be possible to wait until the spacecraft occupies a point on the line of nodes of the two orbits; he would then make the transfer using an optimum impulse. In this case, minimum characteristic velocity, and hence minimum energy, is used to intersect, or osculate with the destination orbit. In the event that the destination planet is not at the point of intersection of the two orbits upon the arrival of the craft, the spacecraft might choose to continue to follow the transfer orbit as long as necessary for interception to occur. Alternatively, the navigator might elect to transfer the craft to an orbit in the plane of the destination and with a period only slightly perturbed from that of the destination body. The spacecraft would then await the time to be overtaken by its destination, or vice versa. In reality, it will usually be required that more dispatch be exercised in the transfer. Indeed, for missions involving living payloads, there will be a premium associated with the prompt completion of the mission. Consequently the work that follows will assume that interplanetary transfers will be made from a configuration of planets such that the first common point of the transfer and destination orbits will be occupied by the destination planet upon the arrival of the spacecraft.

6.1.3 Setting the Course for an Interplanetary Transfer

In this section we shall discuss a procedure which will permit the space navigator to determine the maneuver which he will require in order to effect an interplanetary transfer. As a first step, the navigator must select a heliocentric orbit which will carry him from a selected point on his present orbit to a closure point, or rendezvous, with his destination which, itself, is in an orbit about the Sun. It will be shown that the choosing of a transfer orbit can not be done without setting up a criterion for the choice of the orbit. Typical examples of suitable criteria are minimum characteristic velocity, cotangential departure (or arrival), fixed transfer time, or minimum transfer time. The choice of these criteria will be discussed at the conclusion of the section.

The initial configuration of the spacecraft and the planets will be set by the time of the departure of the spacecraft from its orbit of origin, t_d. The terminal configuration will be set by the time of arrival, $t_d + \tau$. This situation is complicated since the interplanetary transfer orbit must ordinarily be preceded by an escape ascent trajectory and hyperbola leaving the originating planet. Similarly, the transfer must be concluded with a capture and descent hyperbola as it approaches the destination planet. While these extensions of the transfer orbit affect the complete time for the transfer and present a problem of transition from planetocentric hyperbolae to heliocentric ellipse, it will be convenient to consider only the heliocentric elliptical sector of the transfer orbits.

As a first step in navigation, see Figure 6.7, it will be necessary to determine the time relations of the flight. The *departure time* is usually a matter of operational importance and not a decision left to the navigator. The *transfer time* is the time which elapses while the spacecraft is in transfer flight from departure to destination. *Arrival time* is, of course, determined by the time of departure and the transfer time. The transfer time may be computed by application of the time Equation (2-38)

$$(t - t_p) = \frac{1}{n}(A_e - e \sin A_e) \qquad (2\text{-}38)$$

This equation specifies the time which has elapsed since the spacecraft was at periapsis, the transfer time will be given as the time difference between the times for the initial and final positions on the transfer orbit. The point of departure may not be the periapsis (in the case of interplanetary flight, the perihelion) and consequently the transfer time must be computed as follows:

$$\tau = \frac{1}{n}[A_{ef} - A_{e0} + e(\sin A_{e0} - \sin A_{ef})] \tag{6-8}$$

Thus the transfer time for the spacecraft will be defined by the initial and final positions of the spacecraft in the transfer orbit, the eccentricity of that orbit, and the orientation of the transfer orbit.

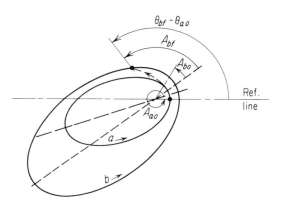

Fig. 6.7. Transfer geometry:

A_{e0} = true anomaly in orbit a at departure
A_{b0} = true anomaly of destination in orbit b
       at time of departure maneuver
A_{bf} = true anomaly in orbit b at arrival
θ_{bf} — θ_{a0} = transfer angle.

In the special case where transfer is between two circular orbits with a tangential departure, $\Delta\varphi_0 = 0$, we have a convenient example for discussing the mechanics of an interplanetary transfer. For convenience, a reference line is chosen which is the heliocentric position vector of the spacecraft at the time of departure, see Figure 6.8. The position of the periapsis of a circular orbit ($e = 0$) is arbitrary, consequently we are free to choose the perihelion of both orbit a and of orbit b to be points on the reference line. Since the transfer orbit is tangent to a circular orbit in this special case, the reference line is also the line of apsides for the transfer orbit. The departure point will be the perihelion of the transfer orbit for an outward transfer and the aphelion for an inward transfer. The transfer time for these journeys will be determined from the application of Equation (6-8) with A_{e0} vanishing;

$$\tau = \frac{1}{n}(A_{ef} - e \sin A_{ef}) \tag{6-9}$$

where

A_{ef} = the transfer angle in terms of eccentric anomaly
e = the eccentricity of the transfer ellipse
n = the mean motion for the transfer orbit

$$\left(n = \frac{2\pi}{T} \right)$$

The transfer time is shown graphed in a non-dimensional form as a function of the transfer angle in Figure 6.9.

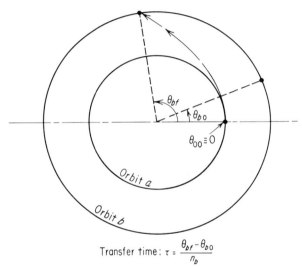

Transfer time: $\tau = \dfrac{\theta_{bf} - \theta_{bo}}{n_b}$

Fig. 6.8. Transfer between two circular orbits; tangential departure.

A transfer orbit will necessarily pass through the point of departure and the terminal point. The transfer will be in a plane orbit. The plane will be defined by three points; the departure point, the terminal point, and the center (or focus) of the gravitational field of the Sun. The transfer may be studied as a two-dimensional motion which occurs in this transfer plane. Such an orbit will satisfy the orbit equation at the departure and terminal points:

$$r_a = \frac{p}{1 + e \cos A_{to}} \tag{6-10}$$

$$r_b = \frac{p}{1 + e \cos A_{tf}} \tag{6-11}$$

where

r_a = the radius of the orbit of the departure planet
r_b = the radius of the orbit of the destination planet
A_{t0} = the true anomaly of the spacecraft at departure ($A_{t0} = \theta_{a0}$ c.f. Figure 6.7)
A_{tf} = the true anomaly of the spacecraft at the terminal point ($A_{tf} = \theta_{bf}$ c.f. Figure 6.7).

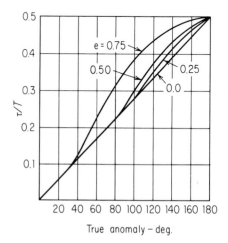

Fig. 6.9. Transfer time vs. true anomaly of transfer (tangential departure, transfer between circular orbits).

These two simultaneous Equations, (6-10) and (6-11), permit the determination of only two of the three parameters which appear in them; these two parameters will be given in terms of the third. The three parameters are the angular momentum of the transfer ellipse, p; the eccentricity of the transfer orbit, e; and the orientation of the transfer orbit which is given by θ_p or the reference to the angle A_t. In order to specify the transfer orbit, an additional relationship, or constraint, is needed. In the tangential departure example of transfer between circular orbits, the orientation of the transfer orbit is defined by the geometry and Equations (6-10) and (6-11) may be taken together with the departure configuration to determine the transfer orbit. In more general examples, it will be necessary to introduce another constraint on the parameters of the transfer before it will be possible to specify an unique orbit transferring the spacecraft from one planet to another. Typical examples of these constraints are as follows

1. Minimum characteristic velocity
2. Cotangential departure
3. Cotangential arrival
4. Fixed transfer time
5. Minimum transfer time

A transfer which is specified to occur between two points which are fixed in space, one on the departure orbit and the other on the terminal orbit, will be a transfer having fixed transfer time. The transfer time is fixed by the time required for the destination to move from its position at the time of departure to the terminal point for rendezvous.

The time for transfer has been discussed above. The transfer orbit must be selected in such a way that the time of transfer is matched to the motion of the destination planet as it approaches the terminal point. As a meaningful example, let us consider the transfer of a spacecraft between two planetary orbits. It will be assumed that the two planets are in orbits which are circular and coplanar. The transfer is to be initiated at a selected point in space and time; the arrival is to be at another specified point in space. The time for arrival will be implied by the configuration of the planets at the time of departure and by the location of the specified terminal point. The transfer time will be such that the destination planet will have motion during the transfer, which is given by

$$\tau = \frac{1}{n_b}(A_{tf} - A_{t0}) \tag{6-12}$$

where

n_b = the mean motion for the destination planet and the true anomalies given refer to the destination orbit.

While it is not possible to solve for the parameters of the transfer orbit explicitly until the specific problem and its constraints have been defined, it is nevertheless possible to employ the pertinent relations to obtain the significant parameters as mathematical functions of one another. Combining Equations (6-10) and (6-11), the eccentricity of the transfer orbit will be given as

$$e = \frac{r_a - r_b}{r_b \cos A_{tf} - r_a \cos A_{t0}} \tag{6-13}$$

where
A_{tf} = final value of A_t in transfer orbit
A_{t0} = initial value of A_t in transfer orbit.

The eccentricity of the transfer orbit is, then, an implicit function of the orientation of that orbit. The following special cases are of frequent interest.

1. Departure point on the line of apsides.

$$e = \frac{r_a - r_b}{r_b \cos A_{tf} - r_a} \qquad \text{(outward transfer)}$$

$$e = \frac{r_a - r_b}{r_b \cos A_{tf} + r_a} \qquad \text{(inward transfer)}$$

2. Terminal point on the line of apsides.

$$e = \frac{r_b - r_a}{r_b + r_a \cos A_{t0}} \qquad \text{(outward transfer)}$$

$$e = \frac{r_a - r_b}{r_b - r_a \cos A_{t0}} \qquad \text{(inward transfer)}$$

3. Terminal point and departure point *both* on the line of apsides.

$$e = \frac{r_a - r_b}{r_b + r_a} \qquad \text{(outward transfer)}$$

$$e = \frac{r_b - r_a}{r_b + r_a} \qquad \text{(inward transfer)}$$

Equations (6-10) and (6-11) may also be combined to obtain an expression for the semi-latus rectum of the transfer orbit.

$$p = \frac{\cos A_{tf} - \cos A_{t0}}{\dfrac{\cos A_{tf}}{r_a} - \dfrac{\cos A_{t0}}{r_b}} \qquad (6\text{-}14)$$

In the special examples, Equation (6-14) will be reduced to the following forms.

1. Departure point on the line of apsides.

$$p = \frac{\cos A_{tf} - 1}{\dfrac{\cos A_{tf}}{r_a} - \dfrac{1}{r_b}} \qquad \text{(outward transfer)}$$

$$p = \frac{\cos A_{tf} + 1}{\dfrac{\cos A_{tf}}{r_a} + \dfrac{1}{r_b}} \qquad \text{(inward transfer)}$$

2. Terminal point on the line of apsides.

$$p = \frac{1 - \cos A_{t0}}{\dfrac{1}{r_a} - \dfrac{\cos A_{t0}}{r_b}} \qquad \text{(outward transfer)}$$

$$p = \frac{1 + \cos A_{t0}}{\dfrac{1}{r_a} + \dfrac{\cos A_{t0}}{r_b}} \qquad \text{(inward transfer)}$$

3. Terminal point and departure point *both* on the line of apsides.

$$p = \frac{2r_a r_b}{r_a + r_b} \qquad \text{(transfer both ways)}$$

When the parameters of the transfer orbit have been determined using the relations which have been discussed above, it will be possible to specify the velocity components which will establish the transfer orbit. These components may be computed in terms of the velocity magnitude and the flight path angle which obtains at the conclusion of the maneuver into a transfer orbit. These quantities may be obtained from the relations

$$p = \frac{h^2}{k} = \frac{r^2 v^2 \cos^2 \varphi}{k} \qquad (6\text{-}15)$$

and

$$e = \sqrt{1 + \frac{(v^2 - 2k/r)r^2 v^2 \cos^2 \varphi}{k^2}} \qquad (6\text{-}16$$

When the transfer parameters have been determined, Equations (6-15) and (6-16) may be used to solve for the velocity and the flight path angle. These are given by

$$v = \frac{\sqrt{kp}}{r \cos \varphi} = \sqrt{k\left[\left(\frac{e^2 - 1}{p}\right) - \frac{2}{r}\right]} \qquad (6\text{-}17)$$

and

$$\cos \varphi = \frac{1}{\sqrt{\dfrac{r^2}{p}(e^2 - 1) + \dfrac{2r}{p}}} \qquad (6\text{-}18)$$

The velocity vector of the spacecraft relative to an inertial reference located at the center of the force field will be specified by the values of flight path angle and velocity which may be calculated from these relations. Maneuver requirements must be calculated as the difference between the velocity vector before and after the departure maneuver. The transfer navigation, like any navigation, may be accomplished as a series of approximations to the ideal maneuver. The number of approximations and the precision required in monitoring the maneuvers will be related to fuel and efficiency requirements. The initial transfer maneuver from the orbit of the departure planet to an orbit that is designed to carry the spacecraft to another planet will be computed, in many instances, as a systems design optimization problem using large computers to take into account the spacecraft flight mechanics. Following the execution of this maneuver, midcourse maneuvers may be necessary in order to adjust the transfer orbit. These maneuvers will be required to compensate for the errors in guidance, to adjust for inaccuracy in our knowledge of fundamental constants of the solar system[1] and the action of orbit perturbations which have not been predicted accurately. The timing of the departure maneuver is an operational matter and will be based on mission requirements, propulsion capability, and the configuration of the solar system when the mission is to be attempted.

While the timing of the departure maneuver is a matter of operational decision, the timing of the correction maneuvers will be a matter of navigation. In general, maneuvers that are made late in the flight will require more fuel than if the same correction is made early in the flight. The precision of measurement of the orbit parameters must be greater for maneuvers which are made early in the flight. Unless the navigation corrections are executed with precision, it can be expected that it will become necessary to repeat them later in the flight with a consequent fuel consumption which would not have been needed if precision corrections had been made. The theory of optimum spacing of corrective maneuvers in an interplanetary transfer has been discussed in Reference 6.7 and will not be discussed further here. The theory of navigation corrections is discussed in Section 6.3.

The preceding discussion has been presented in the context of a transfer between coplanar orbits. Although mission planning must account for the inclinations of the individual orbits, the transfer orbit is indeed confined to a plane. The techniques which have been discussed above may be used to approximate the situation with inclined orbits by treating the motion of the planets as though it were projected into the transfer orbit plane.

6.2 TRANSFER ORBIT GUIDANCE

The previous section discussed the means by which the transfer orbit may be specified in terms of the various orbit parameters and the transfer time. The interrelations of initial and final planet configurations to the transfer time were calculated. The mathematical discussions of orbit dynamics which were presented in Chapter 2 treated the means to relate the orbit parameters to the

---

[1] For example, the astronomical unit, defined as the mean distance between the Sun and the Earth, is known only to about one part in ten thousand.

future position and velocity of the spacecraft. In Chapter 3, the parameters were shown to be functions of measured values of position and velocity of the spacecraft when these coordinates are measured with respect to the focus of the gravitational field in which flight occurs. Transfer orbit guidance may, therefore, be treated as equivalent to the measurement of the position and velocity of the spacecraft and the subsequent computation of corrective maneuvers.

One of the first steps which is encountered in the guidance of an interplanetary spaceship is the control of the maneuver in which the vehicle escapes from the Earth. The guidance system provides commands to control its injection into a precalculated transfer orbit. In the consideration of interplanetary guidance, one is immediately attracted to the possibility of making measurements of spacecraft position and velocity with respect to the Sun. It will be shown later that direct measurements relative to the Sun will be extremely difficult to perform with the precision which is required when these measurements must be made from the great heliocentric distances which apply to interplanetary orbits.

This section will discuss the general properties of the flight mechanics in which the interplanetary spacecraft ascends to escape from the departure planet; the concept of a *virtual launch point* will be introduced to account for the transition from the escape orbit to the heliocentric mid-course transfer orbit. Brief discussions will be included treating the techniques of interplanetary guidance. The precision which may be expected from a system of navigation by dynamical measurements (inertial navigation) will be discussed. The use of interplanetary celestial navigation will be treated briefly to show how these techniques are applicable to the special situations arising in Solar System travel. The discussions of the methods for steering the spacecraft during its ascent to an escape orbit and for providing a suitable mid-course transfer orbit will conclude the section. Computation of mid-course corrections will be deferred here as they are the subject of Section 6.4.

6.2.1 THE ASCENT TO ESCAPE

In studying interplanetary travel, it is necessary to consider the gravitational effects of the Sun and those of the departure and terminal planets. It is essential to treat these more than one at a time during at least some portions of the flight in order to compute the trajectory with extreme precision. However, spaceflight navigation may be analyzed adequately by treating the flight in three parts. These parts are successions of inverse square-law central force field conics, each of which represents the flight as the result of the major effects of gravity during each of the three most important phases of the trajectory. In a sense, this is equivalent to approximation of the flight path by three distinct arcs which are linked together. The three phases of flight are illustrated in Figure 6.10; they are described below.

The Escape Phase

This is the geocentric hyperbola along which the craft escapes. At the conclusion of booster ascent flight, the spacecraft has gained sufficient velocity to escape the departure planet. In this phase of flight, the trajectory may be characterized by the vector representing the hyperbolic excess velocity of the spacecraft relative to the center of the planet, v_∞. This is the velocity which the vehicle approaches asymptotically as it escapes from the gravitational field of the departure planet.

The Heliocentric Phase

This is the mid-course orbit in which the major influence on the craft is due to the gravity field of the Sun. Initial conditions for the heliocentric phase are established in transition from the escape phase. Consequently, the heliocentric velocity at the time of entry into the second phase of flight is the vector sum of the heliocentric velocity of the departure planet and the hyperbolic excess velocity of the spacecraft, that is

$$\mathbf{v}_2 = \mathbf{v}_\oplus + \mathbf{v}_\infty \qquad (6\text{-}19)$$

The initial position of the spacecraft will be approximated as that of the planet at the time of escape. The quantity of interest for guidance purposes is the distance of closest approach between the spacecraft and the destination planet as the craft proceeds along the transfer orbit.

The Terminal Phase

This is the region in which the gravity field of the terminal planet predominates in its influence on the spacecraft. The gravity due to the Sun has an effect which is less than that of the nearby planet. It is a region of hyperbolic flight similar to the escape phase except that it is a region of hyperbolic *approach* rather than one of departure. The initial conditions characterize the terminal trajectory; they are the hyperbolic approach velocity, v'_∞, and the assymptotic distance, d. The figure which measures guidance performance during the terminal flight is the *Keplerian periapsis*, which is the distance from the center of the planet at the point of closest approach if the orbit were not perturbed by atmospheric drag.

The third phase of the transfer orbit becomes important when a close pass is necessary or when a final maneuver for landing or satellite orbit injection is intended. In those situations a terminal, or homing, guidance system will normally be employed. This terminal guidance will be the subject of a separate discussion in a later section.

It is necessary to define a boundary between phases one and two; this same definition may also be applied to the boundary between phases two and three. The critical radius of the activity sphere as defined by Equation (6-1) suggests the basis for such a boundary. For example, the radius of the activity sphere for the Earth is about 575,000 miles, while the heliocentric transfer trajectory to the nearest planet is many times this distance. One may consider, then, that the greatest part of the mid-course trajectory is outside of the activity sphere of the Earth. Consequently, it is predominately influenced by the gravitational field due to the Sun. While it does not appear explicitly in the mathematical

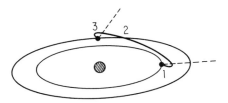

Fig. 6.10. Interplanetary transfer. Phase 1: escape; phase 2: heliocentric transfer; phase 3: terminal.

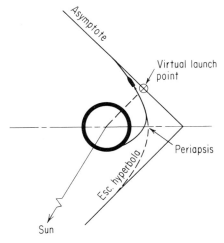

Fig. 6.11. Virtual launch point.

descriptions, the acceleration due to the Sun is not ignored during the escape or the terminal phases of flight. During these portions of the flight, the predominant effect is that of the gravity field due to the Earth (or other planet). Both the Earth and the spacecraft are influenced in a similar manner by the Sun's gravity during this period. The heliocentric acceleration that acts during the hyperbolic phases of the flight is accounted for by the treatment of these phases of flight in terms of motions that are reckoned relative to the nearby planet. A change of coordinate reference from a planetocentric to a heliocentric reference and back again must be made at the times of transition from one phase of flight to another.

In order that the transition in flight between hyperbolic phases and the mid-course may be discussed in a useful manner, it will be convenient to extend the flight conditions along the heliocentric ellipse to a *virtual launch point* and to a *virtual terminal point*. These may be considered to be points of origin and of arrival for the mid-course phase of flight. The virtual launch point is illustrated in Figure 6.11. The *virtual launch point* is chosen as the point where the asymptote of the hyperbolic escape arc is perpendicular to the local vertical. The *virtual terminal point* is defined in a similar manner. The virtual launch point derives its significance from the fact that it represents a point through which the craft would have passed had it been on the mid-course trajectory and its path had not been perturbed by the gravity field of the Earth, or other planet. The virtual terminal point is a point where it is found to be convenient to consider that the transition to hyperbolic approach has occurred. At this point, the change in coordinate systems from a heliocentric to a planetocentric reference will be made.

6.2.2 Interplanetary Navigation by Dynamical Measurements

It is theoretically possible to perform space navigation without any reference to external bodies or landmarks provided that the initial position and velocity of the spacecraft is known and that the characteristics of the gravity field in which the motion is occurring are also known. When navigating in this manner, the non-gravitational accelerations which act on the craft are measured using accelerometers and the gravitational accelerations are computed from a knowledge of the three-dimensional distribution of gravity in the region of flight. Since this system is to operate without reference to external bodies, the spacecraft must carry its own internal attitude reference system. Such a reference may be constructed using a configuration of gyroscopes which are gimballed in such a way as to permit motions of the craft about the three primary body axes without loss of attitude reference. Because it employs instruments depending upon the inertia of their sensitive elements for its operation, such a system is called an *inertial navigation system*. The theory of these devices is discussed in Reference 6.8.

The techniques of inertial navigation may be applied to interplanetary guidance. (For a description of inertial navigation systems in terms of the terrestrial environment see Reference 6.9.) The inertial navigation system is sometimes called an accelerometer system. It operates on a principle of measuring and integrating the non-gravitational accelerations acting on the spacecraft; these are added to the gravitational accelerations which are computed as a function of the position of the craft. The sum of these accelerations is accumulated in the guidance computer to provide a source of position and velocity data which may be used for navigation purposes. See Figure 6.12. In application to a spaceflight, an accelerometer system will require a computer which has been programmed to compute the accelerations which are due to the gravitational fields of the Sun and the nearby planets during the period when the craft is launched and is gaining altitude and velocity for escape from the departure planet. Indeed, the gravity of both the Sun and nearest planet must be considered whenever the spacecraft is within the sphere of influence of any planet. In a similar manner, the gravity computer must consider the effects of the Sun and the terminal planet during the homing portion of the flight. The mid-course phase of flight requires only the consideration of the solar gravity field.

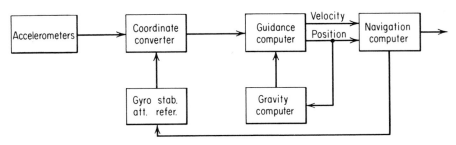

Fig. 6.12. Guidance computer.

Some of the more important techniques for solution of the general problem of inertial navigation are discussed in some detail in Reference 6.8. Several useful approximations for the gravitational acceleration have been analyzed and are discussed in the reference. For example, the gravitational field of the Earth may be approximated for terrestrial navigation purposes by an inverse square-law central force field. The equations of motion of the craft which is being navigated may be linearized without excessive loss of accuracy in the terrestrial example since the variations in the gravitational field acting on the earth-bound vehicle are small in magnitude. (The gravity vector changes in direction but it retains approximately a radial orientation.) Studies of the theory of errors in guidance systems of this kind have shown that errors in the value of gravity calculated by the "g" computer will diverge unless a direct measure of the altitude of the craft is available, Reference 6.10. An interplanetary navigation system which is based on this concept will be approximating the solution of the n-body problem; the precision of measurement and the complexity of computation required for this mode of operation are perhaps not warranted and other methods will be shown to be adequate for these purposes. The long time of flight of an interplanetary journey will permit even the most stable gyroscope to drift excessively and to degrade the quality of the coordinate conversion reference in the navigation device. The expected errors due to gyro drift in an inertial navigation system are indicated by the graph in Figure 6.13.

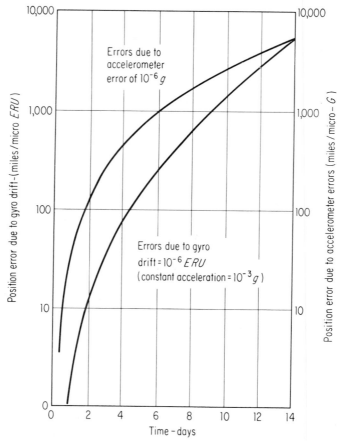

Fig. 6.13. First order errors in inertial navigation—applied to interplanetary flight.

6.2.3 INTERPLANETARY GUIDANCE USING CELESTIAL BODIES

A useful and direct method for determining the position and velocity of a spacecraft is by measurement of those quantities relative to celestial bodies whose motions relative to the Sun are known from astronomical measurements. Since the motions of the celestial bodies are known as a function of time, it is implied in the discussions which follow that an accurate time reference, or clock, is available.

A star, or planet, used as a reference for measurements of this kind acts as a navigation aid in the same sense as landmarks and beacons are used in nautical and aerial navigation. Several examples of measurement systems which may be applied to this problem have been discussed in considerable detail in Chapter 3, where the context was one of terrestrial tracking stations. The extrapolation of these to configurations of measurement stations on one or more celestial bodies is of some passing interest but will not be discussed at this time. When spacecraft position measurements have been made, velocity may be calculated from the time-position differentials or explicit measurements that yield velocity directly may be devised. The orbit parameters which may be calculated from the position and velocity data using methods described in Section 3.1 may be used to extrapolate the spacecraft orbit over time in order to evaluate its effectiveness as a transfer trajectory.

It was shown in Chapter 3 that the trajectory of a spacecraft may be measured from a point on the surface of the Earth and then transformed to a geocentric coordinate reference system to yield the parameters of the geocentric orbit. In a similar manner, one may measure the path of a spacecraft from the Earth and transform this motion to a heliocentric reference to provide a description of the heliocentric orbit of the craft. For space navigation purposes, it will frequently be convenient, or perhaps even necessary, to perform this latter operation using measurements that are made from the spacecraft itself. Applications of celestial body tracking of this particular kind will be known as *offset navigation* and will be most effective when the spacecraft is moving in the vicinity of the reference celestial body or planet. In addition, techniques of range-only and angle-only measurements, which are made from the observation of a number of celestial bodies, may be employed. Of these methods, special interest arises in a system which requires measurements of angles exclusively; systems of this kind will be called *triangulation systems*. The precision which is available in this application of instruments for triangulation is generally greater than is available for instruments which measure range. The boundaries of the region for most favorable application of one of these systems over the other is a function of the relative precision of the instruments used for each purpose. These boundaries will depend upon the state of the art at the time of the design of any specific instrument. The methods of offset navigation and of triangulation will be discussed in the paragraphs that follow.

Offset Navigation

Offset navigation is particularly convenient when a tracking system has been located on a planet, say the Earth, and this tracking system has capability to determine the position and, perhaps, the velocity of the spacecraft relative to the Earth. The offset systems may also be employed where a vehicleborne radar or other tracking system is available to measure the position of the planet nearest to the spacecraft with relation to the craft. The following discussion will be placed in the context of the latter situation where the measurements are made from observations from on-board the spacevehicle.

The heliocentric position of a spacecraft may be given in terms of the position of the craft measured relative to a nearby reference such as the Earth, provided the heliocentric position vector of the Earth is also known. The vector relations may be expressed as follows. (See Figure 6.14.)

$$\mathbf{R}_c = \mathbf{R}_\oplus - \boldsymbol{\rho} \qquad (6\text{-}20)$$

A similar expression will be obtained for the heliocentric velocity vector of the spacecraft.

$$\dot{\mathbf{R}}_c = \dot{\mathbf{R}}_\oplus - \dot{\boldsymbol{\rho}} \qquad (6\text{-}21)$$

where

$\mathbf{R}_c$ = the heliocentric position vector of the spacecraft
$\mathbf{R}_\oplus$ = the heliocentric position vector of the Earth
$\boldsymbol{\rho}$ = the position vector of the Earth measured relative to the spacecraft.

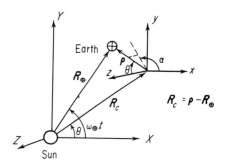

Fig. 6.14. Position reference.

Before discussing the offset systems further, it is necessary to define a coordinate frame for the reference of position and velocity vectors. A non-rotating heliocentric-ecliptic system as described in Section 3.2 has been chosen for this purpose. The most important characteristics of this reference system are summarized below; see also Figure 3.8.

Origin— center of the Sun
X axis— directed outward from the origin toward the first point of Aries, ♈
Y axis— directed so as to form a right-handed set with X and Z
Z axis— directed outward from the origin in the positive sense of the vector representing the annual rotation of the Earth about the Sun

This reference may be established on board the spacecraft using a three-axis stabilized gyro platform which is supervised by a set of star trackers to eliminate the effects of gyro drift. Radar data which have been obtained on the spacecraft may then be referred to the heliocentric-ecliptic reference system to yield the components of the relative position vector, $\boldsymbol{\rho}$. These components will be noted by the Greek letters (ξ, η, ζ).

A special application of offset position measurement was analyzed in Section 3.12. In that example, the offset was the geocentric position vector of a terrestrial tracking station; the motion of the tracking station was due only to the rotation of the Earth. In the interplanetary example which is of present interest, the spacecraft is capable of general motions with relation to the Earth. The heliocentric position vector of the spacecraft is given by the expression of Equation (6.20)

$$\mathbf{R}_c = \mathbf{R}_\oplus - \boldsymbol{\rho}$$
$$= \mathbf{i}(X_\oplus - \xi) + \mathbf{j}(Y_\oplus - \eta) + \mathbf{k}(\zeta) \tag{6-22}$$

The velocity of the spacecraft will be given by the time derivative of (6-22); substituting for the known motions of the Earth relative to the Sun the velocity of the craft will be approximated by

$$\mathbf{R}_c = \mathbf{i}(\Omega_\oplus R_\oplus \cos \Omega_\oplus t - \dot{\xi}) - \mathbf{j}(\Omega_\oplus R_\oplus \sin \Omega_\oplus t + \dot{\eta})$$
$$+ \mathbf{k}(\dot{\zeta}) \tag{6-23}$$

where

$\Omega_\oplus$ = the angular velocity of the Earth in its annual rotation about the Sun

t = the time since the vernal equinox

Triangulation Systems

A number of plans for space navigation based on angle only measurements have been suggested in the literature. This seems to be a natural system for navigation. Among other things in its favor, it involves measurements which may be made with the aid of optical instruments such as telescopes and employs methods which are familiar to astronomy. The standard techniques of celestial navigation depend upon the craft being constrained to a thin shell near the surface of the Earth. Therefore, these are not directly applicable to the measurement of heliocentric orbit parameters where the distance from the Sun to the spacecraft may vary over a wide range.

Sightings of the Sun and of nearby planets, together with a knowledge of the ephemerides of these planets offers a solution to this problem (Reference 6.11). In this solution, the spacecraft is assumed to be in or near the ecliptic plane and the spacecraft navigator determines his position in much the same way as a surveyor calculates ground positions from the azimuth to several benchmarks. The principles involved are illustrated in Figure 6.15. The descriptions of Reference 6.11 deal with a means for determining position only; methods have also been proposed to take account of the motions of the craft and the planets during the time that angle measurements are being made to provide a measurement of the velocity of the spacecraft (Reference 6.12). A technique of this kind depends upon the assumption that the spacecraft is on an orbit which differs only slightly from the nominal, or precalculated trajectory.

A different, and somewhat more general method resembles celestial navigation in some ways but is indeed an inversion of that familiar technique, since it depends upon a reference to the stars and observations are made of the solar vertical. In this system the spacecraft carries a stabilized reference to the helio-centric-ecliptic reference frame which has been described above. The spacecraft position is then defined on a line of position which is a heliocentric radial line. The line of position is identified in terms of Solar System longitude, L_c, and solar system latitude, Λ_c. These quantities are derived from a single observation

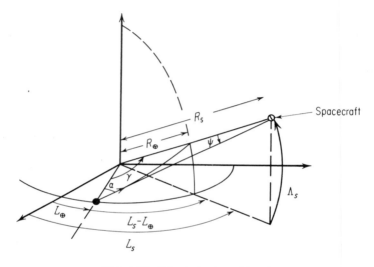

Fig. 6.15. Solar latitude and longitude.

$$R_s = \frac{R_\oplus \sin \alpha}{\sin \psi}$$

$$\sin \alpha = \sin (\psi + \gamma)$$

$$\text{hav } \Lambda_s = \text{hav } (L_s - L_\oplus - \gamma)$$

$$\gamma = L_s - L_\oplus - \Lambda_s$$

$$R_s = \frac{R_\oplus \sin (\psi + L_s - L_\oplus - \Lambda_s)}{\sin \psi}$$

of the direction of the line of sight to the Sun. The Solar System longitude is the angle measured in the ecliptic plane from the vernal equinox counter-clockwise to the projection of the line of position into the ecliptic plane. The Solar System latitude is the angle between the spacecraft line of position and the ecliptic plane. An additional measurement will be required to fix the position of the spacecraft at a point on the l.o.p. This additional measurement may be obtained from observations of the distance from the spacecraft to the Sun (Reference 6.13). The methods of triangulation may also be extended to provide this additional measurement from a sighting of a nearby planet. This depends upon straight-forward geometry as illustrated in Figure 6.15. While the method described in the figure shows the measurement of position only, gyroscopic instruments may be applied to the mechanization of such a system to permit the observation of velocity data as well.

6.2.4 STEERING THE SPACECRAFT DURING ITS ASCENT

When an interplanetary transfer orbit has been specified in terms of the position and the velocity of the craft at the time of injection into a heliocentric orbit the spacecraft control system may be programmed to fly an ascent trajectory which will terminate in flight along the prescribed orbit. In theory, this will involve a flight control program which observes and matches six coordinates in space and the time. As a practical matter, however, the position of injection may be considered to be that of the departure planet at the time when injection occurs. The time of flight will not vary over so great a range as to require special allowance for these variations. Consequently, the transfer orbit may be defined by the three parameters which define the velocity vector at the time of injection. The nature of the transition between the hyperbolic escape orbit and the heliocentric transfer orbit will be shown to justify this simplification.

In order to place the spacecraft in its transfer orbit, it is launched on its ascent trajectory with the control system autopilot supervised from a pre-computed program. This program brings the spacecraft into the vicinity of the predicted injection point with its velocity approximately equal to that which is required to accomplish the transfer. If no further guidance or navigation were exercised, the craft would still be injected into an orbit which approximates the desired heliocentric orbit. The means for improving this approximation will be discussed in the following paragraphs.

The escape orbit is illustrated in the sketch of Figure 6.16. The escape trajectory will be specified in a plane by the specification of a point on its asymptote, the slope of the asymptote relative to the chosen line of apsides, and the hyperbolic excess velocity. These may be given in terms of the heliocentric flight conditions at the virtual launch point. The booster rocket will, generally, be shut down prior to attainment of the escape conditions. As a consequence, it will be necessary to take account of the effect which the gravity of the departure planet will have on the remainder of the trajectory until escape. Guidance computations must be made on the basis of flight conditions which are measured before escape may be considered to have occurred; these measurements are then used to calculate the flight conditions which would be obtained if the engine were to be shut down immediately. When suitable results are obtained, engine shut-off commands will be given. A steering doctrine must also be programmed for the autopilot to assure that the rocket will approach a point in space where the flight conditions are suitable for engine shut-down before the fuel is exhausted.

The transfer orbit will be specified in terms of the heliocentric velocity vector which is required at the virtual launch point. The hyperbolic excess velocity vector which will yield a specified value of the heliocentric velocity will be obtained from the relation

$$\mathbf{v}_\infty = \mathbf{V}_c - \mathbf{V}_\oplus \tag{6-24}$$

where

$\mathbf{V}_c$ = the heliocentric velocity required of the spacecraft after escape from its planet

$\mathbf{V}_\oplus$ = the heliocentric velocity of the Earth, or other applicable planet

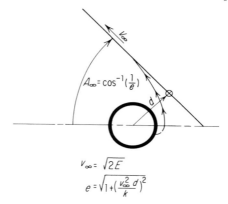

$$V_\infty = \sqrt{2E}$$

$$e = \sqrt{1 + \left(\frac{v_\infty^2 \, d}{k}\right)^2}$$

Fig. 6.16. Escape orbit.

The properties of the hyperbolic escape orbit may be inferred from the flight conditions which are specified for the heliocentric transfer orbit as follows.

1. The flight plane: The plane which represents a combination of the velocity of the craft with the heliocentric velocity of the departure planet to provide the desired heliocentric transfer orbit. Derivable from the vector relations of Equation (6-24).
2. Hyperbolic excess velocity: The magnitude of $\mathbf{v}_\infty$ as determined from Equation (6-24).
3. The slope of the asymptote: This is related to a selected reference line in space through the value of the eccentricity. The direction of the asymptote is established by the direction of the velocity vector at the virtual launch point. The line of apsides for the escape hyperbola will be in the flight plane and will make an angle to the asymptote so that

$$\cos A_\infty = \frac{-1}{e} \tag{6-25}$$

4. The asymptotic distance: This is related to the semi-latus rectum, p, and the angular momentum of the orbit as follows

$$d = \left(\frac{kp}{v_\infty^2}\right)^{1/2} = \frac{h}{v_\infty} \tag{6-26}$$

5. The time to launch: This time must be selected as suitable for the booster to place the spacecraft within an acceptable distance of the desired burn-out point. The tolerances on this burn-out point and the characteristics of the booster set these limits and thus determine the so-called *launch window*.

The control of the spacecraft in its ascent will be simplified by reduction of the number of flight coordinates which are subject to control. The critical parameters of the escape orbit which require control are (1) the flight plane, (2) the hyperbolic excess velocity, and (3) the slope of the asymptote. The asymptotic distance, d, is not considered to be critical here since its variation introduces only a second order perturbation to the heliocentric transfer orbit. Further, the nominal ascent flight program will be chosen in such a way as to place the spacecraft on a trajectory that is within a few miles of the desired asymptote. The time for launch is, of course, controlled by its very selection; ascent time variations introduce second order variations in the transfer errors and hence will not be considered further at this time. The effect of these errors on the transfer flight will be discussed in some detail in a later section.

Guidance for the spacecraft will employ a trajectory computer which uses the observed values of the flight path coordinates to calculate the critical parameters. These parameters are then compared to the desired values of e^Δ and v_∞^Δ for the desired ascent flight and the parameter errors, expressed by Δe and Δv_∞, are determined in a steering computer. The parameter errors are used to determine steering commands, $\Delta\varphi$, and the engine shut-down command, Δv_∞. A block diagram of the system to perform this is shown in Figure 6.17. The critical parameters are related to the measureable flight parameters by the following relations:

$$v_\infty = \frac{h}{d} = \frac{rv}{d}\cos\varphi \tag{6-27}$$

and

$$e^2 = \left[1 + \frac{(v^2 - 2k/r)r^2v^2\cos^2\varphi}{k^2}\right] \tag{6-28}$$

The control equations are obtained by differentiation. Since it is desired to steer the spacecraft until the velocity direction is correct for the desired orbit, the control equations are developed assuming that $\Delta r = 0$. The control equations are given by

$$\Delta v_\infty = \frac{rv}{d}\left[\cos\varphi\left(\frac{\Delta v}{v}\right) - \sin\varphi(\Delta\varphi)\right] \tag{6-29}$$

and

$$\Delta e = \frac{-(v^2 - 2k/r)r^2v^2}{k^2}\left[2\cos\varphi\left(\frac{\Delta v}{v}\right) + \sin 2\varphi\,(\Delta\varphi)\right] \tag{6-30}$$

The indicated parametric differences are made to vanish by steering commands which are computed from the solution of these Equations (6-29) and (6-30) when $\Delta v_\infty = \Delta e = 0$. The spacecraft is programmed for steering to adjust and maintain $\Delta = 0$ and when the velocity error vanishes, $\Delta v = 0$, the engines will be shut down.

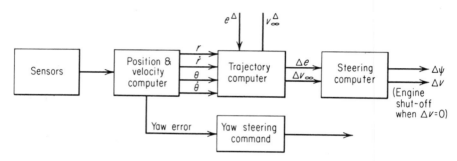

Fig. 6.17. Escape orbit guidance system.

6.3 ANALYSIS OF ERRORS IN INTERPLANETARY FLIGHT

In the previous section the three phases of flight, escape, heliocentric (mid-course), and terminal, were described. In each of these phases, where guidance is employed, errors in guidance are to be expected. These errors will, in general, occur early in the flight and their effects will be carried forward, or propagated, along the flight path in a manner that depends largely on the geometry of the transfer orbit. The errors obtained at the termination of one phase in the flight must be applied as initial errors in the following phase. Subsequent applications of guidance reduces the effect of errors which have been accumulated in the previous flight; the errors in the remaining flight must be reckoned in terms of a new set of initial errors which are realized at the conclusion of the mid-course guidance maneuver.

The errors occurring in the guidance of a spacecraft will be in the form of displacement errors (that is, errors in position), errors in velocity, and errors in timing. The application of first order error theory to these will assume that displacement and velocity errors can each be resolved into three orthogonal components. The six resulting error quantities and the timing error are assumed to be independent of one another and their effects are assumed not to interact. These assumptions simplify the error analysis but they also permit the isolation of the effects of specific forms, or sources, of inaccuracy in the guidance system for the purpose of evaluating guidance performance.

Displacement errors will appear in the form of radial errors, Δr; as errors in the true anomaly, $\Delta\theta$; and as out-of-plane errors, $\Delta Z'$. Velocity errors will be resolved into errors in magnitude, Δv; as errors in the flight path angle, $\Delta\varphi$; and as errors in velocity normal to the plane of flight, $\Delta\dot{Z}'$. The flight plane will be in error by an angle which is given by $\Delta i = \Delta\dot{Z}'/V$. Velocity direction errors will be the result of either of two sources. These are: (1) errors in the guidance and control system, its sensors or computer elements; and (2) errors in the directional reference for the guidance system and its sensors. At some points in the analysis it will be convenient to work with the velocity errors when they have been resolved in a cylindrical coordinate reference system. In this case, the error components will be radial, $\Delta\dot{r}$; tangential, $r\Delta\dot{\theta}$; and axial, $\Delta\dot{Z}'$.

Timing errors will be the result of clock errors in the guidance system or the result of accumulation of time in the trajectory which is different from the program which has been established in calculating the nominal flight path. In general, the errors in timing which cause guidance errors will be relatively small; they will be the result of inaccurate measurement of small intervals of time. The errors which are caused by a drift in the navigators chronometer can be corrected to within a few seconds by the use of frequent time checks with an astronomical observatory on the Earth, or elsewhere.

The effects of each class of errors described in the previous paragraphs will be analyzed for the ascent, or escape, flight in order to determine the effects of guidance errors during the powered flight when these are permitted to influence the subsequent phases of the flight. The results will be stated in a standardized form, that is they will be given in terms of the errors which are effective at the virtual launch point. The errors which are obtained at the virtual launch point will, in turn, be analyzed to determine the way in which they affect the flight in the vicinity of the terminal planet.

In the absence of a terminal guidance, the guidance errors will be measured in the vicinity of the destination by the *miss-distance*. The miss-distance will be determined by the errors in the heliocentric, or mid-course, flight; it is defined as the magnitude of the separation at the time of closest approach to the destination planet. When one, or more, mid-course corrections are employed, the errors which are the result of their execution will propagate in the same manner as though the mid-course guidance point were a new virtual launch point. Velocity errors in the vicinity of the terminal planet will not be evaluated here since they do not affect the miss distance directly. These errors do, however, introduce a first order interaction between time and position errors in the computation of the miss distance; errors of this kind have been treated in detail in Reference 6.14.

The following paragraphs will discuss these various errors in the context of each of the phases of flight. The means of interpreting these errors as displacements and velocity deviations at the virtual launch point will be presented. The evaluation of the miss distance in the vicinity of the destination planet will be described in some detail at the conclusion.

6.3.1 Errors in the Escape Phase

The errors which are obtained at the end of the escape phase of the interplanetary flight will be the result of errors in the guidance that cause inaccurate determination of the flight conditions at the termination of the rocket boost flight. These errors in guidance may be projected forward on the trajectory

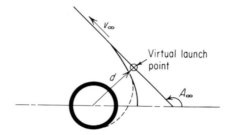

Fig. 6.18. Escape orbit.

to give a set of equivalent errors which may, in turn, be applied as initial conditions for the determination of the errors in the mid-course flight. The point which has been selected for the projection of errors in the escape is the *virtual launch point*. The virtual launch point has been defined in Section 6.2.1; it is a point on the asymptote of the escape hyperbola with minimum distance from the center of the Earth.

The coordinates of the virtual launch point will be defined in terms of the polar (cylindrical) coordinates from the center of the Earth, or other nearby planet, as follows, see Figure 6.18.

$$r^* = \frac{rv \cos \varphi}{(v^2 - 2k/r)^{1/2}} \tag{6-31}$$

where

$r^* = d =$ the radial distance from the center of the planet force field to the virtual launch point.

The virtual launch point is defined in such a way that the true anomaly corresponding to its position vector is unambiguous. Consequently, the errors in its true anomaly are assumed to vanish.

Position Errors

The errors in the position of the spacecraft at the virtual launch point are a fiction, however it will be possible to discuss the mid-course transfer trajectory in terms of the displacement of this point from the predicted, or nominal, value. The displacement of this point will be represented by the displacements in the slope and distance of the asymptote. The radial displacement of the virtual launch point as a result of variation of the flight conditions is obtained from differentiation of Equation (6-31)

$$\Delta r^* = \frac{rv \cos \varphi}{v_\infty} \left[\left(1 - \frac{V_c^2}{v_\infty^2} \right) \frac{\Delta r}{r} + \left(1 - \frac{V^2}{v_\infty^2} \right) \frac{\Delta v}{V} - \tan \varphi \Delta \varphi \right] \quad (6\text{-}32)$$

where

$$v_c^2 = \frac{k}{r}$$

The virtual launch point will be displaced tangentially as a result of changes in the slope of the asymptote. The angle between the line of apsides and the asymptote is shown in Figure 6.18. It is related to the flight parameters as follows

$$\cos A_\infty = \frac{-1}{e} \quad (6\text{-}33)$$

Variations in the boost to orbital flight will introduce an error in the slope of the asymptote. The polar angle from the line of apsides to the vertical passing through the virtual launch point is related to A_∞ as follows

$$A_t^* = A_\infty - \frac{\pi}{2}$$

$$\cos A_t^* = \sin A_\infty = \frac{(e^2 - 1)^{1/2}}{e}$$

$$\sin A_t^* = - \cos A_\infty = \frac{1}{e}$$

A change in the flight conditions which leads to a change in the orbit eccentricity will cause a tangential displacement of the virtual launch point which is given by

$$\Delta A_t^* = \frac{- \sin^2 A_t^*}{\cos A_t^*} \Delta e = \frac{- \Delta e}{e(e^2 - 1)^{1/2}} \quad (6\text{-}34)$$

The eccentricity of the orbit is related to the flight conditions by the expression

$$e^2 = 1 + p \left(\frac{v^2}{k} - \frac{2}{r} \right) \quad (6\text{-}35)$$

Differentiating Equation (6-35)

$$\Delta e = \frac{p}{ek}\left[\left(v^2 - \frac{k}{r}\right)\left(\frac{\Delta r}{r} + \frac{2\Delta v}{v}\right) - \left(v^2 - \frac{2k}{r}\right)\tan\varphi\Delta\varphi\right] \tag{6-36}$$

If preferred, Equation (6-36) may also be written

$$\Delta e = \frac{r^2 v^2 \cos^2\varphi}{ek^2}\left[\left(v^2 - v_c^2\right)\left(\frac{\Delta r}{r} + \frac{2\Delta v}{v}\right) - v_\infty^2 \tan\varphi\Delta\varphi\right] \tag{6-37}$$

When the substitutions indicated by Equations (6-34) and (6-37) have been made, the tangential displacement of the virtual launch point may then be calculated.

$$\Delta A_t^* = \frac{-r^2 v^2 \cos^2\varphi}{k^2 e^3 (e^2 - 1)^{1/2}}\left[\left(v^2 - v_c^2\right)\left(\frac{\Delta r}{r} + \frac{2\Delta v}{v}\right) - v_\infty^2 \tan\varphi\Delta\varphi\right] \tag{6-38}$$

The virtual launch point may be further displaced in the direction normal to the intended flight plane. This displacement will be related to the effective error in the flight azimuth by an amount given below.

$$\Delta Z' = r^* \sin\Delta Az \tag{6-39}$$

where

ΔAz = the error in the azimuth of flight which is effective at the time o booster burn-out.

Velocity Errors

The velocity of the spacecraft at the virtual launch point is taken as equal to the hyperbolic excess velocity, v_∞, in both magnitude and direction. The magnitude of v_∞ is given by the orbit relations discussed in Chapter 2. Specifically recall Equation (2-14)

$$E = \frac{v^2}{2} - \frac{k}{r}$$

The velocity at a very great distance will then approach the value

$$v_\infty = \sqrt{2E} = \sqrt{v^2 - \frac{2k}{r}} \tag{6-40}$$

From differentiation, the variations in hyperbolic excess velocity may be related to the flight conditions in the orbit.

$$\Delta v_\infty = \left(\frac{v}{v_\infty}\right)\Delta v + \left(\frac{k}{2v_\infty r^2}\right)\Delta r \tag{6-41}$$

The velocity direction, or flight path angle, at the virtual launch point will be determined by the orientation of the asymptote. The orientation of this line was mentioned with the discussion of the tangential displacement of the virtual launch point. The flight path angle, relative to the departure planet, at the virtual launch point will be zero because of the way in which this reference point is defined. Variations in the flight path due to variation in the ascent flight conditions may be assessed however, the variation in the flight path angle will be

$$\Delta\varphi = \Delta A_t^*$$

(6-42)

This was given previously in Equation (6-38)

Out-of-plane components of the velocity will be the direct result of errors within the guidance system. Consequently, analysis of these errors will depend upon a detailed knowledge of the guidance mode which is employed. The out of plane velocity component can, however, be related to an *effective* value of the misalignment of the guidance reference as follows

$$\Delta\dot{Z}' = v_\infty \sin\Delta Az$$

(6-43)

Timing Errors

The errors in the time of arrival at the virtual launch point will be the sum of two error components. These are (1) an error in launch time which reflects in errors in effecting lift-off at precisely the scheduled time; and (2) an error in the duration of booster flight. Error components of the first kind are the result of variations in operational procedures and will not be analyzed here. Error components of the second kind are related to the performance characteristics of the booster rocket and the way in which these are controlled by the autopilot system. The effect of timing errors is important for two reasons. First, the Earth is rotating in space about its North-South axis while the asymptote along which the spacecraft must escape is not rotating in space. Second, the virtual launch point is moving relative to the center of the Earth. The mode of this motion depends upon the detailed plans of the flight which is being anticipated but, in general, the virtual launch point may be considered to be in motion in the orbit of the departure planet.

The virtual launch point has been defined as a specific point on the asymptote of the escape orbit. In addition, it is a point of the mid-course transfer orbit which will provide the initial point for reckoning the interplanetary flight. In this sense, we may consider the virtual launch point to be a point in the orbit of the departure planet but which is moving in such a way as to maintain a constant difference in Solar System longitude (that is a constant transfer angle) from the destination planet. An estimate of the rate of motion of this point in space may be obtained by taking the angular velocity of the point in question to be the same as that of the destination planet, that is

$$\Omega^* = \frac{2\pi}{T_{\text{dest}}} \tag{6-44}$$

where

T_{dest} = the period of the destination planet which is assumed to be in an orbit that is approximately circular.

The velocity of the virtual launch point relative to the Earth will be given by

$$V^* = (\Omega^* - \Omega_\oplus)R_\oplus \tag{6-45}$$

$$= 2\pi R_\oplus \left(\frac{T_\oplus - T_{\text{dest}}}{T_\oplus T_{\text{dest}}} \right)$$

$$V^* = V_\oplus \left(\frac{T_\oplus - T_{\text{dest}}}{T_{\text{dest}}} \right) \tag{6-46}$$

Examples are shown on the graph of Figure 6.19.

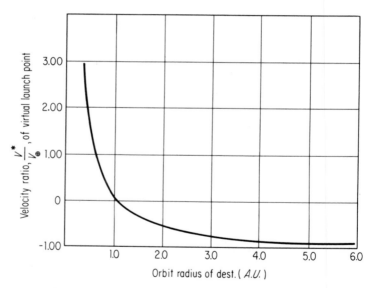

Fig. 6.19. Velocity of virtual launch point relative to Earth.

The ability of the craft to make adjustments of timing errors to account for the diurnal rotation of the Earth is a function of the booster performance and will depend upon the margin of performance which is available in the propulsion system. This can not be evaluated here; for information of this kind, the reader is referred to standard works on the mechanics of spaceflight, c.f. Reference 6.15.

6.3.2 Errors in the Mid-Course Flight

The mid-course transfer orbit will be a heliocentric conic (ellipse, parabola, or hyperbola) with a tangent coincident with the asymptote of the escape hyperbola. While the analysis of the escape orbit neglected the gravitational field

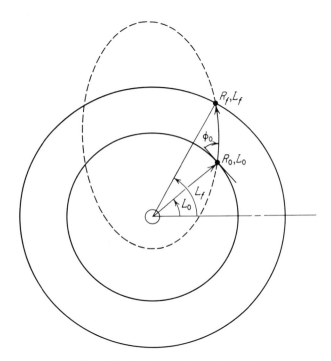

Fig. 6.20. Helicoentric transfer orbit.

of the Sun, the effects of this field were, indeed, taken into account. The escape orbit was analyzed in terms of motion relative to the Earth; the Earth is in free fall about the Sun and as a consequence its center is moving under the influence of solar gravity. No loss in accuracy results from the assumption that the spacecraft and the departure planet are both influenced by solar gravity in precisely the same manner during the escape.

The selection of an heliocentric transfer orbit has been discussed in Section 6.1.3. The orbit will be designed to be within the performance capability of the spacecraft boosters and to carry the vehicle in free fall, under the influence of solar gravity, from a designated initial point (the virtual launch point) to a specified terminal point where the vehicle will rendezvous with the destination planet, see Figure 6.20. A transfer orbit will usually be specified in terms of an initial point; R_0, L_0, Λ_0, and a final point; R_f, L_f, Λ_f, where R specifies the radial distance from the Sun, L gives the longitude of the point measured in the ecliptic plane from the Vernal Equinox, and Λ specifies the latitude measured vertically from the ecliptic plane. Most planetary orbits have inclination angles less than 4 deg; consequently, the values of Λ_0 and Λ_f will usually be small and may be neglected here. It should be noted, however, that although the latitude values are usually small at the initial and terminal points, the spacecraft transfer orbit may nevertheless be inclined to sufficient angle that it will pass through regions of relatively high latitude.

Both the departure and the destination planets are, themselves, in orbital motion about the Sun. Consequently, they will have relative motion which makes the selection of a transfer orbit a function of time. The mid-course transfer angle, $(L_f - L_0)$, and the configuration of the two planets at the time of take-off determine the time allowed for the transfer. The permissible transfer time will be determined from the geometry of this initial configuration as follows.

$$\tau = \frac{\Delta L_{\text{dest}}}{2\pi} T_{\text{dest}} \tag{6-47}$$

where

ΔL_{dest} = angle traversed by destination from initial to final points.

The criteria for the transfer orbit must, then, include passage through the two specified points with elapsed time precisely as specified in Equation (6-47).

The initial point of the mid-course orbit has been defined as the virtual launch point of the escape orbit. Although the craft does not actually pass through this point it is a useful reference position. The heliocentric orbit has such a large radius that a segment of that orbit in the vicinity of a departure planet may be considered to be a straight line. In order to assure coincidence of these two orbits (escape and mid-course), this straight line segment of the heliocentric orbit defines the direction of the vector representing the sum of the hyperbolic excess velocity, v_∞, and the orbit velocity of the departure planet, V. These two vectors are summed in space at the *virtual launch time*; this is the time at which the spacecraft would pass through the virtual launch point if it were travelling along the mid-course orbit unperturbed by the gravitational field of the departure planet. The geometry of this situation is illustrated in Figure 6.21. Because the departure planet is in relative motion with a free-fall point in the mid-course orbit, it is necessary to consider the virtual launch point to be a point in motion. This point will not be suitable as a launch point except at the instant it coincides with the asymptote of the escape orbit (the virtual launch time). The velocity with which this reference point crosses the heliocentric transfer orbit was discussed briefly in Section 6.3.1. The effect of errors due to timing of this intersection will depend upon the value which is chosen for the initial solar flight path angle, Φ_0. Since most of the planets are in orbits which are nearly circular, the optimum value of the solar flight path angle will frequently be approximated by $\Phi_0 = 0$; consequently, the virtual launch point will ordinarily approach and cross the path of the selected transfer orbit at a very small angle. The major effect of advanced, or delayed, arrival at the virtual launch point will appear as an advanced, or retarded, position in the mid-course transfer orbit.

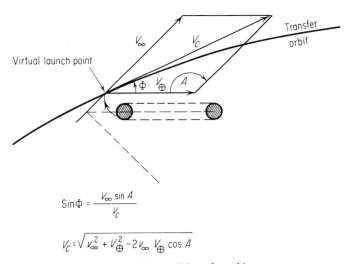

$$\mathrm{Sin}\,\Phi = \frac{V_\infty \sin A}{V_c}$$

$$V_c = \sqrt{V_\infty^2 + V_\oplus^2 - 2 V_\infty\, V_\oplus \cos A}$$

Fig. 6.21. Initial conditions for mid-course.

Errors in booster guidance can be transformed to provide the errors in the initial conditions of the heliocentric flight. The transformation will depend upon the way in which the orbit of the departure planet meets the transfer orbit. The transformations are indicated on Figure 6.22 which illustrates the geometry of this intersection. The initial conditions for the mid-course flight will be in error as a result of displacement of the virtual launch point due to guidance errors and also as a result of errors in the velocity of the spacecraft at the virtual launch point. These deviations in the initial conditions may be calculated by application of chain-rule differentiation to the transformation equations.

$$\Delta R^* = \sin\left(A_{tp}^* + \beta\right)\Delta r^* + r^* \cos\left(A_{tp}^* + \beta\right)(\Delta A_{tp}^* + \Delta\beta) \tag{6-48}$$

$$\Delta L^* = \cos\left(A_{tp}^* + \beta\right)\frac{\Delta r^*}{R_\oplus} - \frac{r^*}{R_\oplus}\sin\left(A_{tp}^* + \beta\right)(\Delta A_{tp}^* + \Delta\beta) \tag{6-49}$$

$$\Delta Z^* = \sin(l - l_n)\sin i\,\Delta r^* + r^*[\sin(l - l_n)\cos i\,\Delta i + \cos(l - l_n)\sin i\,\Delta(l - l_n)] \tag{6-50}$$

$$\Delta V_c^* = \frac{-v_\infty}{V_c}\,\Delta v_\infty \tag{6-51}$$

$$\Delta \Phi^* = \frac{1}{V_\oplus \cos \Phi_0}[\cos(A_{tp}^* + \beta - \Phi_0)\Delta v_\infty - v_\infty \sin(A_{tp}^* + \beta - \Phi_0)(\Delta A_{tp}^* + \Delta \beta)] \tag{6-52}$$

$$\Delta \dot{Z}^* = \Delta v_\infty \sin i + v_\infty \cos i\,\Delta i \tag{6-53}$$

where

R^* = the heliocentric position vector of the virtual launch point
L^* = the heliocentric longitude of the virtual launch point
Z^* = the axial distance of the virtual launch point from the ecliptic plane. (Cylindrical coordinate system)
V_c^* = the heliocentric velocity of the craft at the virtual launch point
Φ^* = the flight path angle of the craft with respect to the local (solar) horizontal at the virtual launch point
A_{tp}^* = the planetocentric true anomaly of the virtual launch point. (The added subscript will be used in the present context to avoid confusion.)

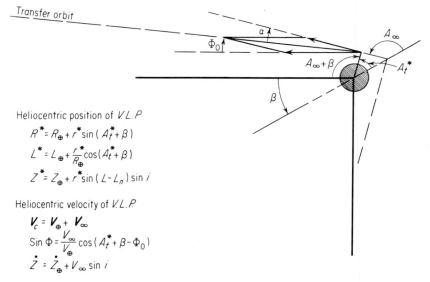

Heliocentric position of V.L.P
$R^* = R_\oplus + r^* \sin(A_t^* + \beta)$
$L^* = L_\oplus + \dfrac{r^*}{R_\oplus}\cos(A_t^* + \beta)$
$Z^* = Z_\oplus + r^* \sin(L - L_n)\sin i$

Heliocentric velocity of V.L.P
$V_c = V_\oplus + V_\infty$
$\sin \Phi = \dfrac{V_\infty}{V_\oplus}\cos(A_t^* + \beta - \Phi_0)$
$\dot{Z} = \dot{Z}_\oplus + V_\infty \sin i$

Fig. 6.22. Transformation—escape to mid-course.

The displaced initial flight conditions that are obtained from Equation (6-48) through (6-53) will, in turn, propagate as errors in the heliocentric orbit and their effects can be evaluated in terms of the displacement of the spacecraft from the intended rendezvous point; this point will be called the *reference point*. These effects in the vicinity of the reference point may be calculated in much the same way as the errors in the escape flight were calculated.

Position Errors

Before attempting to analyze the errors in position of the spacecraft, it will be necessary to consider the way in which the miss-distance is to be calculated from the reference point. This displacement may be computed in several ways. For example, one might consider the radial error which obtains when the longitude of the spacecraft is equal to the longitude of the reference point. On the other hand, one could count the miss-distance as the error in longitude which occurs when the radial distance is equal to that for the reference point. A third condition arises when we consider the miss-distance to be the displacement of the craft from the reference point after the predicted transfer time has elapsed. Combinations of these three possibilities might, of course, be considered. Each of these cases is treated in some detail in Reference 6.14, however we shall deal only with the displacement between the craft and the reference point which is reckoned when the longitude of the craft is equal to the longitude of the reference point. Consequently, in the following discussion, errors will be evaluated under the assumption that the error in longitude vanishes, that is

$$\Delta A_t = \Delta L_f = 0$$

The mid-course orbit satisfies the same orbit equation which was developed in Chapter 2, this is Equation (2-24)

$$R = \frac{P}{1 + e \cos A_t} \tag{2-24}$$

Differentiating Equation (2-24), we obtain the error equation for the radial displacement of the spacecraft from the nominal orbit as a function of the orbit parameters.

$$\Delta R = \frac{R\Delta P}{P} - \frac{R^2 \cos A_t}{P} \Delta e \tag{6-54}$$

The semi-latus rectum, P, for the orbit is related to the flight conditions obtaining at the virtual launch point by the equation

$$P = \frac{R^{*2}V^{*2} \cos^2 \Phi^*}{k} \tag{6-55}$$

Differentiating Equation (6-55)

$$\Delta P = \frac{2P\Delta R*}{R*} + \frac{2P\Delta V*}{V*} - P \tan \Phi * \Delta\Phi * \tag{6-56}$$

Equation (6-56) may also be stated in the alternative form

$$\Delta P = \frac{R*^2 V*^2 \cos^2 \Phi *}{k} \left[\frac{2\Delta R*}{R*} + \frac{2\Delta V*}{V*} - \tan \Phi * \Delta\Phi * \right] \tag{6-57}$$

The expression for the differential of the eccentricity was developed in the previous section; recall Equation (6-37)

$$\Delta e = \frac{R*^2 V*^2 \cos^2 \Phi *}{ek^2} \left[\left(V*^2 - V_c*^2 \right) \left(\frac{\Delta R*}{R*} + \frac{2\Delta V*}{V*} \right) \right.$$
$$\left. - (V*^2 - V_e*^2) \tan \Phi * \Delta\Phi * \right] \tag{6-37}$$

When Equations (6-54), (6-56) and (6-37) are combined, the expression for the radial displacement is obtained; it is

$$\Delta R = \frac{\Delta R*}{R*} \left[2R - \left(V*^2 - V_c*^2 \right) \left(\frac{R^2 \cos A_t}{ek} \right) \right]$$
$$+ \frac{2\Delta V*}{V*} \left[1 + \frac{R^2 \cos A_t}{ek} \left(V*^2 - \frac{k}{R*} \right) \right] \tag{6-58}$$
$$- \Delta\Phi * [1 - (V*^2 - V_e*^2)] \tan \Phi *$$

The out-of-plane component of the position of the spacecraft will be given as a function of the longitude of the craft by the expression

$$Z = R \sin(L - L_n) \sin I \tag{6-59}$$

where

$(L - L_n)$ = the longitude of the spacecraft relative to the longitude of the node between the transfer orbit and the reference plane

I = the inclination angle between the heliocentric orbit and the reference plane.

The displacement out of the reference plane will be sensitive to the parameters in the manner described by the equation

$$\Delta Z = \Delta R \sin(L - L_n) \sin I - R \sin(L - L_n) \cos I \, \Delta I$$
$$+ R \sin I \cos(L - L_n) \Delta(L - L_n) \tag{6-60}$$

Velocity Errors

The velocity of the spacecraft in the vicinity of the reference point may be calculated from the equations which express the conservation of energy and of angular momentum, that is

$$\frac{V^{*2}}{2} - \frac{k}{R^*} = \frac{V^2}{2} - \frac{k}{R} \tag{6-61}$$

$$R^* V^* \cos \Phi^* = RV \cos \Phi \tag{6-62}$$

Solving these equations, we obtain the velocity of the spacecraft at a point on the orbit in terms of the velocity and the flight path angle at the virtual launch point (or at any other guidance point for that matter)

$$V = \sqrt{V^{*2} + \frac{2k(R^* - R)}{RR^*}} \tag{6-63}$$

and

$$\cos \Phi = \frac{R^* V^* \cos \Phi^*}{RV} \tag{6-64}$$

The out-of-plane velocity is expressed by

$$\dot{Z} = V \cos \Phi \cos (L - L_n) \sin I \tag{6-65}$$

Differentiating the above expressions, we obtain

$$\Delta V = \frac{V^*}{V} \Delta V^* + \frac{k \Delta R^*}{VR^*} \tag{6-66}$$

and

$$\Delta \Phi = - \cot \Phi \left(\frac{\Delta R^*}{R^*} + \frac{\Delta V^*}{V^*} - \tan \Phi^* \Delta \Phi^* \right) \tag{6-67}$$

The out-of-plane component of the velocity error is likewise given by

$$\Delta \dot{Z} = \Delta V \cos \Phi \cos (L - L_n) \sin I$$
$$- V \sin \Phi \cos (L - L_n) \sin I \tag{6-68}$$
$$+ V \cos \Phi \cos (L - L_n) \cos I$$

Timing Errors

The transfer time for an interplanetary flight was discussed in a previous section; an expression was developed giving the transfer time as a function of the orbit parameters and the eccentric anomaly. This was expressed by Equation (6-8)

$$\tau = \frac{1}{n} [A_e - A_e^* + e(\sin A_e^* - \sin A_e)] \tag{6-8}$$

The time variations in the flight which arise as a result of guidance deviations from the nominal trajectory may be obtained by differentiation of Equation (6-8).

$$\Delta\tau = \frac{\tau\Delta n}{n} + \frac{1}{n}[(1 + e\cos A_e)\Delta A_e - (1 + e\cos A_e^*)\Delta A_e^* \\ + \Delta e(\sin A_e^* - \sin A_e)] \tag{6-69}$$

where

$$\Delta A_e = \sqrt{1 - e^2}\,\Delta A_t - \frac{\sin A_t}{\sqrt{1 - e^2}}\Delta e$$

$$\Delta A_e^* = \sqrt{1 - e^2}\,\Delta A_t^* - \frac{\sin A^*}{\sqrt{1 - e^2}}\Delta e$$

$$1 + e\cos A_e = \frac{(1 + e^2) + 2e\cos A_t}{1 + e\cos A_t}$$

$$1 + e\cos A_t^* = \frac{(1 + e^2) + 2e\cos A_t^*}{1 + e\cos A_t^*}$$

$$\sin A_e = \frac{\sqrt{1 - e^2}\,\sin A_t}{1 + e\cos A_t}$$

$$\sin A_e^* = \frac{\sqrt{1 - e^2}\,\sin A_t^*}{1 + e\cos A_t^*}$$

$$n = \sqrt{\frac{k}{|a^3|}} = \frac{k^2\sqrt{(1 - e^2)^3}}{R^{*3}V^{*3}\cos^3\Phi^*}$$

When the indicated substitutions have been made, Equation (6-69) has the form

$$\Delta\tau = \tau\Delta n + \frac{1}{n}\left\{\left[\frac{(1 + e^2) + 2e\cos A_t - \sqrt{1 - e^2}}{1 + e\cos A_t}\right]\sin A_t \\ + \left[\frac{(1 + e^2) - 2e\cos A_t^* - \sqrt{1 - e^2}}{1 + e\cos A^*}\right]\sin A_t^*\right\}\Delta e \\ + \frac{\sqrt{1 - e^2}}{n}\left\{\frac{(1 + e^2) + 2e\cos A_t}{1 + e\cos A_t}\Delta A_t - \frac{(1 + e^2) + 2e\cos A_t^*}{1 + e\cos A_t^*}\Delta A_t^*\right\} \tag{6-70}$$

where

$$\frac{\Delta n}{n} = 3\left[\frac{\Delta e}{1 - e^2} - \left(\frac{\Delta R^*}{R^*} + \frac{\Delta V^*}{V^*}\right) - \tan\Phi^*\,\Delta\Phi^*\right] \tag{6-71}$$

Further simplification of Equation (6-70) yields an alternative form as follows:

$$\Delta\tau = \frac{\tau\Delta n}{n} + \frac{1}{nP}[(1 + e^2 - \sqrt{1 - e^2})(R \sin A_t + R^* \sin A_t^*)$$

$$+ 2e(R \sin 2A_t + R^* \sin 2A_t^*)]\Delta e$$

$$+ \frac{\sqrt{1 - e^2}}{nP}\left\{[(1 - e^2) + 2e \cos A_t] R\Delta A_t\right.$$

$$\left. - [(1 + e^2) + 2e \cos A_t^*]R^* \Delta A_r^*\right\}$$

6.3.3 Calculation of the Miss Distance

The previous two sections have dealt with the problem of calculating the errors that occur in an interplanetary flight as a result of errors in the guidance and control systems. Section 6.3.1 discussed the errors in ascent flight with relation to a point of reference on the transfer orbit, that is, the virtual launch point. Section 6.3.2 showed how the flight deviations which obtain at the virtual launch point must be transformed to heliocentric coordinates for application as initial conditions to the mid-course transfer. The initial errors which were calculated for the virtual launch point must be extrapolated forward on the orbit to determine the effect which these will have on the encounter which occurs in the vicinity of the destination. This was done by finding the radial errors, the timing errors, and the out-of-plane errors which occur when the spacecraft is at a point on its orbit with solar longitude, L, equal to that of the chosen rendezvous point. This chosen point, called the *reference point*, is selected as the point where the nominal transfer orbit meets the orbit of the destination planet; it is also the position of the destination when the transfer time has elapsed. Consequently, if the transfer were to be performed with precision guidance and timing the reference point is precisely the point of impact where the spacecraft and the destination will meet.

The measure of navigation effectiveness which is of greatest interest is the *miss distance*. This is defined as the minimum value of the separation between spacecraft and the destination planet as they proceed along their respective orbits, each unperturbed by the other. The minimum separation will not usually occur at the time when the spacecraft longitude is equal to the longitude of the reference point. However, a knowledge of these errors and the relative motions of the two bodies in question will provide a useful estimate of the miss distance.

Although the orbits of most of the planets are inclined only a few degrees, or less, from the ecliptic plane, the transfer orbits may depart considerably from this range of inclinations. Consequently, the vectors which represent the velocity of the destination planet and the spacecraft will not generally be coplanar and it will be necessary to take account of the three-dimensional nature of the motion as well as the initial position and time displacements. The miss distance may be defined by a vector $\boldsymbol{\rho}_m$, whose magnitude will be given by the expression

$$\rho_m = \frac{|\Delta \mathbf{r} \times \Delta \mathbf{v}|}{\Delta v} \tag{6-72}$$

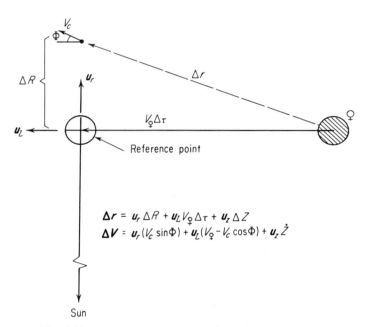

$$\Delta r = u_r \, \Delta R + u_L V_\varphi \Delta \tau + u_z \, \Delta Z$$
$$\Delta V = u_r (V_c \sin\Phi) + u_L (V_\varphi - V_c \cos\Phi) + u_z \dot{Z}$$

Fig. 6.23. Relative motions in vicinity of reference point.

where

$\Delta \mathbf{r}$ = the position vector of the destination planet observed relative to the spacecraft at reference

$\Delta \mathbf{v}$ = the velocity of the destination relative to the destination at reference

The relations of these vectors in a three-dimensional example are developed in detail in Reference 6.14.

The relative motions of the destination and the spacecraft are illustrated in Figure 6.23; the components of the relative position and velocity vectors are also shown in the figure. The miss distance is found from application of Equation

(6-72) where we make the substitutions

$$\mathbf{\Delta r} \times \mathbf{\Delta v} = \mathbf{u}_r[V_\varphi \Delta_\tau \dot{Z} - \Delta Z(V_\varphi - V_c \cos \Phi)] + \mathbf{u}_L[\Delta Z V_c \sin \Phi - \Delta R \dot{Z}]$$
$$+ \mathbf{u}_Z[\Delta R(V - V_c \cos \Phi) - V_\varphi \Delta_\tau V_c \sin \varphi] \qquad (6\text{-}73)$$

$$\Delta v = \sqrt{V_c^2 \sin^2 \Phi + (V_\varphi - V_c \cos \Phi)^2 + \dot{Z}^2} \qquad (6\text{-}74)$$

The above equations may be simplified in the case of a two-dimensional example to the following

$$\frac{|\mathbf{\Delta r} \times \mathbf{\Delta v}|}{\Delta v} = \sqrt{\frac{\Delta R(V_\varphi - V_c \cos \Phi)^2 + V_\varphi V_c \sin \Phi \Delta_\tau^2}{V_c^2 \sin^2 \Phi + (V_\varphi - V_c \cos \Phi)^2}} \qquad (6\text{-}75)$$

In the event that the errors are independent of one another, for example, when they are the result of the accumulated errors in several components and operating modes, the correlation of Equation (6-75) will not be valid and the errors should be summed by a statistical method. The most common statistical sum for this application is the Root Sum Square (RSS).

6.3.4. An Example of Interplanetary Flight

Previous sections have dealt with the methods for calculation of orbit parameters and the analysis of errors in an interplanetary flight. An example of such a flight will be discussed in this section; the effectiveness of navigation will be evaluated in terms of the errors at the destination, or reference point. The analysis will follow the methods which have been described in the previous paragraphs. The flight trajectories that have been chosen include some simplifying assumptions (for example the flight has been confined to the ecliptic plane), however, the example retains the essentials of the procedure which will be demonstrated adequately. In presenting this example, no attempt is made to provide an exhaustive analysis of guidance. To do this involves a computer study which evaluates miss distance as a function of guidance accuracy over a wide range of all the orbit parameters. Studies of this kind do not, in themselves, serve to demonstrate the methods which are employed. An example of this kind of analysis is described in Reference 6.17.

The example to be discussed here is one in which a spacecraft is transferred from a planet that is traveling in a circular orbit at $R = 1.0$ A.U. (An astronomical unit is a distance equal to the mean radius of the orbit of the Earth; it is equal to approximately 93,000,000 miles). The craft is launched into a transfer orbit which will carry it to another planet which is also in a circular orbit but has a radius of $R = 1.5$ A.U. The two planets are assumed to be in orbits which are coplanar; the transfer is further assumed to be one of cotangential departure, that is, $\Phi_0 = 0$ deg. These orbits are illustrated in Figure 6.24. The errors in the transfer have been calculated for transfer angles varying over the range from 120–170 deg. Analysis of the interplanetary transfer orbits yields the parameters that are shown in Table 6.3.

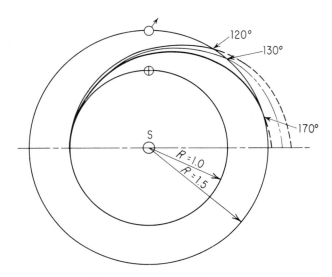

Fig. 6.24. Transfer orbits—Earth–Mars example.

The escape orbit characteristics have been calculated for an escape from the planet Earth on the basis of injection into the designated heliocentric orbits. In calculating the properties of these orbits burn-out has been assumed to occur at 400 miles above the surface of the Earth and at a true anomaly value of 30 deg.

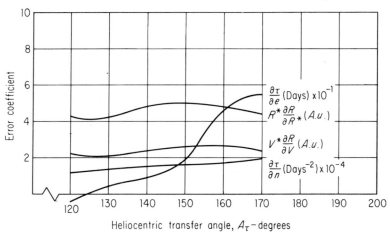

Fig. 6.25. Heliocentric error coefficients—Earth–Mars example.

Table 6.3. Orbit Parameters and Characteristics; Interplanetary Transfer From R = 1.0 to R = 1.5

(Assume: Circular-coplanar orbits with cotangential transfer and E = 0.25)

Transfer Angle	Semi major axis	Eccentricity	Angular momentum	n	Transfer time τ	V^*	v_∞	$V_{\text{Rel.}}$	$\Phi_{\text{Rel.}}$
degrees	A.U.	—	$(A.U.)^2/sec$	day	days	mi/sec	mi/sec	mi/sec	degrees
120	1.37	0.286	2.28×10^{-7}	0.0107	132.5	21.2	2.7	14.9	18
130	1.34	0.254	2.23×10^{-7}	0.0111	159	20.8	2.3	14.2	12
150	1.27	0.218	2.16×10^{-7}	0.0120	193	20.1	1.6	13.2	0
160	1.26	0.208	2.14×10^{-7}	0.0122	225	19.8	1.3	12.9	0
170	1.25	0.202	2.12×10^{-7}	0.0123	242	19.7	1.2	12.3	0

The orbit parameters for escape have been calculated and they appear in Table 6.4; error coefficients for these orbits have been shown graphically in Figure 6.25. The resultant errors which have been obtained at the virtual launch point are summarized in Table 6.5.

Table 6.4. Characteristics of Ascent Orbits for Example

Altitude of Burn-out = 400 miles True
Anomaly of Burn-out — 30 deg.

Heliocentric transfer angle	v_∞	v_p	h	p	r^*	e	$v_{B.O.}$
degrees	mi/sec	mi/sec	mi²/sec	mi	mi		mi/sec
120	2.7	7.44	29800	9240	1010	1.03	7.00
130	2.3	7.30	29200	8880	1270	1.02	6.88
150	1.6	7.09	28400	8400	1780	1.01	6.67
160	1.3	7.05	28200	8270	2170	1.01	6.63
170	1.2	7.03	28200	8210	2340	1.005	6.61

Flight path angle at burn-out = 15 deg
Heliocentric flight path angle at virtual launch point = 0 deg

Table 6.5. Summary of Errors in Ascent Trajectory

Earth–Mars example

Heliocentric transfer angle	Δr^*	ΔA_t^*	$r^* \Delta A_t^*$	Δv_∞	$\Delta \varphi^*$
degrees	mi	millirad	mi	mi/sec	millirad
120	18.06	— 4.05	— 178	0.00585	— 4.05
130	5.08	— 6.70	— 295	0.00681	— 6.70
150	— 65.83	— 13.5	— 595	0.00958	— 13.5
160	— 235.3	— 17.5	— 770	0.0118	— 17.5
170	— 245.2	— 18.8	— 828	0.0126	— 18.8

Assumed Guidance Accuracy:

$$\frac{\Delta r}{r} = 10^{-3}; \qquad \frac{\Delta v}{v} = 10^{-4}$$

The errors in the escape orbit which are shown in Table 6.5 are effective at the virtual launch point and are stated in planetocentric terms. These must be transformed to be stated with reference to a heliocentric reference system before they can be applied to an interplanetary orbit. These transformed errors are tabulated in Table 6.6. The errors in solar longitude which appear at the virtual launch point are so small that they have been neglected in this example.

The radial displacements of the craft position relative to the orbit of the destination planet at the reference point and the tangential displacement of the planet at the reference time are shown in Table 6.7; the error coefficients which apply to this portion of the trajectory are shown in the graph of Figure 6.26.

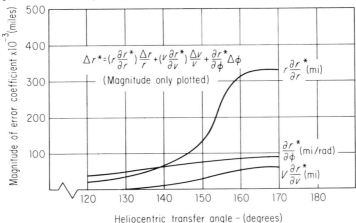

Fig. 6.26. Error coefficients for the ascent trajectory—Earth–Mars example.

Table 6.6. ERRORS IN ASCENT TRAJECTORY REFERRED TO HELIOCENTRIC COORDINATE SYSTEM

Earth–Mars example

Heliocentric Transfer angle	ΔR^*	ΔL^*	ΔV^*	$\Delta \varphi^*$
degrees	mi	rad.	mi/sec	millirad
120	18.06	94.6×10^{-6}	.000745	.292
130	5.08	94.6×10^{-6}	.000754	.248
150	-65.83	94.6×10^{-6}	.000762	.173
160	-235.3	94.6×10^{-6}	.000771	.141
170	-245.2	94.6×10^{-6}	.000771	.130

Assume: System alignment error $= 2 \times 10^{-3}$ rad. relative to Earth.

The possible configurations of the destination planet and the spacecraft in the vicinity of the reference point are illustrated in the diagram of Figure 6.27. The results of an error analysis of this kind provide a measure of the range over which a miss distance may vary; this is indicated by the shaded region of the figure. The statistical nature of this measure of variation will depend largely on the statistical nature of the errors which have been assumed for the guidance equipment and the manner in which these have been accumulated in the calculation.

Table 6.7. SUMMARY OF ERRORS AT REFERENCE POINT

Earth–Mars example

Heliocentric transfer angle	ΔR	$V_{\vartheta}\Delta\tau$	$\sqrt{\Delta R^2 + V^2_{\vartheta}\Delta\tau^2}$	V_{Rel}	Φ_{Rel}
(degrees)	miles	miles	miles	mi/sec	degrees
120	14600	1640	14700	0.1	18
130	13900	3180	14300	0.8	12
150	18800	6320	19800	1.8	0
160	19800	16850	26000	2.1	0
170	19700	19700	27900	2.7	0

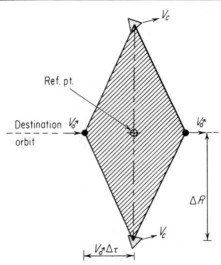

Fig. 6.27. Planet–spacecraft configuration in vicinity of destination showing error region.

When the errors in guidance can be measured at some point in the midcourse in order to provide a refinement of the orbit parameters, it will be possible to predict a specific miss vector in the manner that was discussed in the previous section. This miss vector may be used to form the basis for a mid-course correction. The means for applying these mid-course corrections will be discussed in the following section.

6.4 MID-COURSE CORRECTIONS

In the course of an interplanetary transfer, it may be desirable to adjust the orbit from time to time to make corrections for errors which are detected through measurements which can be made during the flight. These corrections, executed after ascent flight burn-out and prior to terminal maneuvers, will be called *mid-course corrections*. The application of mid-course corrections permits space navigation computations to be made on the basis of a series of measurements made over a long period of time. When mid-course corrections are anticipated a precise solution to the navigation problem will not be required during the brief thrusting interval. A further advantage will accrue from the use of mid-course corrections, the navigation system errors will behave in a manner similar to the errors in a closed loop control system, that is, they will be reduced with time as the navigation data base is increased and as the distance from the destination decreases. In a system which employs mid-course corrections, reliance is not placed on the precision computation of an orbit or the accuracy of the mathematical models used. Indeed, since most instruments may be employed in a mode where they become more accurate as the destination is approached, proper selection of instrumentation and computation techniques will relieve the need for extreme precision of individual measurements. When mid-course corrections are to be used, the errors in the vicinity of the reference point may be calculated in the same way as described in Section 6.3. The errors which are effective at the conclusion of the mid-course guidance maneuvers must be analyzed to determine the way in which they propagate along the remaining sector of the transfer orbit. These follow the same basic rules for error propagation as those which were described for the heliocentric transfer orbit in Section 6.3.3; the mid-course maneuver point is taken as a new virtual launch point with initial condition uncertainty equal to the uncertainty of the guidance system.

The techniques for application of terminal maneuvers, that is, maneuvers on approach to the destination which are made while under the gravitational influence of the destination planet, will not be discussed in this section. They will be the subject of a later section which will deal specifically with the problem of interplanetary homing. (Section 6.5). Before discussing the measurements that are required to compute mid-course corrections, the methods for calculation of these correction maneuvers will be discussed.

The application of mid-course corrections, of course, requires the use of propulsion and, hence, fuel margins must be provided for this purpose. Since the corrections will be applied to correct an orbit that has parameters which initially provided a miss distance within the uncertainty range of the guidance system, it is presumed that the correction maneuvers will be relatively small as a result of subsequent reduction in the uncertainty in the miss distance. Since the magnitude of these maneuvers will be small relative to the total impulse that was required for the journey, it follows that the criterion for application of the correction maneuver need not be minimum characteristic velocity. Rather, since one of the error sources in the mid-course correction will be the control of the direction and magnitude of the maneuver velocity increment, a suitable maneuver criterion might be that the sensitivity of the miss distance to an error in guidance and/or control of the maneuver should be acceptably low while still being high enough to permit corrections to be made within acceptable fuel margins. The evaluation of such a criterion will, of course, depend upon definition of the terms "high enough" and "acceptable fuel margins"; these terms must be defined relative to the specific design configuration of a spacecraft and hence will not be discussed further at this time.

Mid-course maneuvers will be computed to correct the transfer orbit parameters which are known to be in error as a result of measurements which are made on the flight conditions (position and velocity) during the flight. The means for determination of the orbit parameters as a result of the measurements were discussed in Chapter 3. Corrections will be assumed to be made by impulsive velocity maneuvers without abrupt changes in position. Consequently, it will be assumed that the corrections to the orbit parameters will be the result of velocity maneuvers only.

For the purpose of calculating mid-course corrections, it will be convenient to class errors in two groups which may be analyzed and corrected separately. These are the errors which produce a component of displacement from the reference point normal to the plane of the reference orbit and the errors which produce a component of the displacement which is in the reference plane. The plane of the spacecraft orbit is that plane which passes through the center of the Sun and is normal to the angular momentum vector. Errors in the orbit parameters which result in out-of-plane components of the miss vector may be corrected, then, by adjustments to the direction of the angular momentum vector. Displacements in the spacecraft relative to the destination planet which are in the plane of the transfer orbit may be adjusted by changes in the magnitude of the angular momentum vector. They will be radial errors, given by Equation (6-58), and tangential errors resulting from deviations in the transfer time. The effect of time errors, as tangential errors, are measured as

$$R_{ref}\Delta L = V_{\odot}\Delta\tau$$

Where $\Delta\tau$ is defined by Equation (6-70).

The out-of-plane errors will be considered first. As mentioned above, these errors are corrected by changes in the *direction* of the angular momentum vector. The angular momentum is given by the vector product

$$\mathbf{H} = \mathbf{R} \times \mathbf{V} \tag{6-76}$$

An orbit plane change will occur if the angular momentum is changed, such a change may be represented as

$$\mathbf{H} + \mathbf{dH} = (\mathbf{R} + \mathbf{dR}) \times (\mathbf{V} + \mathbf{dV})$$

$$= \mathbf{H} + \mathbf{R} \times \mathbf{dV} + \mathbf{dR} \times \mathbf{V} + \text{2nd order terms} \tag{6-77}$$

For purposes of mid-course corrections, it is desired to adjust the orbit plane of the spacecraft to one which contains the point which is currently occupied by the spacecraft and the point of reference, the maneuver will be assumed to be one of velocity impulse in which $dR = 0$. Consequently the corrective maneuver will be given by

$$\mathbf{dH} = \mathbf{R} \times \mathbf{dV}$$
$$= \mathbf{i}(R_y\,dV_z - R_z\,dV_y) + \mathbf{j}(R_z\,dV_x + R_x\,dV_z) + \mathbf{k}(R_x\,dV_y + R_y\,dV_x)$$

Since we are presently confining our interest to changes in angular momentum for the sole purpose of correcting out-of-plane errors, we shall assume that the in-plane components of the spacecraft velocity are correct, that is, $dV_x = dV_y = 0$. The components of the indicated change in angular momentum are then given by

$$\mathbf{dH} = \mathbf{i}(R_y\,dV_z) - \mathbf{j}(R_x\,dV_z) \tag{6-78}$$

Velocity maneuvers which produce a component of $\mathbf{dH}$ which is parallel to the x axis will cause a precession of the orbit plane and hence will shift the line of nodes defined by the spacecraft orbit and the orbit of the destination planet. Velocity maneuvers which produce a component of $\mathbf{dH}$ which is parallel to the y axis will cause a change in the orbit inclination angle, I. Since the transfer orbit will be designed to have a node with the destination orbit at the reference point, the appropriate correction maneuver will be one which precesses the orbit node until it coincides with the reference point. The change in the orbit node will be given by

$$\Delta L_n = \frac{\mathbf{i} \cdot \mathbf{dH}}{H} \tag{6-79}$$

and the change in the inclination angle will be given by

$$\Delta I = \frac{\mathbf{j} \cdot \mathbf{dH}}{H} \tag{6-80}$$

The anticipated out-of-plane error is given by Equation (6-60), however, at the reference point we assume that

$$\Delta R_{\text{ref}} = \Delta L_{\text{ref}} = 0$$

hence the out-of-plane component of the error will be given by

$$\Delta Z = R_{\text{ref}} \cos I \sin(L_{\text{ref}} - L_n)\Delta I + \sin I \cos(L_{\text{ref}} - L_n)\Delta L_n \tag{6-81}$$

Mid-course corrections to the orbit plane may be made by precessing the orbit until the transfer orbit-destination orbit node is placed at the reference longitude. Since the planet orbit inclination will generally be small, a precession of the nodes in the ecliptic plane will produce a like angle of precession of the transfer orbit when measured in the plane of the destination planet orbit. The indicated correction angle will then be a precession as follows

$$\Delta L_n = \frac{\Delta Z_{\text{ref}}}{R_{\text{ref}} \sin I \cos (L_{\text{ref}} - L_n)} = \frac{\mathbf{i} \cdot \mathbf{dH}}{H} \tag{6-82}$$

and the velocity impulse which will give the desired correction will be

$$dV_z = \frac{\Delta Z_{\text{ref}} V}{R_{\text{ref}} \sin I \cos (L_{\text{ref}} - L_n)} \tag{6-83}$$

It should be noted here that the efficiency of this maneuver will be affected by the longitude at which the maneuver is executed relative to the longitude of the node of the orbit. For example when the correction is made at the nodal point, the entire effect is a change in the orbit inclination. Similarly, a maneuver which is made at a point where $(L - L_n) = \pi/2$ (or any integral multiple of $\pi/2$) will produce only precession of the nodes and none of the velocity impulse will be effective in changing the orbit inclination.

In the discussion which follows, the correction of in-plane errors will be treated as maneuvers which are confined to the plane of the orbit. Out-of-plane errors will be assumed to have been corrected in advance. The vector representing the least separation between the spacecraft and the destination planet is called the miss distance and is given by the expression of Equation (6-72). When the out-of-plane errors have been corrected, the two remaining components of the miss vector will be the radial and the tangential components of the miss distance respectively. The radial errors at the reference point are defined by Equation (6-58) and the errors in the transfer time are given by Equation (6-70). Tangential errors are related to the timing errors by an equation that is shown above. The direction and magnitude of the mid-course correction for in-plane errors will be calculated, then, from the simultaneous solution of the following set of equations.

$$\frac{\partial R}{\partial V} dV* + \frac{\partial R}{\partial \Phi} d\Phi* = \mathbf{u}_R \cdot \boldsymbol{\rho} \tag{6-84}$$

$$V_\text{\textcirclesolid}\left(\frac{\partial \tau}{\partial V} dV* + \frac{\partial \tau}{\partial \Phi} d\Phi* \right) = \mathbf{u}_L \cdot \boldsymbol{\rho} \tag{6-85}$$

where

$dV*$ = the maneuver velocity increment
$d\Phi*$ = the change in the flight path resulting from the maneuver

$$\frac{\partial R}{\partial V} = \frac{1}{V}\left[1 + \frac{R^2 \cos A_t}{ek}\left(V*^2 - \frac{k}{R*} \right) \right]$$

$$\frac{\partial R}{\partial \Phi} = -\left(1 - V*^2 + \frac{2k}{R*} \right) \tan \Phi*$$

$V_{\venus}$ $\doteq$ velocity of destination planet

R^*V^* = flight conditions at maneuver point

$\dfrac{\partial \tau}{\partial V},\ \dfrac{\partial \tau}{\partial \Phi}$ may be calculated from Equation (6-69).

Solving these equations we obtain the following result.

$$dV^* = \frac{V_{\venus}(\mathbf{u}_R \cdot \boldsymbol{\rho})\,\partial \tau/\partial \Phi - (\mathbf{u}_L \cdot \boldsymbol{\rho})(\partial R/\partial \Phi)}{(\partial R/\partial V)(\partial \tau/\partial \Phi) - (\partial R/\partial \Phi)(\partial \tau/\partial V)} \tag{6-86}$$

$$d\Phi^* = \frac{(\mathbf{u}_L \cdot \boldsymbol{\rho})\,\partial R/\partial V - V_{\venus}(\mathbf{u}_R \cdot \boldsymbol{\rho})\,\partial \tau/\partial V}{(\partial R/\partial V)(\partial \tau/\partial \Phi) - (\partial R/\partial \Phi)(\partial \tau/\partial V)} \tag{6-87}$$

The geometric relations of the maneuver are illustrated in the sketch of Figure 6.28. For maneuvers which are of a reasonably small size, $d\Phi^*$ will be small and the maneuver may be approximated as follows

$$dV^* = \left(\frac{T}{M}\right) dt \cos \alpha$$

$$V^* d\Phi^* = \left(\frac{T}{M}\right) dt \sin \alpha$$

where

T = the rocket thrust applied
M = the mass of the rocket craft
dt = the time increment for firing the rocket
α = the angle between the velocity vector before the maneuver and the thrust vector (see Figure 6.28.)

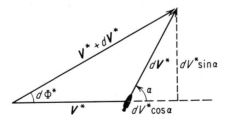

Fig. 6.28. The geometry of the mid-course maneuver.

An example of the general configuration of a mid-course navigation correction computer is indicated in Figure 6.29. Reference is made to other celestial bodies, or to inertial instruments, in order to permit computation of the parameters of the orbit which is being followed by the spacecraft. This orbit is then evaluated to forecast the component miss distances at the destination orbit. A Navigation computer commands the corrective maneuver that will be required to eliminate the predicted miss vector.

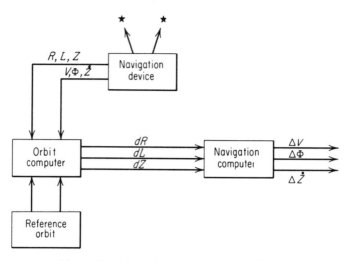

Fig. 6.29. Schematic of a mid-course guidance.

6.5 GUIDANCE FOR ENTRY AND LANDING

The discussions of the previous sections indicate the precision which will be required of interplanetary guidance and navigation systems if the entire navigation problem is to be solved in the vicinity of the departure planet or at a point that is remote from the destination. It is, of course, theoretically possible for an interplanetary spacecraft to be given a controlled boost at the beginning of its flight and subsequently to coast over great distance on a trajectory which is designed to terminate with approach conditions appropriate for landing at the destination. This does not now appear to be within the predictable state of the art; consequently, specific attention has been given to the problem of steering a spacecraft into a suitable landing trajectory as it approaches its destination. In this section this will be referred to as the *homing problem*. The discussion here is confined to a planar encounter, however, no loss in generality results since the chosen plane is defined by the vector representing the approach velocity and by the point at the center of attraction of the destination planet. For many examples, there will be no need to execute maneuvers which will change this plane; however, these maneuvers are given brief consideration later. The homing problem will be treated in terms of relative motion of the spacecraft when referred to the destination planet. The solar gravity field need not be

considered explicitly since the relative motion form of analysis considers the
solar gravity in the same way as it was treated in the analyses of Section 6.3.

Homing is concerned with the guidance and control of a spacecraft to direct
it into an approach trajectory which is suitable for termination of the mission at
the destination planet. It will be assumed here that landing is the desired
terminal maneuver, however, it should be apparent that a number of other

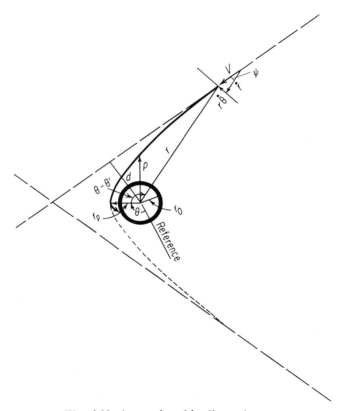

Fig. 6.30. Approach and landing trajectory.

maneuvers in the vicinity of the destination planet can be controlled in the same
manner. Landing will be considered in a broad sense of the term and will not
deal with touch-down maneuvers. The maneuvers that are required to convert
the hyperbolic approach orbit which develops as the spacecraft begins to
respond to the influence of the gravitational field of its destination to an orbit
which leads to safe penetration of the planetary atmosphere will be studied.
The criteria for a satisfactory landing trajectory are developed and discussed
in Reference 6.4 where the concept of a landing corridor is presented and

analyzed. These corridors have been defined in terms of the parameters of the approach trajectory. Safe landing paths are correlated with the configuration of the spacecraft and with the altitude of the *Keplerian periapsis* for the approach trajectory. This is the periapsis (point of closest approach) which would occur if the approach trajectory were not perturbed by the effects of atmospheric drag. Using this correlation, the control of the spacecraft to place it in a landing path will be accomplished if it is controlled in such a way as to place its Keplerian periapsis within a designated landing corridor. This is accomplished by maneuvers which modify the approach trajectory until the orbit relations which may be measured indicate a value of the periapsis radius, r_p, and the velocity, v_p, which are within the indicated landing corridor (see Figure 6.30). The characteristics of the corridor must be determined with reference to the specific planet, its gravity and the properties of the atmosphere, and the configuration of the spacecraft under consideration. These will not be discussed here but rather the landing trajectory will be discussed with the periapsis altitude treated parametrically.

For purposes of analysis and discussion, the homing problem may be divided into three distinct sub-problems; these are described below.

First Application of Corrections

The first corrections should be applied at a point which has sufficient distance to assure that the trajectory will close with the destination permitting fine corrections to be applied at a later time. The first correction is rather simple in application and it will be seen that, for best results, it should be performed at the greatest possible distance from the destination planet to conserve fuel. This distance is limited by the accuracy with which the correction can be computed and applied.

Second Correction

The second correction adjusts the approach trajectory causing it to pass through the narrow landing corridor. It will be seen that this correction should be applied close to the planet when precision measurements of the trajectory will be feasible. Without the first correction, excessive propulsion energy might be required to perform the second correction.

Final Descent

A third maneuver is required to convert the approach orbit from one which has periapsis in the chosen landing corridor to one which actually lands. This may be accomplished by rocket deceleration, (indeed this will be needed when landing is planned on a planet without atmosphere), or it may be accomplished by use of atmosphere-induced drag forces. Since the latter possibility represents the case of greatest efficiency, the following discussions will assume this to be the planned landing mode.

Since the consequences of an inaccurate solution to the homing problem are considered to be intolerable, the use of an open loop solution will be rejected here in favor of a closed loop guidance system in which the flight conditions are continuously monitored and corrections applied as needed. A closed loop system of this kind requires that a suitable prediction system be provided to permit on-board forecasting of the motions of the spacecraft. Corrections may be introduced through application of continuous thrust or through impulses which are applied at selected intervals. A theory of optimum spacing of the correction intervals is discussed in Reference 6.18.

It will be convenient to discuss the homing problem with reference to the requirements which are applicable to these individual steps. They will be treated in the reverse order taking the final maneuver first. The optimum time for conversion from a hyperbolic arc approach trajectory to a planetary orbit or a landing ellipse may be shown to be at the Keplerian periapsis where $r = r_p$. (See Reference 6.20). For all members of an approach trajectory family, each may be identified with a parameter e, and the velocity of the spacecraft at periapsis will be given by

$$v_p = \left[(1 + e) \frac{k}{r_p} \right]^{1/2} \tag{6-88}$$

If the value of r_p is selected properly for the planet concerned and for the configuration of the spacecraft under consideration, then the trajectory which will be followed by the spacecraft is one for which atmospheric drag will contribute the decelerations needed for a safe landing and the on-board environment will not exceed that for a crew. (Reference 6.4). It will be necessary, then, to control the vehicle in its transition trajectory to provide the hyperbolic approach arc which is associated with the appropriate Keplerian periapsis.

The accuracy of an interplanetary transfer orbit has been studied and error analysis expressing the dispersion in the parameters of an approach trajectory has been treated in Section 6.3. The uncertainty in the miss distance for a field-free encounter has been shown to be large. The analysis of the example discussed in Section 6.3.4 indicates, for example, that the uncertainty in the mid-course trajectory will lead to probable errors at the destination of the order of 20,000 miles. The accuracy of guidance needed for landing control can be derived from the work of Chapman (Reference 6.4), who discussed the narrow landing corridors. While these corridors are, to some degree, a function of the spacecraft configuration, we shall consider only the case of vehicles of the ballistic re-entry type (that is, those having $L/D = 0$). For this class of vehicles, the landing corridors are represented at the trajectory periapsis by narrow bands of altitude of about 5 to 10 miles in width. (Reference 6.4). The corridor mentioned is characteristic of the Earth and its neighbor planet Venus.

The homing problem, then, is to provide control of a spacecraft as it approaches its destination and to steer it into a landing corridor. It may be observed to be in a course which differs as much as 20,000 miles from a collision course and the homing guidance must bring it into the landing corridor which is perhaps 10 miles wide at the periapsis. As if this were not a task of sufficient magnitude, this must be done under the increasing influence of the gravity field of the destination planet thus requiring that the effects of this force be taken into account in making the corrections.

6.5.1 DYNAMICS OF THE APPROACH TRAJECTORY

As the mid-course flight progresses, the spacecraft will begin to approach the destination planet where its motions will be strongly influenced by the gravity fields of both the destination planet and the Sun. Since the analysis will consider the motions of the spacecraft relative to the planet, it requires that consideration be given to the gravity field of the planet. For example, a spacecraft approaching Venus at a distance of 100 planet radii (400,000 miles) will experience a solar gravity acceleration which differs from that acting on the planet by an amount less than 1 per cent. The acceleration arising from such a differential in solar gravity is about one tenth of that which is due to the planet directly. Unlike the planet field, this differential term vanishes as the spacecraft approaches the planet, consequently, the effects of solar gravity may be neglected. The trajectory followed by the spacecraft will thus be considered to be determined entirely by the planet gravity and the initial conditions of motion. The planar trajectory may be described mathematically relative to the planet in terms of three parameters. For reasons of convenience, the semi-latus rectum, p, the eccentricity, e, and the argument to periapsis, θ_p, have been chosen. The equation involving the true anomaly, $(\theta - \theta_p)$ will not be required to calculate the corrections for landing unless a specific landing site is demanded. This parameter will not be given further consideration here since it is felt that to include this relation will unduly complicate the problem. Post-entry maneuvers and a capability for soaring are probably more practical as a means of reaching a specific landing site.

The parameters that have been chosen to describe the approach trajectory may be expressed in the coordinates which are used to describe the spacecraft position and velocity relative to the Earth. These coordinates are illustrated in Figure 6.30.

the semi-latus rectum

$$p = r_p(1 + e) = \frac{r^4 \dot{\theta}^2}{k} \tag{6-89}$$

the eccentricity

$$e = \sqrt{1 + p\left(\frac{\dot{r}^2 + r^2\dot{\theta}^2}{k} - \frac{2}{r}\right)} \tag{6-90}$$

the orientation of the line of apsides

$$\frac{er}{p}\sin(\theta - \theta_p) = \frac{\dot{r}}{r\dot{\theta}} = \frac{1}{\tan\varphi} \tag{6-91}$$

Using the first of these two relations, it is possible to predict the altitude of periapsis by measurements of the altitude, the altitude rate, and the turning rate of the line of sight to the destination planet from the spacecraft. The periapsis is given by the relationship

$$r_p = \frac{r^4\dot{\theta}^2}{k\left[1 + \sqrt{1 + \dfrac{r^4\dot{\theta}^2}{k}\left(\dfrac{\dot{r}^2 + r^2\dot{\theta}^2}{k} - \dfrac{2}{r}\right)}\right]} \tag{6-92}$$

By adjusting these coordinates, it will be possible to control the periapsis to bring it into coincidence with the value that is appropriate for the landing corridor.

Homing guidance requires that measurements be made to determine the difference between the periapsis of the approach trajectory and the center of the specified landing corridor. These deviations will be expressed in terms of the orbit parameters by

$$\Delta r_p = \frac{\partial r_p}{\partial r}dr + \frac{\partial r_p}{\partial \dot{r}}d\dot{r} + \frac{\partial r_p}{\partial \theta}d\theta \tag{6-93}$$

Differentiation of Equations (6-89) and (6-90) will permit the error coefficients to be written as

$$\frac{\partial r_p}{\partial r} = \frac{2r_p(1 + e)}{re} - \frac{r\dot{\theta}^2}{g_pe} - \frac{r_p^2}{er^2} \tag{6-94}$$

$$\frac{\partial r_p}{\partial \dot{r}} = -\frac{\dot{r}}{eg_p}, \tag{6-95}$$

$$\frac{\partial r_p}{\partial \theta} = \frac{1}{\dot{\theta}}\left[r_p\left(\frac{1 + e}{e}\right) - \frac{r^2\dot{\theta}^2}{eg_p}\right] \tag{6-96}$$

The homing navigation system will be required to make observations and to determine the magnitude of Δr_p in order to place the trajectory within the landing corridor. The characteristic velocity of these maneuvers should be minimized in order not to make the fuel demands so great as to jeopardize the success of the mission. Accordingly, it will then be desirable that all corrections to the velocity direction be made at the greatest distance possible from the destination planet. The corrections will then be made when the required direction changes are small and before the gravity field of the planet has caused excessive increase in the relative velocity between the planet and spacecraft. The craft must be close enough to its destination, however, to be able to sense and compute the correction needed with sufficient accuracy. On this basis it is apparently desirable to make corrections in two or more steps. These steps are in the nature of coarse and fine corrections as follows:

Step 1: A correction, which is made at a great distance ($r/r_0 = 100$) which modifies the trajectory to place the periapsis at approximately the altitude of the landing corridor.

Step 2: A correction, or series of corrections, to place r_p precisely within the landing corridor and to maintain it there.

A detailed development of this theory of multiple step homing guidance is presented in Reference 6.18.

The technique for control will be illustrated by means of an example. Assume that a spacecraft is approaching its destination and has sensed the need for a correction in the predicted periapsis as expressed by Equation (6-92). The correcting maneuver is specified by Equation (6-93). The maneuver will be specified in terms of velocity increments which are independant; one increment is parallel to the line of sight to the planet and the other is perpendicular to this line of sight. Since this line of sight presents a convenient reference line, it will be used for instrumentation purposes. The possibility of an impulsive change in the vehicle position will not be considered. Consequently, the adjustment in periapsis which will result from a change in the velocity vector is given by

$$\Delta r_p = - \frac{\dot{r}}{e g_p} dv_\parallel + \frac{1}{r\dot{\theta}} \left[r_p \left(\frac{1+e}{e} \right) - \frac{(r\dot{\theta})^2}{e g_p} \right] dv_\perp \qquad (6\text{-}97)$$

where

$dv_\parallel$ = the velocity increment parallel to the line of sight
$dv_\perp$ = the velocity increment perpendicular to the line of sight.

The coefficients of $dv_\parallel$ and $dv_\perp$ have been calculated for a typical range of variables and have been shown in Figures 6.31 and 6.32. In general, the correction velocity vector in the orbit plane will make an angle with the line of sight to the destination such that

$$\tan \psi = \frac{\partial r_p / \partial r\dot{\theta}}{\partial r_p / \partial \dot{r}} \qquad (6\text{-}98)$$

When tangential velocity is low, that is, at very great distance from the center of gravitational attraction of the destination planet, corrections should be made substantially in the cross velocity direction only.

For purposes of a specific example, we have selected a typical flight plan from the tables of Reference 6.7. This flight plan is summarized in Table 6.8. These

parameters may be used to determine the guidance coefficients for the approach
flight.

After Step 1 has been executed as described above and as the vehicle
approaches its destination, an on-board computer will calculate the periapsis
of the trajectory to determine the final correction, or corrections, needed to

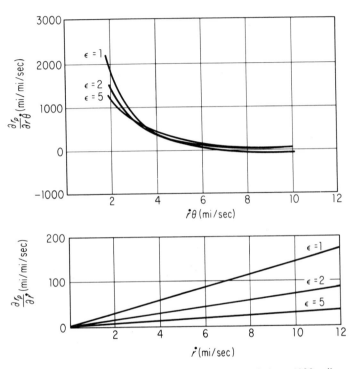

Fig. 6.31. Guidance coefficients Earth approach ($r_p = 4100$ mi)

Table 6.8. HOMING GUIDANCE PARAMETERS–EARTH TO MARS EXAMPLE

Parameter	Mars	Earth
1. Date of approach	September 1, 1966	November 1, 1967
2. Transit time (days)	260.	382.
3. Hyperbolic excess velocity (mi/sec)	3.7	7.4
4. Eccentricity ($p = 10^5$ mi)	4.2	7.8
5. Flight path angle (rad) ($r/r_0 = 100$)	0.0313	0.111
6. Radial velocity (mi/sec)	4.16	7.75
7. Tangential velocity (mi/sec)	0.131	0.866
8. $\partial r_p / \partial \dot{r}$ (mi/mi/sec)	410.	165.
9. $\partial r_p / \partial r\dot{\theta}$ (mi/mi/sec)	20,200.	5380.

place the vehicle in a desired landing corridor. This correction is computed with the use of Equation (6-97). The orientation of the thrust vector during the correction will depend upon the relative magnitude of the two guidance coefficients at the time of execution of the command. The velocity and the flight

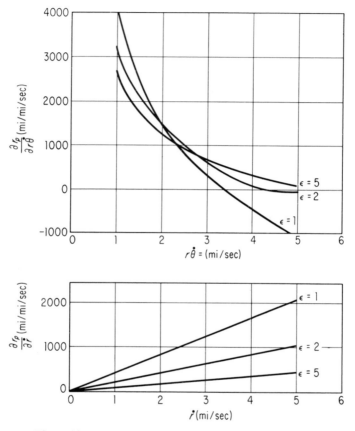

Fig. 6.32. Guidance coefficients Mars approach ($r_p = 2300$ mi)

path angle for the post-Step 1 trajectory in the examples are shown in Figures 6.33 and 6.34; these data have been used to calculate the guidance coefficients along the new Earth-approach trajectory. The guidance coefficients indicate that maneuvers which will change the velocity direction are favored for the greater distances from the destination (see Figure 6.35). Final corrections to the trajectory that are made near the periapsis should be made by adjustment of the velocity magnitude.

The analysis that has been described thus far has not considered corrections

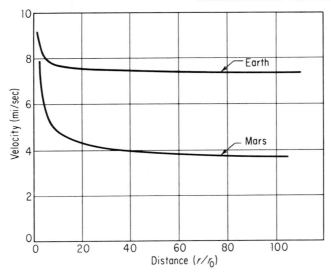

Fig. 6.33. Approach velocities for the example shown in Table 1.

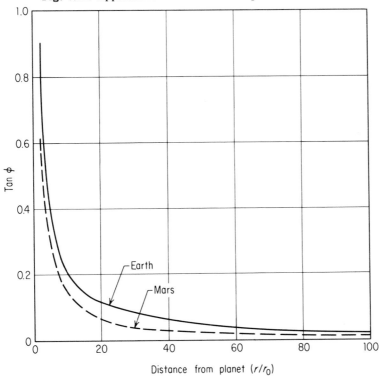

Fig. 6.34. Flight-path angle on approach trajectory.

to the plane of the trajectory. It is possible to extend this homing concept to provide a determination of the maneuvers that are required to place the vehicle into another trajectory plane. This correction capability will permit a two-dimensional freedom in the selection of a landing site. It will not be necessary to select a landing site from within the plane of the approach trajectory. By extensions of this technique of homing it is possible to place the vehicle in a path through any desired point. For landing purposes, however, it will normally be adequate to consider only the altitude of the periapsis and the inclination of the approach trajectory plane. Final landing adjustments may then be made after entry into the planetary atmosphere.

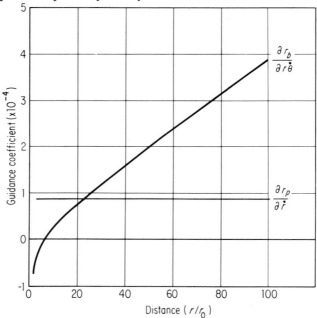

Fig. 6.35. Guidance coefficients along an Earth approach trajectory.

In order to rotate the trajectory plane through an angle λ, a new velocity maneuver, dv_z, must be introduced. This maneuver is directed normal to the orbit plane, along the z axis, with a magnitude

$$dv_z = v \sin \varphi \sin \lambda \tag{6-99}$$

The magnitude of this velocity correction will be minimized if it is executed at a point which is distant from the planet and when $v \sin \phi = r\dot{\theta}$ is at a minimum. This three-dimensional correction can be accomplished in a single maneuver if desired. The magnitude of the maneuver velocity and its direction will be a function of the actual change in periapsis required, but the velocity increment will be minimized only if the maneuver is executed in a plane called the *critical plane*. This plane is defined as the plane containing the normal to the trajectory plane and the velocity vector for the optimal correction to the periapsis as defined by Equation (6-98).

6.5.2 Instrumentation of the Homing Guidance

In the previous section, the nature of the homing problem was discussed and a mathematical model was presented for the computation of maneuvers to modify an interplanetary transfer orbit so that it will pass through a corridor which sets the conditions for an air-drag entry. Measurements of range r, range rate $\dot{r}$, and the rate of change of the line of sight, $\dot{\theta}$, are required in order to compute the necessary flight parameters for determination of the maneuvers required. In this section, a configuration of instruments suitable for the measurement of these coordinates will be described.

Before discussing a particular configuration of instruments, a few comments will be made relative to the means that are available for the measurement of the individual coordinates which are needed to define the trajectory and to predict the periapsis.

Range to Destination (r)

The use of radar methods for this measurement would be desirable provided sufficient signal strength could be reflected from the planet. Where a radar beacon may be located on the planet in advance, this would certainly be feasible; however, in many cases this will not be so. It will be assumed that surface reflection from the planet must be used with a radar set. The result of a typical calculation of radar range is illustrated in Figure 6.36; it shows that the average transmitted power must be in the megawatt regime in order to permit range sensing at distances up to 400,000 miles. At the distances where the homing observations must be made, optical measurements of the planetary disk appear to be adequate for sensing range. Figure 6.37 shows the angle that is subtended by the planet as the spacecraft approaches it. The error in range for a 4000 mile planet radius where telescope accuracy for angle measurement is assumed to be 1 part in 10^{-4} is also shown.

Range Rate (ṙ)

If a radio system were determined to be feasible for range measurements, then range rate should be obtained from the radar data or from a doppler frequency shift in the received radar frequency. An optical system such as the one described above for range measurements will not give range rate data directly. However, if adequate range accuracy may be achieved a satisfactory measurement of range rate may be derived. The accuracy of such a measurement is enhanced if the dynamics of the range and range rate are known to be well behaved and if the observations of range may be made over an extended time interval. (More detail in the accuracy of differentiating range data to obtain velocity information is given in Chapter 3.)

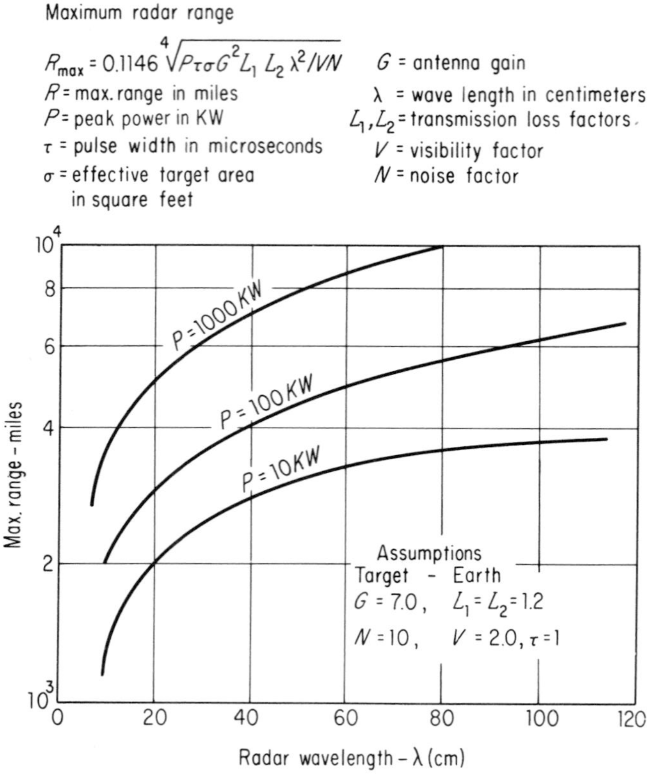
Maximum radar range
$R_{max} = 0.1146 \sqrt[4]{P\tau\sigma G^2 L_1 L_2 \lambda^2 / VN}$
R = max. range in miles
P = peak power in KW
τ = pulse width in microseconds
σ = effective target area in square feet
G = antenna gain
λ = wave length in centimeters
L_1, L_2 = transmission loss factors
V = visibility factor
N = noise factor
P = 1000 KW
P = 100 KW
P = 10 KW
Assumptions
Target - Earth
G = 7.0, $L_1 = L_2 = 1.2$
N = 10, V = 2.0, τ = 1
Max. range - miles
10^4
8
6
4
2
10^3
0
20
40
60
80
100
120
Radar wavelength – λ (cm)
Fig. 6.36.

Turning Rate of the Line of Sight ($\dot{\theta}$)

For this measurement, it will be sufficient to note the torquing signals from the tracking servo to the gyroscope that stabilizes the tracking telescope. The precision stabilization gyros must be rigidly mounted to the tracking telescope and be capable of acting as command receivers for the tracking servos. A three axis gyro-stabilized gimbal system will be desirable to isolate the angular motions of the spacecraft from the telescope. The turning rate will be related to the flight parameters and the coordinates by the following expression

$$\theta = \frac{vd}{r_0^2}\left(\frac{r_0}{r}\right)^2 \tag{6-100}$$

This relation has been graphed and is shown in Figure 6.38 for a selected range of parameters. A gyro capable of sensing 0.001 times the Earth's angular rate (1 milli-Earth rate unit, or 1 MERU, is equal to 0.015 deg/hr) will sense this turning rate in time to permit application of the first corrections at distances of 100 times the planet radius.

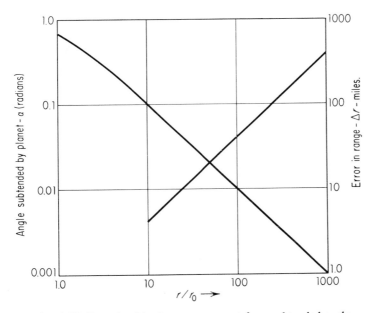

Fig. 6.37. Error in altitude—measurement from subtended angle.

A set of tracking telescopes, gyros, and computers designed to operate in accordance with the principles outlined above is shown in Figure 6.39. Since the function of these instruments is to compute and to command the application of velocity corrections, accelerometers have been included on the platform to provide the means to monitor the thrust magnitude and the direction of the thrust relative to the stabilized reference. Integration of the accelerometer output will provide a measure of the velocity change which results from the maneuver.

An estimate of the accuracy that is required of a set of homing instruments may be obtained considering the error coefficients defined by Equations (6-94), (6-95), (6-96) as they are computed along the trajectory of approach to the destination. The error in prediction of periapsis will be related to the errors in measurement by the relation that is expressed by Equation (6-93). A unit contribution to the error in predicted periapsis defines a quantity which we shall call the *coefficient of unit error*. This coefficient expresses the error in measurement of a single flight coordinate that will contribute an error of unit magnitude in the desired parameter. In this case, the desired parameter is the periapsis distance, r_p. The coefficients of unit error are obtained for the homing example as follows:

Error in r leading to unit error in periapsis

$$\delta r = \frac{1}{\partial r_p / \partial r}$$

Error in $\dot{r}$ leading to unit error in periapsis

$$\delta \dot{r} = \frac{1}{\partial r_p / \partial \dot{r}}$$

Error in θ leading to unit error in periapsis

$$\delta \theta = \frac{1}{\partial r_p / \partial \theta}$$

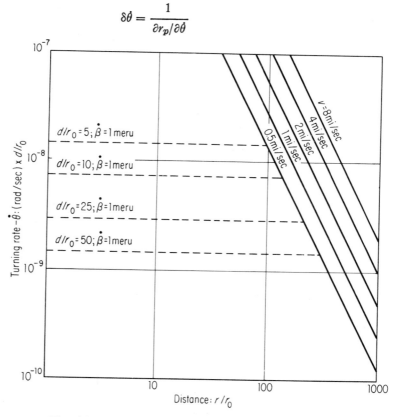

Fig. 6.38. Turning rate of line-of-sight to destination planet.

These coefficients of unit error have been calculated and are shown for the example in Table 6.9.   From the data shown in the table, it is apparent that, although the requirements are exacting, an instrument may be constructed which will provide the accuracy needed to permit adjustment of the spacecraft trajectory

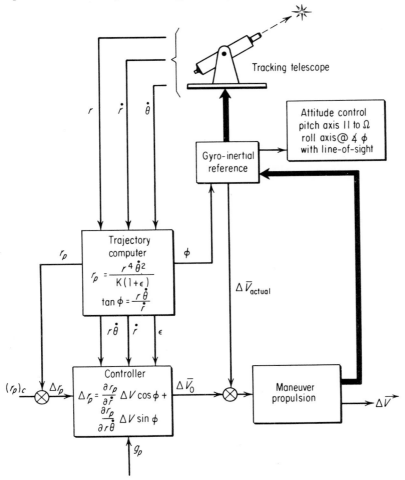

Fig. 6.39. Interplanetary landing guidance system.

in order to place its periapsis within a corridor that is 5 to 10 miles wide provided that a one micro-radian accuracy may be obtained from the telescope measurement of a planet disk.   Accuracy of instruments of this kind is predicted to meet this quality, see Reference 6.13.

Range rate accuracy requirements will be satisfied if the differentiation intervals of 100 seconds or more may be employed.   As the spacecraft approaches the planet, the accuracy of measurement that is required will decrease rapidly, as indicated by the decrease in the magnitude of the unit error coefficients shown in Table 6.9. More precise corrections of the altitude of periapsis may be applied in the manner of an iterative solution to permit a moderate quality instrument system to provide a high accuracy in the end result without requiring excessive maneuvers late in the flight.

Table 6.9. Unit Error Values Along the Earth Approach Trajectory

	$r/r_0 = 100$	$r/r_0 = 50$	$r/r_0 = 25$	$r/r_0 = 10$
Error in r leading to a 1 mile error in r_p	0.3 mi	0.15	0.075	0.0375
Error in $\dot{r}$ leading to a 1 mile error in r_p	0.0159 mi/sec	0.0156	0.0155	0.0153
Error in θ leading to a 1 mile error in r_p	0.145×10^{-9} rad/sec	4.85×10^{-9}	19.7×10^{-9}	100×10^{-9}

6.6 SPECIAL PROBLEMS OF RETURN

The return leg of an interplanetary flight presents many special problems which are not present on the departure. Several of these will be discussed briefly, the emphasis here will be on the navigational aspects of the problems. The general considerations of interplanetary navigation which have been discussed are, of course, still applicable. Interplanetary return flight represents an operation from a remote base under conditions where supporting services will be limited. In addition, each planet will have its own characteristics that require special consideration. Table 6.1 has presented a summary of the activity spheres of the various planets. The escape velocity for several planets is shown in the Appendix.

Return flight operations will frequently be necessary under conditions of limited supply. This will certainly be the case until the planets have been colonized for purposes of industrial exploitation. The supply limitations affecting the operation may apply to fuel, to electrical power, to instrumentation, or to life support supplies and equipment. The limitations may be due to a planned austerity in the operation or they may be the result of an accident, an emergency, or some unexpected system failures. In any event, the planning for the return journey must recognize the high probability that some such limitations will exist and the probable effect that they may have on the choice of return orbits. The major navigational result of these limitations is that there may be a premium on trajectory optimization. The exact nature of the optimization required, that is, minimum velocity, minimum transfer time etc, will depend largely on the kind of emergency situation which may exist and can not really be predicted in advance.

If the return trajectories are to be carefully optimized, there is a strong inference that digital computing equipment will be required on the spacecraft. The Earth-based computers that are used for trajectory optimization are usually high capacity, high speed machines. However, this is a matter of convenience rather than of necessity; a limited capacity computer could be programmed to provide a satisfactory result at a proportionately reduced speed. As an alternative, it may be desired to have the computations performed at a central base on the Earth and to transmit the results of the optimizing computation to the waiting spacecraft by means of a radio data link. This implies that the crew of the craft will be capable of evaluating their own limitations and those of the craft. They must, further, be capable of transmitting these limitations to an Earth-based computing station where the needed computation can be performed. The data link to be used for this purpose need not be operated as a wide-band data link nor does it need to be operated for long periods of time since the data to be transmitted will be in the form of orbit parameters, flight parameters, or limitations to these; guidance coefficients to be used on the return journey will also be transmitted.

In addition to data relative to the return orbit, the spacecraft navigator will, of course, require a knowledge of the ephemeris of the Earth and that of the planet to be departed. These data, too, may be obtained by radio transmissions, however, it may be more convenient to carry these data aboard the spacecraft in a form that is analogous to a navigator's map-kit. Ephemerides which have been constructed from Earth-based astronomical observations will be prepared with "Earth time" as an independant variable. Unless a precision clock is carried aboard the spacecraft and protected from the environmental changes that may affect its accuracy the spacecraft will require means to check and calibrate its chronometer to eliminate the effects of drifts and other errors. This check will be necessary in order to synchronize the local timepiece with the time system for which the ephemerides are valid. Time signals transmitted from the Earth would seem to provide the best source of data for this check.

A precision self-contained timepiece, or chronometer, to be used for navigation purposes can be constructed from atomic clock devices. These have been made practical for space applications with the advent of the maser; such a timing system is discussed with some applications in Reference 3.8. An atomic chronometer may be checked by comparison with an Earth transmitted time signal or it may be checked by means of local observations when the observer's position is known. The technique for doing this from a point on a distant planet is discussed in Reference 6.12.

Launch operations from the planets will necessarily be restricted in their scope. The use of elaborate erectors, gantry cranes, and extensive check-out equipment is not expected to be feasible. Neither will the use of ground handling transporters be readily available. Specially sited tracking and/or guidance radar stations will not be available except, perhaps, in special situations. It may also be assumed that refuelling for the return flight will not be available[1] and that the entire launch operation will be carried out using fuel and equipment that was transported to the planet in the spacecraft. The limited scope of the launch operations implies that the guidance, or navigation, to be used in the return journey should be self-contained to the escape, or burn-out point. This will preclude the use of systems that demand the use of an array of guidance stations requiring local surveys. The self-contained navigation systems used need not be inertial systems but they should provide the crew of the spacecraft with the capability of observing their own orbit parameters using measurements which can be made and processed on-board the craft. The spacecraft navigation after burn-out will be similar to that which has been discussed in the previous sections of the Chapter. Navigation for a landing on return to the Earth has already been discussed in Section 6.5.

PROBLEMS

1. Compute the hyperbolic excess velocity that is required for a Hohmann transfer from the Earth to the orbit of Mars. What velocity increment is needed at the orbit of Mars in order to place the spacecraft in a circular orbit with radius equal to that of Mars?

2. Repeat Problem 1, above, for a Hohmann transfer from the circular orbit in the vicinity of Mars to a circular orbit about the Sun having radius equal to the orbit of the Earth.

3. Compute the total velocity impulse that is required for the departure phases of the two previous problems. Assume that departure is from the surface of the planets mentioned.

4. Determine the hyperbolic excess velocity for an Earth–Mars flight leaving Earth on the Julian Calendar date J 244 0950 and arriving at Mars on J 244 1125. What is the Mars arrival velocity? Assume a 35 day stopover at Mars, find the velocity of departure and arrival for return to Earth arriving at J 244 1400. Hint: Use the chart of Figure 6.5.

5. Determine the departure velocity, minimum orbit eccentricity, and transfer time for a transfer orbit which will carry a spacecraft from a point at $R = 1.0$ A.U., $L = 30$ deg to a point at $R = 1.5$ A.U., $L = 120, 150, 160$ and 180 deg.

6. The error in Solar System Latitude and Longitude will be approximately equal to the error in angle measurements to the line of sight to celestial bodies. Plot a graph showing the error in position in statute miles, which is the result of a unit angular error in celestial body sights.

[1] An exception to this is perhaps the use of a heat–exchanger nuclear rocket. In a rocket of this kind, a single gas is used as the coolant–propellant. Liquid hydrogen is commonly used because of the advantages of its low molecular weight. It occurs to us that this propellant might be collected efficiently at the destination rather than to carry it for the entire trip.

7. Find the error and relative velocity for a 180 deg transfer using the parameters of the example discussed in Section 6.3.4. What is the 180 deg transfer time between these two orbits?

8. Compute the displacement in spacecraft position which is obtained at the reference longitude as a resut of a 1 mile per second increase in velocity when this increase is applied tangentially at a transfer angle of 90 deg in the orbits that are discussed in Section 6.3.4.

9. Repeat Problem 8 for radial velocity increments of 1 mi/sec.

REFERENCES

6.1. Ehricke, K. A., *Space Flight: Vol. I Environment and Celestial Mechanics*, D. Van Nostrand Co. Inc., Princeton N.J., 1960.

6.2. Hohmann, W., *Die Erreichbarkeit der Himmelskorper*, R. Ouldenbourg, Munich, 1925.

6.3. Vertregt, M., *Interplanetary Orbits*, Journal of the British Interplanetary Society Vol. 16, No. 6, March–April, 1958.

6.4. Chapman, D. R., *On the Corridor and Associated Trajectory Accuracy for Entry of Manned Spacecraft into Planetary Atmospheres*, Transactions of the Xth Congress, IAF, London, 1959.

6.5. Lawden, D. F., *Optimal Programming of Rocket Thrust Direction*, Astro. Acta, Vol. 1, No. 1, p. 41, 1955.

6.6. Edelbaum, T. N., *Some Extensions of the Hohmann Transfer Maneuver*, ARS Journ. Vol. 29, No. 11, p. 864–865, Nov., 1959.

6.7. Breakwell, John V., R. W. Gillespie and S. Ross, *Researches in Interplanetary Transfer*, ARS Paper No. 954–59, 1959.

6.8. Gilvarry, J. J. and S. H. Browne, *Theory of Blind Navigation by Dynamical Measurements*, The Rand Corporation R-144, Santa Monica, Calif., July, 1949.

6.9. McClure, Connie L., *Theory of Inertial Guidance*, Prentice-Hall, Inc., Englewood Cliffs, N.J., 1960.

6.10. Browne, S. H. and J. J. Gilvarry, *Theory of Errors in Inertial Navigation Systems*, The Rand Corporation R-154, Santa Monica, Calif., 1949.

6.11. Stearns, E. V., *An Interplanetary Navigation System*, Proc IXth Congress IAF, Amsterdam, 1958.

6.12. Battin, R. H. and J. H. Lanning, Jr., *A Navigation Theory for Round Trip Reconnaissance Missions to Venus and Mars*, MIT Instrumentation Laboratory R-240, Cambridge, Mass, August, 1959.

6.13 Larmore, Lewis, *Celestial Observations for Space Navigation*, Inst. for Aero Sci, National Summer Meeting, Los Angeles, Calif., July 8–11, 1958.

6.14. DeBra, D. B., *The Effect of Guidance Errors in Astroballistic Trajectories*, Proc IRE, Third National Convention on Military Electronics, July, 1959.

6.15. Benesch, S. E., *Exterior Ballistics*, Prentice-Hall, Inc., Englewood Cliffs, N.J. (indef.).

6.16. Ehricke, K. A., *Error Analysis of Keplerian Flights Involving a Single Central Force Field and Transfer Between Two Central Force Fields*, Navigation, Vol. 6, No. 1, Spring, 1958.

6.17. Magness, T. A., J. B. McGuire and O. K. Smith, *Accuracy Requirements for Interplanetary Ballistic Trajectories*, Proc. IXth Congress, IAF, Amsterdam, August, 1958.

6.18. Harry, David P. and Alan L. Friedlander, *Exploratory Analysis of Planet Approach-Phase Guidance Schemes Using Range, Range-Rate and Angular-Rate Measurements*, NASA TN–D–268, Lewis Research Center, Cleveland, Ohio, March, 1960.

6.19. Harry, David P. and Alan L. Friedlander, *An Analysis of Errors and Requirements of an Optical Guidance Technique for Approaches to Atmospheric Entry with Interplanetary Vehicles*, NASA TR R–102.

6.20. DeBra, D. B. and R. W. Gillespie, *Minimum Maneuver Circular Capture Orbits*, Astronautical Sciences Review, 1959.

6.21. *Space Handbook: Astronautics and its Applications*; Staff Report of the Select Committee on Astronautics and Space Exploration. U.S. Government Printing Office, Washington D.C., 1959.

6.22. Breakwell, John V., *The Spacing of Corrective Thrusts in Interplanetary Navigation*, Proceedings of the Third Annual West Coast Meeting, The American Astronautical Society, August 8–11, 1960, Seattle, Washington.

6.23. Eckel, K., *Optimum Transfer Between Non-Coplanar Elliptical Orbits*, Astronautica Acta, Vol. VIII, No. 4, 1962.

7

NAVIGATION TO THE MOON

7.0 INTRODUCTION

Of all the spaceflight missions that have attracted man's serious contemplation, the one arousing the most universal interest seems to be that of flight to the Moon. Perhaps this is simply because the Moon is the nearest and most inviting of the celestial bodies that is seen from the Earth. For the same reason, the Moon may be reached with the expenditure of less booster energy than is required for more remote spaceflight destinations. The flight time for such a trip is also relatively brief. A one-way trip may be made in a very few days; this is compared to several months as required for an interplanetary journey. This chapter will treat the mechanics of lunar transit in general terms and will discuss the means for navigation of lunar flight vehicles. Some of the more interesting characteristics of lunar flight will be described. Before going into detail on the subject of lunar flight and the techniques for navigation to the Moon, a brief description of the lunar and cis-lunar environments will be presented.

The Earth and the Moon are frequently treated as a single dynamical system. Taken together, these two bodies resemble a double star system more closely than do any other two bodies in the Solar System. The common center of mass, called the *barycenter*, lies about 3100 miles from the center of the Earth along the line that joins the centers of the two bodies. The center of the Earth will be shown to describe a closed orbit about the barycenter with a period of about a month. When a double star system is considered alone, the determination of the orbit parameters of one of the components of the system is not difficult since both of the components move about the barycenter in accordance with Kepler's laws of motion for a body in a central force field. In the case of the Earth–Moon system, however, this concept yields only a rough approximation. The gravity field of a third body, the Sun, has a strong perturbing influence in the vicinity of the Earth and the Moon. This makes the net effective field of gravity depart from the field of mutual attraction between the two bodies. The orbital plane of the Moon is inclined to the ecliptic plane by about 5 deg but it varies rapidly over a range of about ± 23 minutes. The various perturbations acting on the Moon in its orbit about the Earth and the Sun are described in more detail in classical texts on lunar theory, cf. Reference 7.1.

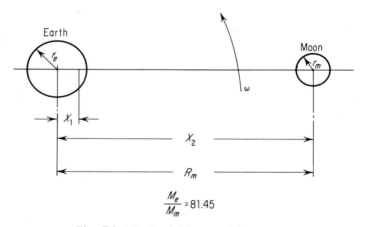

Fig. 7.1. The Earth-Moon model.

Physical Data regarding the Moon and its characteristics have been collected and are presented in Table 7.1. The general characteristics of a free-flight lunar transfer orbit may be studied with reference to the simplified model of the Earth–Moon system that is shown in Figure 7.1. In this model the Earth and the Moon are both assumed to be spherical bodies with gravitational fields identical to those that would be associated with equivalent point masses. This two body system is assumed to be isolated in space but revolving about the barycenter of the system. This simplified model neglects such factors as the following

Rotation of the Earth and associated effects
Oblateness of the Earth
Eccentricity of the orbit of the Moon
Gravitational effects due to the Sun.

Table 7.1. PHYSICAL CHARACTERISTICS OF THE MOON

Period of revolution	27.32 days
Distance from the Earth	
minimum	221,500 mi
mean	238,900 mi
maximum	252,700 mi
Eccentricity of lunar orbit	0.0549
Inclination of lunar orbit to equatorial plane	
of the Earth	28° 35′ (max)—18° 19′ (min)
Inclination of lunar orbit to ecliptic	5° 9′ (mean)
Direction of rotation	Direct
Gravitational parameter	1.727×10^{14} ft³/sec²
Escape velocity at surface of Moon	7873 ft/sec
Surface gravity (Earth = 1)	0.1650 (4.94 ft/sec²)
Mass of Moon (Earth = 1)	0.1286
Barycenter of Earth–Moon system	
at minimum distance	1250 mi below surface of Earth
at mean distance	1020 mi below surface of Earth
at maximum distance	863 mi below surface of Earth

7.1 CHARACTERISTICS OF CIS-LUNAR SPACE

In contemplation of flight through cis-lunar space it becomes necessary to consider two potential sources of perturbing forces which might influence the trajectory of the spacecraft. The first of these arises because the aggregate gravity fields of the Sun, the Earth, and the Moon do not approximate the simple inverse square-law central force field described in the Kepler theory. Consideration must also be given to the magnitude of the drag forces that may arise when the spacecraft travels through cis-lunar space at high speed. The effect of these two forces will be analyzed briefly in this section in order to permit an estimate to be made of the effect that they will have on the navigation of lunar spacecraft.

The acceleration due to gravity at the surface of the Moon is about $\frac{1}{6}$ of that which is due to the Earth's gravity field at its own surface, that is $g_{lunar} = \frac{1}{6} g_{earth}$. The effect of these accelerations acting upon a spacecraft will decrease as the square of the distance of the spacecraft from the Moon and the Earth respectively. In addition, the Earth–Moon system is immersed in the solar gravity field as a part of the Solar System. Consequently, the gravitational acceleration acting on a spacecraft that is travelling in cis-lunar space will be represented by the vector sum of the gravity due to the Sun, the Earth, and the Moon. The magnitude of the components of this sum are shown graphically in Figure 7.2.

A graph of the magnitude of the components of a gravitational field such as the one that is shown in Figure 7.2 is not fully descriptive of the situation. Perhaps a more descriptive representation is obtained if we consider a plane in which the Earth and Moon are shown at fixed positions. This plane, if observed from inertial space will appear to rotate. The axis of rotation will be the line that passes through the barycenter and is normal to the plane of the lunar orbit. The period of revolution of the plane will be the lunar period, $T = 27.3$ days. Other components of rotation will exist with much longer periods but they will be neglected here. A contour plot of the aggregate gravity acceleration field may be constructed in such a plane to show the acceleration acting on a vehicle which might be located at any point in the plane. Such a contour map would have the general appearance of the one that has been sketched in Figure 7.3.

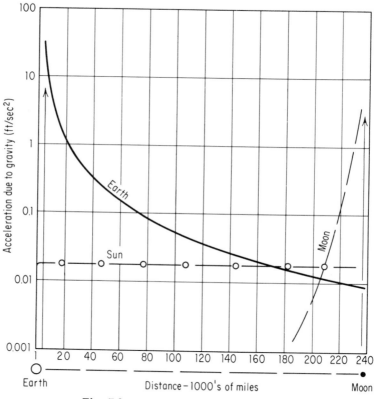

Fig. 7.2. Gravity fields in cis-lunar space.

The Sun's gravity vector will appear to rotate with relation to an Earth–Moon system of reference. The rotational period will, of course, be the lunar period. The gradients of the solar gravity field may be obtained from the inverse-square law of gravity; that is, the gravitational acceleration is

$$g = g_{ref}\left(\frac{R_{ref}}{R}\right)^2 \tag{7-1}$$

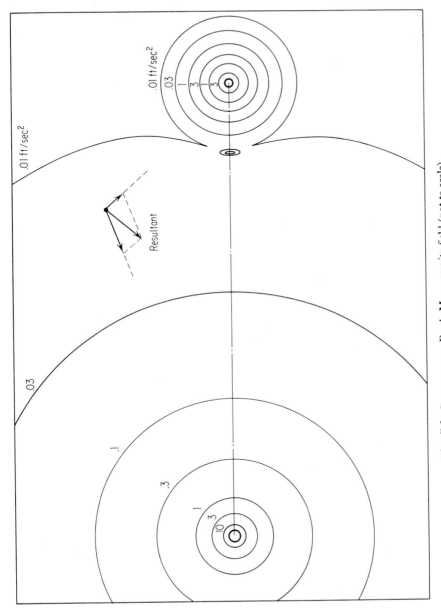

.01 ft/sec²

.03

1

3

3

.01 ft/sec²

.03

Resultant

.1

.3

1

3

10

Fig. 7.3. Contour map. Earth-Moon gravity field (not to scale).

283

The gradient of the gravitational acceleration is

$$\frac{dg}{dR} = -2g_{ref}R^2_{ref}R^{-3} \qquad (7\text{-}2)$$

but

$$k = g_{ref}R^2_{ref} = 3.96 \times 10^{-14} \text{ A.U.}^3/\text{sec}^2\text{: } R = 1.0$$

consequently

$$\frac{dg}{dR} = 7.92 \times 10^{-14} \text{ sec}^{-2}$$

$$= 4.14 \times 10^{-10}(\text{ft/sec}^2)\text{ mi}^{-1}$$

The maximum variation occurring within the lunar orbit will be less than

$$\mathbf{u_r} \cdot \Delta \mathbf{g} = 1.05 \times 10^{-4} \text{ ft/sec}^2$$

The tangential component of the solar gravity acceleration within the lunar orbit arises as a result of the convergence of the solar gravitational field. Within the region that is bounded by the lunar orbit this will be within the limits of

$$\mathbf{u_\theta} \cdot \Delta \mathbf{g} = g_{ref} \tan \theta = g_{ref}(243 \times 10^3/10^8)$$

$$= 4.86 \times 10^{-5} \text{ ft/sec}^2$$

The Earth–Moon system is moving as a unit through the solar gravity field in a free-fall orbit. The period of this orbit is the period of the Earth in its orbit, that is 365.24 days. Consequently, the motion of a spacecraft that is travelling in this field must be calculated considering the effect that the Sun's gravitational field has on the orbit. A useful degree of approximation may be obtained, however, if calculations are made under the simplifying assumption that the solar gravity field is uniform in both direction and magnitude throughout cis-lunar space. Such an assumption permits the field to be neglected when the spacecraft orbits are calculated relative to the barycenter of the Earth–Moon system. The accelerations due to the solar gravity acting on the Earth, the craft, and the Moon would then all be identical. In that event, the relative motion of these bodies that would arise from these accelerations in this uniform field will vanish.

The density of the atmosphere in space in the regions of cis-lunar orbits is discussed in some length in Reference 7.2 where evidence is presented showing that a cis-lunar atmosphere exists and that its density is substantially that of the interplanetary atmosphere. The *logarithmic density ratio*, (log ρ/ρ_0) of this atmosphere is given as approximately

$$\log \frac{\rho}{\rho_0} = -19$$

where

$\rho_0 = 0.0025$ slug/ft³ (the standard density for the atmosphere of the Earth at its surface)

The effective drag that arises from the atmosphere as it acts on a body travelling through cis-lunar space is given by the familiar relation

$$F_D = \tfrac{1}{2}C_d A \rho v^2 \tag{7-3}$$

Assuming

$$C_d = 1$$

$$\rho = \rho_0 \times 10^{-19} = 2.25 \times 10^{-22} \text{ slug/ft}^3$$

$$v = 10^4 \text{ ft/sec}$$

The resulting acceleration that acts on a body having $\dfrac{W}{A} = 20$ will be

$$a = \frac{1.125 \times 10^{-14}}{W/A}g = 0.54 \times 10^{-16}g$$

The effects of an acceleration of this magnitude can be neglected for periods as long as 30 to 60 hours, consequently, the effect of this perturbing force may be neglected in most lunar flights.

7.2 LUNAR TRANSFER TRAJECTORIES

A complete study of the parameters for Earth–Moon transfer trajectories is beyond the scope of the present work. However, a few general remarks regarding the characteristics of these trajectories will be appropriate before discussing lunar navigation. The relatively large perturbations that act on the orbit of a spacecraft that is moving in cis-lunar space are largely the result of the interactions of the lunar gravity field with that due to the Earth. These interactions make the two-body central force field (Keplerian) theory inadequate for lunar navigation purposes. A thorough analysis of these trajectories will be found in References 7.3 and 7.4. Although the lunar orbits are distorted in shape near the Moon, the segment of the orbit which is in the close vicinity of the Earth may be described in terms of the Keplerian theory. Consider, now, a fictitious transfer orbit that is designed to carry a spacecraft from the Earth to the Moon's orbit. In doing so, the problem may be idealized by neglecting the effects of the gravity field due to the Moon. The resulting idealized trajectory will have the following properties:

Perigee r_p	= 4000 statute miles
Apogee r_a	= 238,000 statute miles
Major axis a	= 243,000 statute miles

Eccentricity e = 0.98
Velocity at perigee v_p = 6.68 mi/sec
Orbit period T = 7.34 days

An example of such an orbit is shown in the sketch of Figure 7.4.

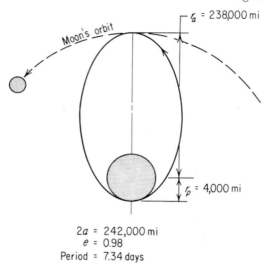

$$2a = 242,000 \text{ mi}$$
$$e = 0.98$$
$$\text{Period} = 7.34 \text{ days}$$

Fig. 7.4. Idealized lunar transfer orbit (not to scale).

The foregoing list of parameters represents an idealized "minimum transfer" example that was calculated under the assumption that the Moon is a massless point. Indeed, such an orbit would be so badly distorted in the vicinity of the Moon that we would expect it to miss the destination altogether. These values do, however, provide some limiting parameters that are useful in evaluation of lunar flight systems. The orbit described above is one in which the spacecraft velocity is approximately minimum for the transfer to the Moon. This orbit places the craft under the influence of the Moon's gravitational field for a greater time than do the orbits which have greater energy. As a result, the effects of those orbit perturbations that arise from the gravity due to the Moon will be greater than for faster orbits having higher energy, or higher eccentricity. Briefly, then, lunar transfer orbits will be expected to have the following general properties:

$r_p \geqslant 4000$ statute miles
$r_a \geqslant 238,000$ statute miles
$a \geqslant 242,000$ statute miles
$e \geqslant 0.98$
$v_p \geqslant 6.68$ mi/sec = 35,300 ft/sec

An important result of the work that has been reported by Lieske (Reference 7.3) is a parametric study of lunar transfer orbits. The interrelations of these parameters are discussed in some detail in the reference; several of the more significant results of that study are discussed in the following paragraphs.

A typical example of a lunar flight trajectory is shown in Figure 7.5. The departure portion of the trajectory is a sector of an ellipse having high eccentricity; however, as the spacecraft approaches the Moon, the lunar gravity field acts on the orbit causing the craft to depart from the initial ellipse and to be drawn closer to the Moon. This distortion is evident in Figure 7.5. If the conditions of the encounter between the spacecraft and the Moon, as indicated by the velocity vector of the spacecraft relative to the Moon, are within certain bounds, a collision landing on the Moon will occur. *High energy* transfer orbits requiring injection velocity at the Earth exceeding the minimum will show a reduced distortion due to this perturbation and give Earth-Moon transfer times shorter

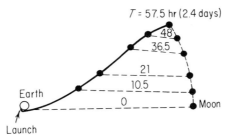

Fig. 7.5. Typical Earth-Moon transfer, 2.4 day transfer time.

than is shown in Figure 7.5. These higher energy transfers will be characterized by increased eccentricity over the idealized conic departure segment of the orbit. As the departure velocity increases to Earth escape velocity, the departure orbit segment becomes parabolic in shape and the eccentricity approaches unity. Further increases in the velocity of injection into the transfer orbit will further increase the eccentricity and the orbit becomes an arc of an hyperbola.

The relation between the transfer time for the Earth–Moon trip and the velocity of injection into the transfer orbit is displayed in Figure 7.6. This curve has been computed using the simplified Earth–Moon model that was described in the previous section. The flight conditions for the curve shown apply to a cut-off altitude of 300 miles ($R = 4300$ mi). A point has been placed on the figure to show a comparison with the idealized trajectories that were discussed previously.

As the spacecraft progresses along the transfer orbit, its velocity follows a pattern similar to that which would result from the law of conservation of angular momentum in unperturbed flight. Indeed, the flight is perturbed and it is necessary to calculate the velocity profile by electronic computation. The velocity profile that corresponds to a 1.4 day transfer orbit is shown in Figure 7.7. The high velocity that was obtained in the vicinity of the Earth falls off rapidly to a plateau. In the vicinity of the Moon, this velocity increases again

Burn-out conditions at 300 miles

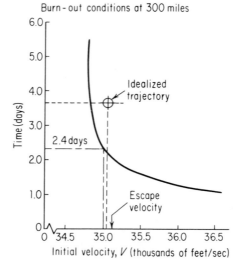

Fig. 7.6. Transfer time from Earth to Moon.

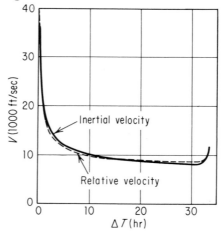

Fig. 7.7. Velocity profile for Earth-Moon transfer, 1.4 day transfer time.

under the influence of the gravity field of the Moon. The velocity of the spacecraft relative to the Moon as well as the inertial velocity of the craft is shown in the graph of Figure 7.7. It should be noted that these two curves do not differ greatly from one another.

A set of coordinates that may be used as a reference for the description of lunar transfer trajectories is shown in Figure 7.8. The initial position of the spacecraft is given in two-dimensional polar coordinates—the radial distance from the center of the Earth, r, and the angle between this radius and a reference line, θ. The reference line is chosen to be the initial position vector of the Moon. The initial velocity vector is defined by a magnitude, v, and a flight path angle, γ,

Parameters used to describe
initial conditions

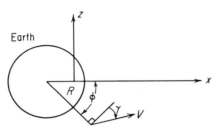

Fig. 7.8. Parameters used to describe
initial conditions.

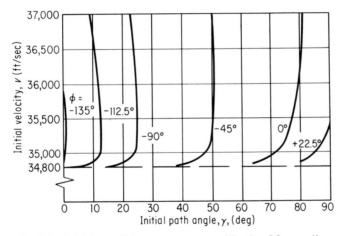

Fig. 7.9. Initial conditions required to hit the Moon—direct
motion.

(the angle relative to local horizontal). A final parameter is defined to describe the sense of the motion. The motion is said to be *direct* or *retrograde* relative to the Earth–Moon model, depending on whether the angular velocity of the Earth–Moon system is parallel or anti-parallel with the angular velocity vector of the spacecraft orbit.

Curves showing the initial velocity-path angle combinations for which lunar impact is attainable are shown in Figure 7.9. A similar curve has been prepared for retrograde flights; this is given in the curves of Figure 7.10. The initial conditions at the Moon that are required for a return flight to the Earth are shown in Figure 7.11.

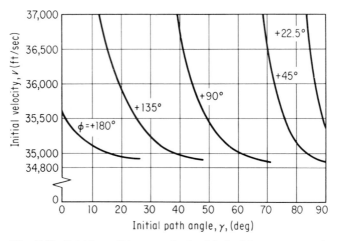

Fig. 7.10. Initial conditions required to hit the Moon—retrograde motion.

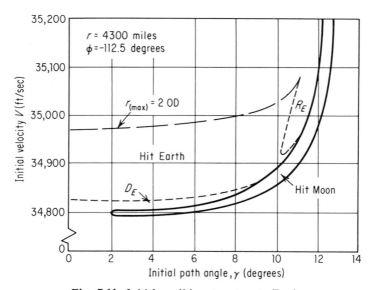

Fig. 7.11. Initial conditions to return to Earth.

7.2.1. Effect of Relative Earth-Moon Motions

In establishing an Earth–Moon transfer orbit, it is important to consider the motions of the Moon relative to the Earth. It will be shown here that this motion introduces important temporal variations in the injection maneuvers that will be required for lunar flights. Recalling the Earth–Moon model which was shown in Figure 7.1, the motion of the Moon relative to the Earth may be described in terms of the angular motions of the system about its barycenter. The applicable angular velocity vectors are listed below.

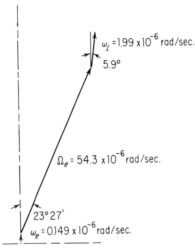

Fig. 7.12. Angular velocity vectors for Earth-Moon motions (lengths not to scale).

Terrestrial orbit angular velocity (The reference vector): The vector representing the heliocentric motion of the Earth, it is normal to the ecliptic plane and has magnitude of $\omega_e = (2\pi \div 365 \times 24 \times 3600)$ rad/sec. ($\omega_e = 0.149 \times 10^{-6}$ rad/sec.)

Terrestrial angular velocity: The vector representing the diurnal rotation of the Earth, it is inclined at an angle of $23° 27'$ to the reference vector and lies in a plane with azimuth that corresponds to the time of the year; its magnitude is $\Omega_e = (2\pi \div 24 \times 3600)$ rad/sec. ($\Omega_e = 54.3 \times 10^{-6}$ rad/sec.)

Lunar orbit angular velocity: The vector representing the angular velocity of the Moon in its orbit, it is inclined at $5° 9'$ to the reference vector in an azimuth plane that also depends on the time of the year. Its magnitude is $\omega_e = (2\pi \div 27.3 \times 24 \times 3600)$ rad/sec. ($\omega_l = 1.99 \times 10^{-6}$ rad/sec.)

These vectors are shown in relation to one another in the sketch of Figure 7.12.

The path of the Moon, as seen from the Earth, is approximately a great circle which is inclined to the ecliptic at an angle of about 5° 9'. The orbit of the Moon intersects the ecliptic plane at two opposing *nodes*; the ascending node is the one where the Moon passes through the ecliptic while going northward. The descending node is the one where the Moon passes through the ecliptic as it travels to the south. These nodes exhibit a motion that is called regression. This regression is a westward movement of the nodes in the ecliptic plane, it is similar to the way in which the equinoxes slide westward in their

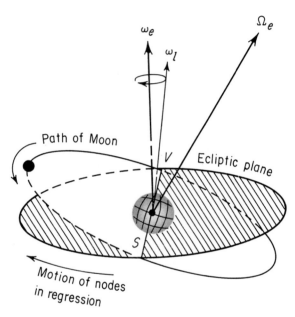

Fig. 7.13

precession but the lunar regression is at a faster rate. The nature of the motion is illustrated in Figure 7.13. A complete revolution of the lunar nodes is accomplished in 18.6 years. As a result of the regression, and other changes that occur in the Moon's orbit for which the gravitational field of the Sun is largely responsible, the apparent path of the Moon in the celestial sphere will differ considerably from month to month.

While the Moon's path carries it some 25,000 miles above and below the ecliptic plane, the angular variation, when observed from the Earth, is quite small. Consequently, the Moon appears to move north and south during each month about as much as the Sun will during the course of a year. Near the position of the summer solstice[1] the Moon rises in the northeast, sets in the northwest, and is high in the sky (in the northern hemisphere) at its upper transit. Near the winter solstice, about two weeks later, the Moon rises in the southeast, sets in the southwest, and crosses the meridian at a lower apparent altitude.

When the inclination of the Moon's path to the ecliptic is taken into account, it appears that the range in declination varies perceptibly as the nodes regress. When the ascending node is coincident with the vernal equinox, the path of the Moon in inclined to the celestial equator at $23° 27' + 5° 9' = 28° 36'$. This situation occurred in 1950. Nine years later, the ascending node was coincident with the autumnal equinox and the inclination of the lunar orbit to the equator was $23° 27' - 5° 9' = 18° 18'$. This variation is illustrated in Figure 7.14,

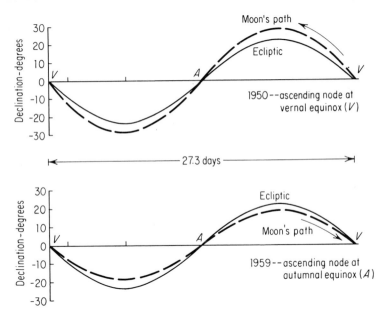

Fig. 7.14. Effect of regression of the nodes on lunar declination.

the curves illustrate the declination of the Moon as it proceeds through its 27 day period. The variation of 10° in the Moon's declination is chiefly responsible for the nutations of the axis of the Earth which accompanies its precessional motion.

The Moon rotates on its axis in the same period as its revolution around the

---

[1] It is convenient to define the *summer solstice* as a point on the projection of the lunar orbit in the ecliptic plane. This is the point that is farthest north of the equatorial plane. The winter and summer solstices occupy points with azimuth 90° from the line of the equinoxes.

Earth. Furthermore, the equator of the Moon is approximately coincident with the plane of its orbit relative to the Earth. As a consequence, the Moon presents nearly the same hemisphere towards the Earth at all times. Small changes in this aspect of the Moon, called *librations*, may be noted with careful observations. This characteristic of constant aspect relative to the Earth permits important simplifications in the procedures for *aiming* at the Moon in flights where it is planned to approach the Moon directly and to "land" by hitting the front surface of the Moon. Landing dynamics will be discussed briefly, with respect to a lunar flight, in a later section.

7.2.2 THE LAUNCH WINDOW

In a previous section, the range of initial flight conditions that lead to a lunar transfer orbit terminating with lunar impact was discussed. The tolerance in initial flight conditions for arrival at the Moon from an Earth departure provides a range of values for R_0, ϕ_0, V_0, and γ_0. The family of limiting orbits will form an elongated corridor in space. This corridor is shaped something like a funnel that leads to the Moon's orbit; the terminus will be shaped open or closed depending on the presence, or absence, of the Moon at the end. A satisfactory transfer orbit is one on which the craft may enter the funnel at a time when the Moon will move to the opposite end of the funnel in time for the arrival of the craft. The opening of this corridor near the Earth might be referred to as the *launch window*. It will be shown that, although the window is of specific dimensions, it is "open" for only a brief interval of time. The launch vehicle, its performance characteristics, and its guidance will determine the range of ascent trajectory parameters which will permit the vehicle to be injected into an orbit passing through this window; see Figure 7.15. This range of parameters includes a range of allowable values for the launch time that are related to the rate of rotation of the Earth. This range of the launch time is frequently used to define the launch window. Consequently, the launch window characteristics will depend upon the design of the launch vehicle as well as the characteristics of the Earth–Moon system.

Suppose that the ascent trajectory of a spacecraft may be characterized as imparting a specified shift in position and velocity to the craft. These changes must be accomplished within certain bounds which are set by the constraints of flight operations. The boundaries are applied largely to the early portions of the flight, that is, those portions which occur near the surface of the Earth and under the influence of the atmosphere. Consequently, the effects of these boundaries are felt most strongly in terms of the velocity of the craft. After leaving the atmosphere, and sufficient velocity has been gained to give the craft relative freedom from so called "gravity losses", the guidance and control system of the craft will be able to exert only a limited influence on the trajectory. It will be necessary, then, to insure that the spacecraft is launched at a time when one of the members of the family of ascent trajectories that are available to the craft will pass into the launch window.

The detailed structure of the launch window will depend upon several factors. Among these factors are flight safety regulations, the location and field of view of the several ground guidance and tracking stations to be used, and vehicle fuel reserves. No attempt will be made here to define all of these nor to describe the window in detail. As an example, however, consider a flight in which an adequate transfer orbit will be obtained if injection occurs over a range of

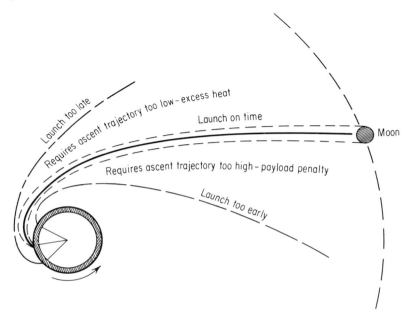

Fig. 7.15. Illustrating the launch window.

position defined by $\varphi = \varphi_0 \pm 5°$. It has also been determined for this flight that the guidance system is capable of making adjustments of all orbital parameters to account for a range of $\pm 1°$ in the position angle, φ. The total range in φ is then $\pm 6°$. The Earth turns on its axis at a rate of 15° per hour; hence the launch time tolerance is ± 24 minutes. This time interval may also be expressed by saying that the launch window is open for 48 minutes.

In addition, another boundary appears in the azimuth of the velocity vector at injection into the transfer orbit. When a space vehicle is injected into its transfer orbit at a point that is not, per se, in the plane containing the orbit of the destination body, a non-coplanar flight occurs. If the latitude (λ) of the launch site is given by an angle that is less than the declination of the lunar orbit, α_1, then the launch site will pass through the plane of the Moon's orbit twice a day.

If the latitude of the point under consideration is greater than 28° 36', the launching point will never be in the plane of the lunar orbit. Launch points that are located between 18° 18' and 28° 36' latitude will be in the lunar orbit plane twice a day during certain portions of the 18.6 year cycle of the nodes, depending on the current value of α_1. Launch sites having latitude less than 18° 18' will always pass through the plane of the lunar orbit twice a day.

An example of this azimuth boundary might arise when a spacecraft is launched to the Moon from a site at Cape Canaveral, Florida (latitude 28° N). At a particular time each day, the spacecraft may be launched into the plane of the orbit of the Moon. The firing azimuth for such a flight may be stated with relation to an inertial reference sphere at the time of launch. It is

$$\psi = \alpha_1 R_e \cos (l - l_n) \qquad (7\text{-}4)$$

where

$l =$ the longitude of the launch site

$l_n =$ the longitude of the ascending node of the lunar and the equatorial planes.

At some other time, a different launch azimuth will be required in order to obtain a new value for the inclination of the transfer orbit.

Frequently, there will be limitations that are placed on the launch azimuth for space launchings; these will be the result of range safety requirements or some other operating rule which may not be anticipated here but which must be applied to the selection of the orbit. These limitations may be expressed in terms of allowable deviations in the launch azimuth which are symmetrical about a nominal value. The deviation in this quantity will be determined by the time of launch and the difference between the latitude of the launch site and the current declination of the Moon. Since the Earth subtends an angle of less than 2° when observed from the Moon, this deviation need not be greater than about ± 1°.

7.2.3 LANDING DYNAMICS

Before proceeding to the discussion of more specific navigation problems, it will be interesting to consider some of the navigational aspects that arise when a landing on the Moon is planned. The methods for computing and steering a course to the Moon will be quite similar to the methods that were discussed in Section 6.5 under the heading *Guidance for Entry and Landing*. The applicable constants and the details of the trajectory will, of course, be somewhat different.

The lunar spacecraft will be placed in an orbit that is designed to carry it to the Moon. As the craft recedes from the Earth and approaches the Moon it will be possible by means of observations that are made from the Earth or from the craft to estimate the parameters of the lunar approach orbit. These parameters will permit calculation of the periapsis distance. (In the case of lunar flight, the periapsis is sometimes referred to as the *periselene*.) The approach path can be evaluated in terms of this parameter, r_p, the orbit eccentricity, and the orientation of the orbit. The periapsis can be adjusted to correct the approach orbit using the methods described in Section 6.5. The coefficients for the computation of these corrections have been calculated for a family of lunar approach trajectories and are shown in Figures 7.16 and 7.17.

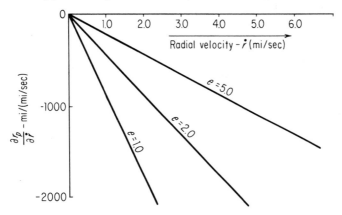

Fig. 7.16. Homing guidance coefficients—approaching the Moon.

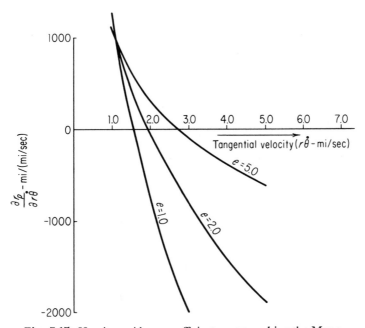

Fig. 7.17. Homing guidance coefficients—approaching the Moon.

Unlike the Earth and the near planets, that is, Mars and Venus, the Moon has no atmosphere. Consequently, a craft that will land on the Moon will not be able to dissipate the energy that is associated with its approach velocity through transfer of that energy to heat in the atmosphere. It will be necessary, therefore, for a lunar craft to be equipped with a special device for the purpose of reducing and absorbing the shock of a straight-in landing. The requirements for such an energy absorber are discussed in some detail in Reference 7.5. In order to evaluate these requirements, consider the velocity at which the spacecraft would be travelling on impact at the surface of the Moon in the event that no deceleration system were employed. This velocity is a function of the relative velocity between the Moon and the spacecraft before entry into the effective lunar gravity field; that is the *hyperbolic excess velocity*. The hyperbolic excess velocity of approach to the Moon is shown as a function of the orbit transfer time in Figure 7.18.

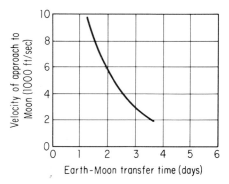

Fig. 7.18. Hyperbolic excess velocity of approach to Moon.

The velocity of impact that would occur in the absence of a deceleration may be calculated through integration of the equations of motion of the craft as it approaches the Moon. These equations must take into account all of the forces of significant magnitude that will act on the craft. The evaluation of this integral will yield a time history of the velocity magnitude and will depend upon the exact trajectory followed by the craft. An equivalent result may be obtained if we are concerned only with the velocity that would occur at the surface impact. It is assumed that the kinetic energy at the instant of impact is the sum of the kinetic energy due to the hyperbolic excess approach velocity and the velocity that the craft acquires as it falls through the lunar gravity field. Thus, the velocity of impact will be derived as follows

$$\tfrac{1}{2}Mv^2_{\text{impact}} = \tfrac{1}{2}Mv^2_{\infty} + \tfrac{1}{2}Mv^2_{\text{escape}}$$

$$v_{\text{impact}} = \sqrt{v^2_{\infty} + v^2_{\text{escape}}} \qquad (7\text{-}5)$$

The foregoing equation represents the minimum impulse that will be required of a rocket system for the deceleration of a lunar landing craft. The minimum impulse requirement will apply if the deceleration system provides a velocity change in a negligible interval of time, that is, if the acceleration level is infinite, and the deceleration is accomplished just prior to the instant of touchdown. Figure 7.19 presents a graph of the effective value of impact velocity on the Moon. These velocity values are shown for a range of values of the hyperbolic approach velocity.

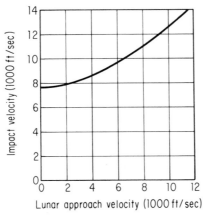

Fig. 7.19. Velocity of lunar impact.

If the vehicle is to touchdown with zero velocity, a cut-off of the engine must coincide with zero velocity and zero altitude. In a system where the engine is to be ignited once only, the altitude at which the signal to fire the engine will be given is determined by the thrust of the engine and the approach velocity. In a trajectory where the terminal approach is substantially vertical, this relation will be as follows

$$h_f = \tfrac{1}{2} a_{eff} t^2$$

where

h_f = the altitude for firing the engine
a_{eff} = the effective acceleration during the thrusting interval
t = the engine burning time.

A more precise estimate will require the integration of the equation of vertical motion, this equation is

$$\ddot{z} - g_1 = \frac{T}{W - \dot{w}t}$$

where

g_1 = the lunar gravity
T = the thrust of the decelerating engine
$\dot{w}$ = the rate of fuel consumption of the engine
t = the time that the engine has burned.

Integration of this differential equation will give rise to an expression involving two constants that are dependent upon the performance of the engine and the propellant flow rate. For a very approximate result, one may neglect the propellant loss and the deceleration of the craft will then be a constant. In this case the altitude for firing the engine will be given by

$$h_f = \tfrac{1}{2}\frac{v_0^2}{(T/W - 1)g_e}$$

7.3 LUNAR NAVIGATION

The discussions that appeared in the previous sections of this chapter have served to summarize the interrelations of the many parameters that apply to lunar flight. They emphasize the extreme dependance of each aspect of the flight on the many others. In addition, emphasis has been given to the individual nature of each flight showing, in every case, how the flight conditions will differ as a result of the special nature of the gravitational fields that are present in cis-lunar space and also as a result of the relative motions of the Earth and the Moon. Accordingly, it is apparent that it will be necessary to calculate each lunar flight orbit for a specific launch time and for a specific launch vehicle-spacecraft combination. The range of parameters for application of one such calculation to a variety of launching conditions defines, in a sense, the "launch window" for the particular operation at hand.

As a result of the absence of a general solution to the three-body problem of dynamical motion, generalizations to lunar transfer flights will not be useful; except, perhaps, as the basis for vehicle and systems design approximations. Precise orbit calculations will be necessary for each flight. These calculations must take account of the Earth-Moon configuration during the entire period of the transfer flight in order to establish the suitable burn-out conditions at the end of the booster flight and to estimate the trajectory to be followed thereafter.

The perturbations to a lunar flight will cause the solution of lunar flight problems to be mathematically non-linear in nature; consequently, it will be difficult to predict the effects that small variations in the booster-guidance systems performance will have on the over-all performance of the spacecraft in its lunar flight. As a consequence, mid-course guidance and subsequent corrections to the orbit are considered to be very important to lunar flight planning. This section will consider some of the problems that may be anticipated in the navigation of a lunar transfer craft. The need for special in-flight computations and for mid-course navigation systems will also be considered. A brief discussion has been included to show the major factors that are applicable to the selection of a guidance system for lunar purposes.

7.3.1 THE THREE-BODY PROBLEM

The most important characteristic of lunar navigation and guidance arises as a result of the complexity of the gravity field in which the flight occurs. As the discussion of Section 7.1 has shown, the flight of a lunar space vehicle must, indeed, be considered as a three-body problem; that is, the spacecraft is a mass-point travelling under the influence of the combined gravity fields of two major massive bodies. A further complication arises as a result of the motions of the Earth–Moon system relative to inertial space and to the other bodies in the Solar System.

Indeed, an explicit analysis of the motions of a spacecraft in cis-lunar space would allow for the following:

The motions of the Moon about the Earth
Perturbations to the orbit of the Earth that are caused by the Moon
The motion of the Earth–Moon system about the Sun
The perturbations of the motions of the Earth and the Moon that are caused by other Solar System bodies
The motion of the Solar System through galactic space.

Although all of these should be considered, an adequate approximation will be obtained if consideration is given to the first motion only, that is, to the motion of the Moon as an orbiting body that is revolving about the Earth. A spacecraft that is in flight from the Earth to the Moon and return may have its motion analyzed as though the barycenter of the Earth–Moon system were the origin of an inertial reference frame. However, the analysis must recognize that the two most important masses in the system, the Earth and the Moon, are both in motion relative to this reference point. The motion may be described as that of a rigid body in rotation about its center of mass (the barycenter) with a constant angular velocity; the period of this motion is about 27 days. This motion is illustrated in Figure 7.20. These motions have been described in some detail in Section 7.2.1.

The description of the motions of a spacecraft that is moving under the influence of the gravity of two massive bodies such as the Earth and the Moon constitutes one of the more important applications of the three-body problem. The three-body problem is classical and is treated in many standard texts dealing with celestial mechanics (cf. Reference 7.2, page 421). A complete and general integration of all of the equations of motion in the three-body problem that is similar to the solution of the two-body problem discussed in Chapter 2 is not recognized to be possible. As a practical matter, motions of a spacecraft in cis-lunar space must be determined using numerical methods, such as an expansion in an approximating series (variation of parameters) or a numerical integration (Enke's method). Two special cases have been found however that do not demand the simplifying assumption that one of the bodies has an infinitesimal mass.

A special form of the three-body problem has been defined by Jacobi and is of particular interest in the study of lunar flight. Jacobi assumed that one of the three masses is much greater than the others. His investigations determine the motion of the body of infinitesimal mass (that is the spacecraft) in the gravitational fields of the two finite masses. The development of the equations of motion for the planar restricted three-body problem is beyond the scope of the present work; it is developed in Reference 7.2 (pages 431–435). Jacobi's

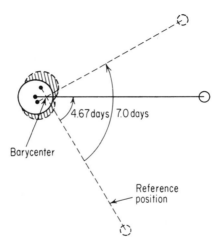

Fig. 7.20. The motion of the Earth-Moon system about its barycenter.

equations may be used to compute the flight path of a particle, or spacecraft, in the gravity field of two large masses. Numerical methods of computation must be employed and the calculations are laborious and time consuming. Modern high speed computing machinery, however, reduces the labor to the point where such trajectories may be calculated with relative ease once the problem has been programmed.

A discussion of the Jacobian planar three-body problem and the non-planar example will be omitted here. The reader is commended to the references for this detail. It should be noted, however, that each individual flight program represents a special case and no useful generalizations may be made. Consequently, it would serve no useful purpose to discuss specific results here.

7.3.2 LUNAR NAVIGATION SYSTEMS

In the following paragraphs, some of the general properties of guidance and navigation systems that might be applied to lunar flight missions will be discussed. The factors contributing to the selection of a system from among those that are treated will be mentioned and the suitability to an actual lunar flight operation will be evaluated. A later section will deal with the instrumentation that is required to implement some of these systems.

The navigation and control of lunar flight operations requires the means to monitor the progress of a flight and to evaluate this progress against some criteria of planned progress. In addition, it will be necessary to compute and to execute corrective maneuvers that will eliminate the effects of flight errors soon after they are detected. Three important kinds of system should be considered. They are listed below.

Open loop system: this describes a system that depends upon the precise calculation of the three-body orbit of a spacecraft. All the forces that will act on the craft are measured or predicted and then they are taken into account in order to calculate a predicted flight path for the spacecraft. A guidance system of this kind must include the capability to observe the trajectory and subsequently to control the motion of the spacecraft so that only limited deviations will be permitted from the nominal, or predicted, trajectory. An example of such a system would be an all inertial system with a programmed gravity correction.

Earth-based tracking and correction: this is a system employing a complex of fixed ground stations for the purpose of tracking the spacecraft. These stations, together with their data reduction systems, determine the position and velocity of the craft and predict its motions in the vicinity of the Moon. In addition to the precision that is gained from the large dimensions that will be permissible in the base-line for such a system, extreme precision and flexibility of operation may be derived from the use of a large ground-based computer installation for high speed orbit calculations and the generation of corrections with high accuracy.

Self-contained homing system: this is a system of instruments, carried in the lunar vehicle, that is used to observe selected flight coordinates relative to the destination in order to determine the corrections that are required to bring the craft to its destination. Although the precision and the flexibility of such a system is less than for an Earth-based system, the self-contained device may be employed to correct the trajectory of a spacecraft with relation to its destination. In a sense, it is a form of closed loop system and a moderate level of approximation will be acceptable provided the propulsion system permits an iterative solution to be accepted.

In the final analysis, the selection of a lunar navigation system will be based on the factors outlined above, but consideration must also be given to some important operational problems. For example, consider how an operational limit that might be placed on the post-burn-out maneuvers of a spacecraft will influence the selection of a navigation system from among the three kinds discussed above. If the payload capability of the craft does not allow for the propulsion equipment that will provide a post-injection guidance maneuver, an open loop system must be employed to insure the precise selection of a satisfactory orbit. If, however, limited guidance corrections are permissible, then extreme precision tracking will be exercised to measure the orbit during the early flight and to compute the corrections required for a single corrective maneuver. An Earth-based system will probably be found most favorable. The precision of the system will, of course, be enhanced by application of a "three-body" system of flight analysis for orbit prediction. Finally, if sufficient payload margins exist to permit application of iterative solutions, a self-contained system may be preferred in terms of flexibility, cost, and over-all performance. The self contained systems will, of course, be useful in those missions where precise orbits in the vicinity of the Moon, or landing maneuvers are required.

Of all the factors that may influence the selection of a system for guidance and navigation of a flight to the Moon, the two most important will be the ability of the system to perform the mission at hand and the total cost associated with the use of that system. No navigation system, regardless of the savings in cost, will be satisfactory unless it is capable of performing in the context of the assigned mission. However, among those systems that are judged to be capable, it will be natural to select the guidance system that will involve the least total cost for the operation. The ability of a given system to perform the lunar flight mission must be evaluated in terms of accuracy, reliability, weight, flexibility, operating range, and environment. Cost is, of course, influenced by reliability, extent of ground based installations, logistical support, and crew operations required.

Under the circumstances that will apply to early exploration of the Moon, it will be expected that lunar flights will be made under the guidance and direct supervision of a ground-based system. Consider the hypothetical complex of three tracking stations shown in Figure 7.21. Three tracking stations are located about the Earth at intervals of 120° in longitude and with latitude to place the stations in the vicinity of the plane of the lunar orbit. This complex of tracking stations will be able to track the spacecraft continuously in its flight to the Moon after the craft has attained a sufficient altitude, say in excess of the Earth's radius. Range, angles, and doppler tracking techniques, together with data smoothing, will permit the orbit parameters to be determined with a high level of precision. The distribution of tracking systems in the current NASA tracking and control network is shown in Figure 7.22.

A ground-based system of the kind that is described above will have a high reliability since the stations can be made arbitrarily free of failure, failures that do occur can be repaired, and failures in a single station need not have a catastrophic effect on the success of the total operation. The cost of such a system will, however, be high when one considers the problems associated with staff,

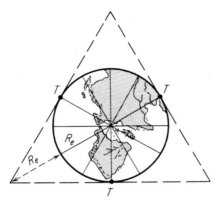

T = tracking station

Fig. 7.21. Coverage of space from three equatorial tracking stations.

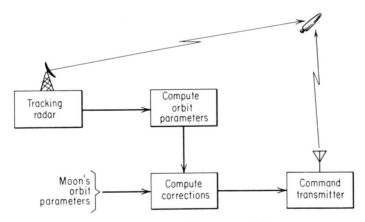

Fig. 7.22. Lunar tracking-command loop.

supply, maintenance, and communications support for such a complex of stations. In the event that only a single transmitting station is employed for transmission of commands to the spacecraft, it will be necessary to assure that this station will have a clear "view" of the spacecraft at the time when it will be necessary to transmit orbit correction commands to the craft.

A self-contained system for lunar navigation requires that sensors of sufficient

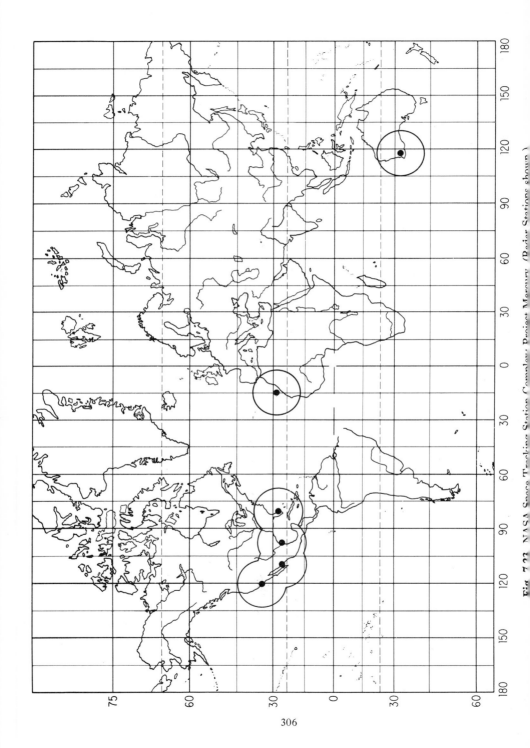

Fig. 7.22. NASA Space Tracking Station Complex, Project Mercury. (Radar Stations shown.)

accuracy be miniaturized and packaged to be carried on-board the lunar craft. Such a system gains inherent accuracy as the craft approaches the Moon, see Section 6.5. However, inaccuracy in the sensors will result in "hunting" by the navigation system and hence by the craft. This hunting will be at the expense of fuel in the propulsion system. Nevertheless, a self-contained system of this kind that permits adjustment of the orbit plane and of the periapsis of the approach orbit is essential if a particular lunar launch trajectory or landing point is required for the mission. Since the navigator makes repeated adjustments of his trajectory as he approaches the Moon, this kind of system will be particularly applicable to lunar navigation. The three-body nature of the trajectory becomes less important as the craft approaches the Moon, or the Earth, on either its outbound or inbound leg of the journey.

7.4 SUMMARY OF LUNAR NAVIGATION

The discussions of the previous sections of this chapter have presented the environment in which lunar flight will occur. The characteristics of cis-lunar space and the trajectories for lunar transfer have been described together with the non-linear character of the lunar navigation problem. This section will summarize these and show how the space navigation techniques that have been discussed in previous chapters of the book may be applied to lunar navigation.

The discussions that appeared in previous sections have shown that it is not possible to define a general solution to lunar navigation and that each flight must be treated as an individual case. Each transfer orbit will be related to an Earth-fixed coordinate system in a special way that is, itself, related to the time of departure, the intended duration of the flight, and the location of the individual terminal points on the Earth and the Moon respectively. No useful repetitive cycle exists that will provide a convenient relation between these conditions and time.

Navigation for lunar flight will require that the ascent from Earth be controlled with sufficient accuracy to place the craft in a transfer orbit that will bring the spacecraft close enough to permit corrective maneuvers to convert the initial orbit to a satisfactory orbit for the lunar landing that has been planned. A definition of the terms *sufficient accuracy*, *close enough*, and *satisfactory* as used in the previous sentence will depend upon the design of an individual flight system, its payload and performance margins, and its propulsion efficiency. These definitions will not be discussed further here, but they will be given as a fundamental part of the navigator's operating procedure in any specific flight. In cases where the desired trajectory at the Moon may be defined in terms of a periapsis distance (in the lunar flight case this is sometimes called the *periselene*), the techniques for corrective maneuvers have been discussed in Section 6.5. Coefficients for calculation of the correction maneuvers are given in Section 7.2.3.

Lunar reconnaissance orbits of specified altitudes call for approach to the Moon on an orbit that gives a pre-established periapsis; conversion to the lunar orbit can then be accomplished at the point of periapsis. Specific landing sites may then be selected from the reconnaissance orbit. The low rate of revolution of the Moon will cause the motion of the ground path of the satellite orbit to be exceedingly slow; that is, the satellite will pass over nearly the same point on the ground each pass. The selection of a ground landing site can be accomplished by the selection of a de-orbiting time and the de-orbiting maneuver.

A mission that calls for a direct flight to a lunar landing will require more careful analysis of the orbits to relate the orbit parameters to the point on the surface of the Moon where impact will occur. The point of impact on the surface of the Moon will lie in the trajectory plane. It will be defined by a polar angle that is measured between the radius through the point of impact and a reference line. The impact point may be calculated by application of the orbit Equation (2-24), the impact point will be given by

$$r_0 = \frac{p}{1 + e \cos (\theta - \theta_0)} \tag{7-6}$$

where

r_0 = the lunar radius, 1080 miles
θ_e = the orientation of the reference line relative to the periselene
θ = the polar angle between the point of impact and the reference line measured in the plane of the trajectory.

Solving, now, for the polar angle of the impact point,

$$\cos (\theta - \theta_0) = \frac{1}{e} \left(\frac{p}{r_0} - 1 \right) \tag{7-7}$$

A more convenient form results when the parameter p is replaced by $p = r_p(1 + e)$.

$$\cos (\theta - \theta_0) = \left(\frac{r_p}{r_0} \right) \frac{1 + e}{e} - \frac{1}{e} \tag{7-8}$$

Figure 7.24 illustrates the relations between the point of impact in the trajectory plane and the orbit parameters of eccentricity and periapsis. These parameters will not be related in any convenient way to the lunar latitude and longitude. This relation will depend upon the orbit inclination and the lunar coordinates of the axis of the approach orbits.

The initial conditions for injection into a lunar transfer orbit were discussed in Section 7.2. These initial conditions and the sensitivity of these parameters for a lunar impact are indicated in Figures 7.9 through 7.11. Briefly, for flights in which the initial velocity exceeds 35,000 ft/sec, lunar impact will be obtained if the velocity direction is controlled within $\pm$ 0.25 deg. Certainly, this accuracy of guidance and control will be adequate where terminal maneuvers such as those that have been described in Sections 6.5 and 7.2.3 can be employed. Instrumentation systems for the guidance and control of the ascent boosters have been described in Chapter 3 and need not be discussed here in the specific context of lunar flight.

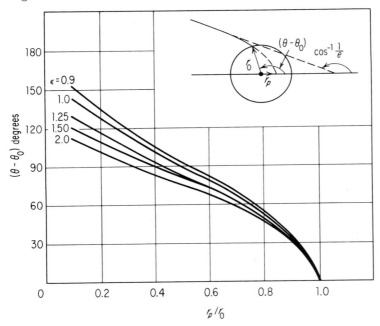

Fig. 7.24. Point of lunar impact as a function of approach trajectory parameters.

REFERENCES

7.1. Moulton, F. R., *An Introduction to Celestial Mechanics* (Chapter IX, Part II—The Lunar Theory), The Macmillan Co., New York, 1914.

7.2. Ehricke, K. A., *Space Flight: Vol. I Environment and Celestial Mechanics*, D. Van Nostrand Co. Inc., Princeton, N.J., 1960.

7.3. Lieske, H. A., *Lunar Trajectory Studies*, The RAND Corporation, P-1293, Santa Monica, Calif., Feb. 26, 1958.

7.4. Walters, L. G., *Lunar Trajectory Mechanics*, Navigation Vol. VI, p. 51, Institute of Navigation, Spring, 1958.

7.5. Stearns, E. V., *Propulsion Requirements for a Soft Lunar Landing*, Proceedings of the National Flight Propulsion Meeting—IAS; Cleveland, Ohio, March 10, 11, 1960.

7.6. Noton, A. R. M., *Post Injection Radio Guidance for Interplanetary Missions*, Jet Propulsion Laboratories TM471, Pasadena, Calif., 1959.

8

NAVIGATION IN INTERSTELLAR

FLIGHT

The previous chapters have dealt with the problems of space navigation in environments where travel has been confined to the Solar System, that is, the Earth, Moon and the planets. While manned flight has just begun to penetrate extraterrestrial space, it is apparent that no region of the Solar System will remain unavailable to navigation as sufficient propulsion energy becomes available. In this brief chapter we will discuss lightly the navigation of a spacecraft that travels from the Solar System to the vicinity of other stars. There are, of course, problems associated with the very great distances between the stars and our Solar System that require special attention. For example, a space ship that escapes from the Earth with 15 mi/sec will have a velocity of about 7.5 mi/sec remaining when it has escaped from the Solar System. If it is headed towards the closest star, Alpha Centauri, which is 4.3 light years distant from the Earth, the journey would take 175,000 years. If the speed of the craft is made to approach the speed of light, the round trip journey to that star would require somewhat more than eight years. The effects of relativity would influence the propulsion requirements for such a spacecraft adversely; indeed, it is doubtful that such a craft might be practicable with any known form of propulsion.

One may conceive of some special problems that will be associated with the long time of such a journey and speculation on the idea of space borne colonies has occupied more than one author, References 8.1 and 8.2. Special aspects of the time paradox may be applied to the space travellers in colonies such as these. We will not discuss these interesting problems but will confine our remarks to a brief discussion of the environment for interstellar travel, some comments on the mechanics of interstellar flight, and finally a few suggestions for specific methods to determine position and velocity in interstellar flight.

8.1 INTERSTELLAR FLIGHT ENVIRONMENT

In terms of its distribution of mass, the universe may be described as a vast expanse of empty space containing widely separated clusters of stars; these clusters are called *galaxies*. The Sun, with its planets making up the Solar System, is clustered with an estimated 150 billion other stars. This cluster, or galaxy, is called the Milky Way. It is roughly 100,000 light years in diameter. This galaxy is disk shaped, since its thickness is roughly one fifth of its diameter, or 20,000 light years. For reference, it would take less than 11 hours for light to travel the length of the major axis of the orbit of Pluto, the outermost known planet of the Solar System. The spatial density of the stars near the center of the galaxy may be more than 1000 times the stellar density in the vicinity of the sun.

The properties of some of the nearer stars have been described in the literature. For example, Gadomski has described 59 known stars within 17 light years of the Sun and Sandage has estimated that 1700 stars lie within 56 light years of Sol. Reference 8.3 and 8.4. It is apparent that an interesting and perhaps rich field of exploration would be available to an interstellar vehicle having a range of 10 to 100 light years from Sol.

There are other galaxies besides the Milky Way. As a matter of fact, galaxies are themselves grouped in ones, doubles, or multiple galaxies, groups (about 10) and clusters of galaxies with membership measured in hundreds or thousands. Star clusters are assemblages of stars having members less widely scattered than are the stars in the fields around the clusters. They are not contemporary congestions; the stars in groups are moving together so that the clusters maintain their identities for a very long time. Star clusters are of two types: *galactic clusters* and *globular clusters*.

Galactic clusters are so named because they are found near the principal plane of the Milky Way. Accordingly, they appear in, or near, the Milky Way when observed from the Earth and appear to be associated with our own galaxy. Also known as *open clusters*, they are not highly concentrated toward their centers. About 500 galactic clusters can be identified. They have a linear diameter of about 6 parsecs (one parsec is about 3.26 light years); their memberships range from around 20 to a few hundred stars.

Globular clusters are more compact and are spheroid in form. They are much larger, more populous, and more distant than the known galactic clusters. They are less confined to the vicinity of the Milky Way. More than 100 globular clusters are recognized in the galactic system. Only a few of these are visible without a telescope.

The space between the stars, in the spiral arms of the Milky Way, contains great quantities of dust and gas. These very tenuous clouds can be observed because they are made luminous by reflection of light from nearby stars; others are observable because they obscure areas of the Milky Way or of the bright nebulae.

There are tens of thousands of galactic clusters known. An estimate has been made of the speed that would be required to escape the potential field of our galaxy; it is on the order of 250 miles per second. Unlike the Solar System, the galaxies are not systems of bodies that orbit about a single massive body whose central gravity field predominates. The stars in a galaxy are moving about under the mutual influence of their collective gravity fields. In addition, the individual clusters and galaxies are in a relative motion that indicates that the universe is indeed expanding.

A craft that is moving about in the Milky Way will find it convenient to define its position in terms of a galactic latitude–longitude system of coordinates. For this purpose, it is necessary to define a new system of coordinates for the celestial sphere. The north and south *galactic poles* are the two opposite points that appear to an Earth observer to be the farthest from the central line of the Milky Way. These appear in the following positions when referred to the equinox of 1900.

Galactic North Pole: R.A. 12^h40^m, decl $+$ 28 deg (Coma Berenices)
Galactic South Pole: R.A. 0^h40^m, decl $-$ 28 deg (Sculptor)

The galactic equator is the great circle that is equidistant from the galactic poles; it runs about a degree north of the central line of the Milky Way when observed from the Earth, such that the Sun is north of the principal plane of the galaxy. The galactic equator is inclined 62° to the celestial equator, the ascending node appears in the constellation of Aquilar and the descending node is in the opposite point to the east of Orion.

Galactic longitude is reckoned in degrees from the ascending node described above (R.A. 18^h40^m). Viewed from the north galactic pole, it increases in the counterclockwise direction. *Galactic latitude* is measured from the galactic equator towards the north or south galactic poles.

The Sun is near the principal plane of the galactic system, but it is a long way from the center. The center is estimated to be about 8000 parsecs (26,000 light years) from the Sun in the direction of the star cloud Sagittarius. When observed from the Earth, the center of the galaxy is estimated to be at longitude 327°, latitude $\pm$ 1°. Consequently the Sun would be found to be located at longitude 147°, latitude $\pm$ 1° when observed from the galactic center.

Like the Sun, the stars are globes of hot gas. Their radiations filter through the stellar atmosphere and permit astronomers to estimate the properties of the star. The effective temperature of a star is taken to be the temperature of its radiating surface when calculated by radiation laws. The temperature of stars measured in this way ranges from 2000°K to 50,000°K.

The stars are mainly hydrogen and helium with impurities of carbon, nitrogen, and oxygen; only traces of other elements appear. Hydrogen constitutes about 55 per cent of the cosmic material, helium 44 per cent and the heavier elements constitute the remaining 1 per cent in about the same proportions as they occur on the Earth.

8.2 INTERSTELLAR/INTERGALACTIC FLIGHT MECHANICS

Before a spacecraft can be described to be in interstellar flight, it is necessary that the spacecraft escape from the Solar System. Bodies within the Solar System are in orbits that are influenced primarily by the Sun. A craft will be considered to have escaped from the Solar System if it has obtained a velocity in excess of the solar escape velocity. This velocity is shown in Figure 8.1.

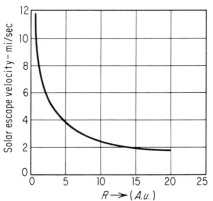

Fig. 8.1. Solar escape velocity.

A spacecraft that has escaped from the Solar System will be moving away from the Sun and, presumably, in the direction of its destination at a velocity that is equal to the hyperbolic excess velocity. The propulsion needed to obtain a departure speed is measured by the characteristic velocity of the maneuver. This represents the total velocity increment required. The characteristic velocity (v_c) that is required to depart the Earth is shown in Figure 8.2 as a function of the hyperbolic excess velocity relative to the Sun (v_∞).

While the hyperbolic excess velocity represents the initial velocity of departure from the Solar System, it is to be anticipated that this velocity will be changed in magnitude and direction by the accelerations of the craft due to the gravity fields of the other stars. Initially, the craft will be at such a great distance from these stars that this influence will be barely perceptible. As the craft comes closer, however, the influence of these fields will increase until, in the near vicinity of a star, the spacecraft will enter into an orbit that is essentially a Keplerian hyperbola and, for this interval, the mutual interactions of these two bodies alone need be considered.

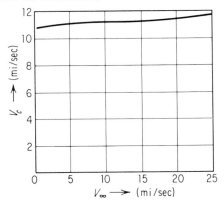

Fig. 8.2. Characteristic velocity as a function of solar hyperbolic excess velocity —take-off from Earth's surface.

The motions of the craft as it passes in the vicinity of a star in this manner will be similar in all respects to the motion of a comet. Unless some disturbing influence, for example drag acceleration, rocket maneuvers, and so forth, is applied to the spacecraft, it will not be captured by the star as it passes but will experience a change in the velocity direction. This change in course may be predicted from the relations illustrated in Figure 8.3.

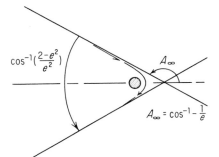

Fig. 8.3. Course change encountering a star.

One, of course, is tempted to speculate on the means for use of this acceleration for course changes and steering. While no net increase in velocity magnitude will be realized from an exchange such as the one described above, these encounters might be used in a controlled fashion to provide the changes of direction that will permit an excursion to be varied. Two or more such encounters may be employed to close a "round trip" journey without requiring further expenditure of rocket propellant except that which is required for corrective maneuvers.

In general, the velocity of an interstellar space voyager will be within a few orders of magnitude of the velocities of the stars with respect to each other. Consequently, it will not be possible to consider the stars as fixed points in space and to navigate the spacecraft with respect to these fixed points. Also, the stars of the galaxy through which the craft is traveling will not be useful for navigation purposes since relatively large parallax angles will develop in their lines of sight as observed from the craft. Useful navigational reference data may, however, be derived from observation of stars in distant galaxies. In order for this to be useful, it is necessary that the galaxy in which the travel is occurring has been mapped with sufficient detail to show the point of departure, the destination, and any important way points or hazards.

8.3 NAVIGATION IN THE GALAXY

Just as in the context of other applications, navigation in an interstellar flight will require the determination of position and velocity of the spacecraft and the subsequent calculation of the course changes permitting the craft to close with its destination. The means for accomplishing each of these steps will be discussed briefly in the following pages. The treatment will not attempt to be exhaustive, to do so would involve extensive speculation relative to the kind of flight systems that might be used for interstellar flights. A few problems will be anticipated and some possible solutions to these will be suggested and discussed in the following pages.

8.3.1 POSITION DETERMINATION

Interstellar navigation will not be possible by a direct application of celestial navigation techniques as we found to be the case for terrestrial and Earth satellite vehicles. Many of the stars that are considered to be fixed for navigation purposes when observed from the Earth can not be considered to be fixed for purposes of interstellar flight. The very great distances that are traveled by the spacecraft will introduce sizeable parallax errors in observations of the closer stars. Furthermore, the long flight times involved in an interstellar journey may, in some cases permit the relative motion of the stars to become apparent. These objections are particularly applicable to observations that are made with respect to stars within the Milky Way galaxy. Stars that are more distant may, however, be used for navigation purposes. Before being used for navigation, each star should be carefully evaluated in this respect.

The manner in which stars are used for determination of position within the Milky Way will be quite different from terrestrial applications. First, the distance from the spacecraft to the center of the galaxy must be calculated as well as the latitude and the longitude of the craft. This requires the use of three stars to determine a position rather than two stars as are used in conventional, or terrestrial, navigation by celestial observations. Since no point will be universally identifiable with the center of the galaxy, it will be necessary to measure the angles between the lines of sight to each of three stars; three angles will be observed. These three angles will then be used with galactocentric values of the positions of these stars to calculate the position of the craft. This position will be most conveniently stated with reference to the galactic latitude-longitude system.

A device for radio ranging to the stars might be employed in a manner similar to that described in Chapter 3 (See Section 3.4.2 or Reference 3.8). While a system of this kind is theoretically feasible, its use would be frustrated by the radio noise to be expected from the stars. The level of this noise would surely exceed the signal strength that might be receivable from a system of interstellar beacons. A further objection would arise to the use of a radio ranging system. This is due to the excessive time delay that would be associated with radio transmission/reception over interstellar distances.

Special techniques for observation of spacecraft position will be applicable on approach to a specific star. These applications are only valid as the relative distances between the star and the spacecraft become small, say 100 to 1000 astronomical units. These will be discussed in a later section. (See Section 8.3.3.)

8.3.2 VELOCITY DETERMINATION

The velocity of the spacecraft may be calculated from a series of position measurements used as a time sequence of data. For many purposes this will probably be adequate. A doppler shift method may also be applied. While theoretically possible, radio frequency doppler techniques do not appear to be feasible because of the long time (several years) required for the transmission of radio signals to and from stellar targets.

Doppler shift techniques that employ spectroscopic methods to determine velocity relative to selected stars have been described in the literature (Reference 8.6). These devices depend upon the universal characteristics of the spectrum from stars and their gaseous atmospheres. If a spacecraft observes the spectra of several stars, a shift in the absorption lines will be noted that indicates the radial components of velocity of the craft relative to the star being observed.

The shift in the spectral line will be the result of the doppler principle and can be analyzed by the applicable theory. A shift of the spectral lines towards the red indicates recession of the star while a shift towards the blue indicates an approach. Observation of the radial velocity of the spacecraft relative to several selected stars will permit calculation of the velocity relative to the galactic reference system.

8.3.3 NAVIGATION RELATIVE TO AN APPROACHING STAR

As the interstellar flight proceeds and the spacecraft approaches a star along its way, it will be desirable to observe, precisely, if the spacecraft is on a course that will bring it to the vicinity of that star. This can be determined by observation of the time rate of change of the direction of the line of sight to the star in question. If the direction of the line of sight remains fixed in space, the craft is on a collision course to the star that is being observed.

The line of sight direction can, in principle, be observed using gyro-stabilized instruments to note the changes. However, a more satisfactory means for the observation will probably be derived from observations of the destination star against a stellar field background. If no relative motions are observed, the craft is on a collision course. Proportional navigation may be employed to correct a non-collision course to place the craft on a true collision course with a selected star. In proportional navigation, the rate of change in heading of the spacecraft is made to be proportional to the observed rate of change of the direction to the star. In the more familiar application of an interceptor missile, this technique is used in a continuous maneuver. In interstellar examples, it will be necessary to make corrections and to monitor the result over a long period of time to assess the effect of the new trajectory after each maneuver. A series of corrective maneuvers will be required to effect an approximate collision.

As the spacecraft approaches its final phase of flight toward a star, the navigator will wish to steer his craft in such a way as to maneuver within a specified distance of the star and, perhaps, to control the eccentricity of the orbit as it approaches the chosen star. The techniques for doing this have been described in Section 6.5 under the title of Interplanetary Landings and will not be discussed further here.

REFERENCES

8.1. Sheppard, L. R., *Interstellar Flight*, The Realities of Space Flight, Edited by L. J. Carter, McGraw-Hill Book Co., New York, 1957.

8.2. Cornog, Robert, *Selected Problems of Interstellar Navigation*, Navigation VII, 2 and 3, Summer, 1960.

8.3. Gadomski, Jan, *Die Sternenskospheren im Radius von 17 Lichtjahren um die Sonne*, Proceedings of the VIIth Congress of the IAF, Barcelona, 1957.

8.4. Sandage, Allan, *The Stars within 15 Parsecs of the Sun*, Stellar Populations, Interscience Publishers, Inc., New York, 1958.

8.5. Baker, Robert H., *Astronomy*, 6th ed., D. Van Nostrand, New York, 1955.

8.6. Sonnabend, David, *Measurement of Velocity in Space*, Proceedings of AAS 4th National Meeting, New York, 1957.

APPENDIX I

GLOSSARY OF TERMS

Anomaly. An angle; for example, true anomaly, mean anomaly, eccentric anomaly.

> *Eccentric Anomaly.* An angle at the center of an ellipse between the line of apsides and the radius of the auxiliary circle through a point having the same apsidal distance as a given point on the ellipse.

> *Mean Anomaly.* The angle through which an object would move at the uniform average angular speed, *n*, measured from the principal focus.

> *True Anomaly.* The angle at the focus between the line of apsides and the radius vector measured in the direction of orbital motion.

Aphelion. The point on an elliptical orbit about the sun that is farthest from the sun.

Apoapsis. The point farthest from the principal focus of an orbit in a central force field.

Apogee. The highest point on an *earth-centered* elliptical orbit. The point of intersection of the trajectory and its semi-major axis that lies farthest from the principal focus.

Apsides. (line of Apsides) In an elliptical orbit, the major axis.

Apsis. The point on a conic where the radius vector is a maximum or a minimum.

Celestial Equator. The great circle on the celestial sphere that is formed by the intersection of the celestial sphere with the plane of the earth's equator. For solar system applications, it is formed by intersection with the ecliptic.

Celestial Sphere. A sphere of infinite radius with its center at the center of the earth upon which the stars and other astronomical bodies appear to be projected. This sphere is fixed in space and appears to rotate counter to the diurnal rotation of the earth. For solar system navigation purposes, the celestial sphere may be considered to be centered at the Sun.

Coordinates on the Celestial Sphere. Polar coordinates are used in specifying the location of a star, or other heavenly body on the celestial sphere. These are the *declination* (δ) and the *right ascension* (R.A.).

Declination. The declination of a star is the angular distance north, or south, of the celestial equator measured on the celestial sphere.

Ecliptic. The great circle on the celestial sphere that is formed by its intersection with the plane of the earth's orbit.

Epoch. Arbitrary instant of time for which elements of an orbit are valid.

First point of Aries (Υ). Vernal equinox.

Geocentric coordinates. Coordinates on the celestial sphere as they would be observed from the center of the earth.

Hyperbolic excess velocity. In the two-body problem, the relative velocity of the bodies after escape from the mutual potential field.

North Celestial pole. This is the point of intersection of the earth's axis of rotation with the celestial sphere. In solar system navigation applications, the celestial poles form a line normal to the ecliptic plane while preserving the sense of the North-South orientation.

Orbital Elements. The orbit of a body that is attracted by an inverse-square central force can be specified unambiguously by nine parameters (See Chapter II). These parameters are known as the elements of the orbit.

Parameters (orbit). Orbital elements.

Parameters (flight). Descriptive quantities that define the flight conditions relative to a selected reference frame.

Periapsis. In an elliptical orbit, the apses closest to the non-vacant focus. In an open orbit, the point of closest approach to the orbit center.

Perigee. The point in the orbit of a spacecraft that is closest to the earth when the orbit is about the earth.

Perihelion. The point of an orbit about the sun that is closest to the sun.

Retrograde. Orbital motion in a direction opposite to that of the planets in the solar system; that is, clockwise as seen from the north of the ecliptic.

Right Ascension (R.A.). The right ascension of a star is the angle, measured eastward along the celestial equator, from the vernal equinox to the great circle passing through the north celestial pole and the star under observation. Right ascension is frequently expressed in hours, minutes and

seconds of sidereal time (1 hour is equal to 15°) because clocks are used
in the terrestrial measurement of right ascension.

Time. In astronomical usage, time is usually expressed as universal time (U.T.).
This is identical with Greenwich Civil Time and is counted from 0 to 24
hours beginning with midnight. A decimal subdivision is often used in
place of hours, minutes and seconds. Thus the following are all identical

> Nov 30.75 UT
> Nov 30; 18^h 00^m UT
> Nov 30; 1800Z
> Nov 30; 1:00 pm EST.

Topocentric Coordinates. Coordinates on the celestial sphere as observed from
the surface of the earth.

Topocentric Parallax. The difference between geocentric and topocentric
positions of a body in the sky.

Vernal Equinox. The point where the sun appears to cross the celestial equator
from south to north. The time of this crossing, when day and night are
everywhere of equal length, occurs at about 21 March.

APPENDIX II

GLOSSARY OF SYMBOLS

The symbols that have been used for mathematical representations of quantities have generally been defined as they are introduced. Nevertheless the following listing of common applications used in this text is presented to assist the reader. Special applications of the symbols are defined as they appear in the text and these definitions should always be interpreted and confirmed in local context where used.

A	Variable angles; area	M	Mass
A_t	True anomaly	R	Radial distance (usually from the sun)
A_e	Eccentric anomaly		
C	Coefficient of drag	R_e	Radius of the earth $=20.9 \times 10^6$ ft.
E	Specific energy, i.e. energy per unit mass	T	Thrust, period
F	Force	V	Velocity
G	Universal constant of gravity	W	Weight
		$\dot{W}$	Rate of burning propellant
H	Angular momentun of a gyroscope	a	Acceleration, semi major axis
I_{sp}	Specific impulse	b	Non-gravitational acceleration; semi minor axis
K	Gravitational constant of the sun $(K=3.17 \times 10^{10}$ mi³/sec²$)$	c	Distance from center of ellipse to a focus
L	Longitude, torque	e	Eccentricity

f	Force; frequency	r	Radial distance
g	Acceleration due to gravity	r_a	Distance to apoapsis
h	Orbit angular momentum; altitude	r_p	Distance to periapsis
i	inclination angle	t	Time (independent variable)
k	Gravitational field constant	t_p	Time of passing periapsis
l	Longitude	v	Velocity
m	Mass	v_∞	Hyperbolic excess velocity
n	Mean motion in orbit	v_e	Escape velocity
p	Semi-latus rectum	v_p	Velocity at periapsis
q	Generalized coordinate		

GREEK SYMBOLS

γ	Flight path angle	σ	Range angle
θ	Angle of position in orbit measured from reference line	τ	Transfer time
		ϕ	Elevation angle, coflight path angle
$(\theta-\theta_p)$	True anomaly	ω	Frequency of angular rotation, $\omega=\dfrac{2\pi}{T}$; a longitude angle (see p. 201)
θ_p	Argument to periapsis		
λ	Latitude		
π	3.1416...		
ρ	Radial distance; density	Ω	Angular velocity

ASTRONOMICAL SYMBOLS

⊙	Sun	♅	Uranus
☿	Mercury	♆	Neptune
♀	Venus	♇	Pluto
⊕	Earth	☊	Ascending node
♂	Mars	☋	Descending node
♃	Jupiter	♈	Symbol for first point of Aries
♄	Saturn		

APPENDIX III

DATA ON THE SOLAR SYSTEM

Planet	Sun	Mercury	Venus	Earth	Mars	Jupiter	Saturn	Uranus	Neptune	Pluto	Moon (relative to Earth)
Mean distance from Sun, miles	—	36×10^6	67.2×10^6	92.9×10^6	141.5×10^6	483×10^6	886×10^6	1783×10^6	2791×10^6	3671×10^6	23.9×10^4
Mean orbital velocity, miles/sec	—	29.7	21.7	18.5	15.0	8.11	5.96	4.22	3.37	2.94	0.636
Mean angular orbital velocity, deg/day	—	4.09	1.602	0.986	0.524	0.083	0.0335	0.0117	0.006	0.004	13.17
Sidereal period, days	—	88.0	224.7	365.26	687.0	4332.0	10.759[1]	30.700[1]	60.200[1]	90.800[1]	27.32
Rotational period, days	24.65 to 33.3	88.0	30(?)	0.998	1.027	0.413	0.431	0.448	0.666	—	27.32
Eccentricity of orbit	—	0.206	0.00681	0.0167	0.0933	0.0484	0.0558	0.0471	0.0086	0.249	0.0549
Inclination of equator to orbit, deg	7.175	—	—	23.45	25.20	3.115	26.745	98.0	29.0	—	6.678
Inclination of orbit to ecliptic, deg	—	7.0	3.395	0	1.85	1.307	2.492	0.772	1.773	17.315	5.141
Mass, lb	4.35×10^{30}	0.725×10^{24}	10.65×10^{24}	13.19×10^{24}	1.41×10^{24}	4150×10^{24}	1240×10^{24}	190×10^{24}	225×10^{24}	12.1×10^{21}	0.162×10^{24}
Density (water = 1.00)	1.41	5.46	5.06	5.52	4.12	1.35	0.71	1.56	2.47	2	3.33
Force constant, $\mu = GM$, miles³/sec²	3.17×10^{10}	5.28×10^3	7.75×10^4	9.60×10^4	1.026×10^4	3.02×10^7	9.03×10^6	1.38×10^6	1.64×10^6	8.8×10^4	1.18×10^3
Solar radiation intensity ($\oplus = 1$)	—	6.7	1.9	1.0	0.43	0.04	0.01	0.003	0.001	0.0006	1.0
Mean diameter, miles	864,000	3010	7610	7918	4140	86,900	71,500	29,500	26,800	3600.0	2160
Oblateness $(a-b)/a$	0	0	0	0.00337	0.00521	0.065	0.1053	0.071	0.0222	—	—
Gravity at surface, ft/sec²	897.0	12.3	28.2	32.2	12.7	84.4	36.9	33.5	48.2	14.3	5.33
Escape velocity at surface, miles/sec	383.0	2.65	6.38	6.97	3.15	37.3	22.4	13.7	15.7	10.0	1.48
Satellite velocity at surface, miles/sec	271.0	1.87	4.51	4.93	2.23	26.4	15.8	9.68	11.1	7.0	1.05
Sun's gravity at planet's orbit, ft/sec²	—	0.129	0.0371	0.0194	0.0084	0.00072	0.00021	0.000053	0.000021	0.000012	0.0194

Note: (1) Years

RELATION BETWEEN COORDINATES & PARAMETERS

The following is a summary of important relations between the flight coordinates of a craft and the parameters that may be used to define its orbit.

The following flight coordinates are used:

$r =$ radial distance from principal focus

$\theta =$ angular distance along trajectory measured at the principal focus from a reference direction to the position vector of the craft

$v =$ the scalar velocity, or speed, of the craft.

$\phi =$ the flight path angle of the craft measured from local horizontal. (Horizontal may be defined here as the plane normal to the geocentric position vector of the craft).

$$h \quad = rv \cos \phi = nab$$

$$P \quad = \frac{1}{k} \left(r^2 v^2 \cos^2 \phi \right)$$

$$E \quad = \left(\frac{v^2}{2} - \frac{k}{r} \right)$$

$$e^2 \quad = 1 + \left(v^2 - \frac{2k}{r} \right) \frac{r^2 v^2}{k^2} \cos^2 \phi$$

$$e \sin A_t = \frac{hv}{k} \sin \phi = (1 + e \cos A_t) \tan \phi$$

$$\cos A_\infty = -\frac{1}{e}$$

$\underline{e = 0}$

$$v^2 = v_c{}^2 = \frac{k}{r} = \frac{h^2}{pr} = gr$$

$$\dot{\theta}^2 = \frac{k}{r^3} = \frac{g}{r}$$

$\underline{e < 1}$

$$v_a{}^2 \quad = \left(\frac{k}{a} \right) \frac{(1 - e)}{(1 + e)}$$

$$v_p{}^2 \quad = \left(\frac{k}{a} \right) \frac{(1 + e)}{(1 - e)}$$

$$\frac{V_a}{V_p} \quad = \frac{(1 - e)}{(1 + e)}$$

$\underline{e > 1}$

$$V_p = (1 + e) \frac{k}{r_p} = v_\infty{}^2 + 2 \frac{k}{r_p}$$

APPENDIX V

THE ORBIT EQUATION AND ASSOCIATED RELATIONS

$$\ddot{r} - \dot{\theta}^2 r = \frac{-k}{r^2} \; ; \qquad g = \frac{-k}{r^2} \; ; \qquad \frac{d}{dt}(r^2\dot{\theta}) = 0$$

$$r = \frac{P}{1 + e \cos A}$$

$$t_2 - t_1 = \sqrt{\frac{a^3}{k}} \left[A_{e2} - A_{e1} - e\,(\sin A_{e2} - \sin A_{e1}) \right]$$

$$p \quad = \frac{h^2}{k} \; ; \quad \text{semi-latus rectum}$$

$$r_p \quad = \frac{p}{1+e} \; ; \quad \text{periapsis radius } (e < 1)$$

$$2a \quad = r_a + r_p = \frac{2p}{1-e^2} = \frac{k}{E} \; ; \text{major axis } (e < 1)$$

$$b \quad = a\,\sqrt{1 - e^2} = \frac{p}{\sqrt{1 - e^2}} \; ; \text{semi-minor axis}$$

$$h \quad = r^2\dot{\theta} \; ; \text{angular momentum}$$

$$E \quad = \frac{\dot{r}^2}{2} + \frac{r^2\dot{\theta}^2}{2} - \frac{k}{r} \; ; \text{specific energy}$$

$$e \quad = \frac{r_a - r_p}{r_a + r_p} \; ; \text{eccentricity}$$

$$n \quad = \sqrt{\frac{k}{|a^3|}} = \frac{2\pi}{T} \; ; \text{mean motion } (e < 1)$$

$$v_\infty \quad = \sqrt{2E} = \sqrt{\frac{-k}{a}} \; ; \text{hyperbolic excess velocity}$$

$$A_t \quad = (\theta - \theta_p) \; ; \text{ true anomaly.}$$

$$A_m \quad = \sqrt{\frac{k}{|a^3|}} \, (t - t_p) \; ; \text{mean motion}$$

$$A_e \quad = \text{eccentric anomaly} \quad (\text{defined by time equation})$$

$$\cos \, A_e = \frac{\cos A_t + e}{1 + e \cos A_t} \; ; \qquad \cos A_t \quad = \frac{\cos A_e - e}{1 - e \cos A_e}$$

$$\sin \, A_e = \frac{\sqrt{1 - e^2} \, \sin A_t}{1 + e \cos A_t} \; ; \qquad \sin A_t \quad = \frac{\sqrt{1 - e^2} \, \cos A_e}{1 - e \cos A_e}$$

APPENDIX VI

CONVERSION TABLES

Authors Note: In the preparation of this text it became apparent that many problems arise that call for operation on orbital data by dynamic functional operations such as force, acceleration, etc. These are most frequently available in different systems of units and conversion to a common system is frequently required. The following tables have been prepared to provide convenient factors for this purpose.

The tables are presented in a form that has been found to be convenient for the application of unit conversion. It will be noticed that conversion factors are presented as a ratio of units such that the ratio has a value of unity. Thus, these may be applied to equations in which a variety of units appear without changing the equality involved.

Units of Length

1 = 0.0032808 ft/cm = 0.3970 in/cm = 2.54005 cm/in
1 = 0.304801 M/ft = 3.28083 ft/M.
1 = 5280 ft/St.Mi = 6076 ft/ N.Mi. = 1.15078 St.Mi/N.Mi.
1 = 0.62137 St.Mi/Km = 1.60935 Km/St.Mi.

Units of Time

1 = 1440 min./mean solar day = 86,400 sec/mean solar day
1 = 365.256 mean solar days/sidereal year
1 = 8766.14 hours/sid. yr. = 3.15583×10^7 sec/sid. yr.
1 = 365 days/cal. yr = 8760 hrs/cal. yr = 3.1536×10^7 sec/cal.yr.

Units of Velocity

$$1 = 5280 \frac{\text{ft/sec}}{\text{St.Mi./sec}} = 1.89394 \times 10^{-4} \frac{\text{St.mi./sec}}{\text{ft/sec}}$$

$$1 = 4.54 \times 10^8 \frac{\text{ft/sec}}{\text{St Mi./day}} = 2.83 \frac{\text{ft/sec}}{\text{Km/day}}$$

330

$$1 = 2.2369 \frac{\text{St.Mi/hr}}{\text{M/sec}} = 0.447041 \frac{\text{St.Mi./sec}}{\text{St.Mi./hr}}$$

$$1 = 1.4667 \frac{\text{ft/sec}}{\text{St.Mi./hr}} = 1.6093 \frac{\text{Km/sec}}{\text{St.Mi./sec}} = 3280.833 \frac{\text{ft/sec}}{\text{Km/sec}}$$

Units of Acceleration

$$1 = 30.481 \frac{\text{cm/sec}^2}{\text{ft/sec}^2}$$

$$1 = 32.16 \frac{\text{ft/sec}^2}{g} = 6.13 \times 10^{-3} \frac{\text{St.Mi/sec}^2}{g} = 0.01095 \frac{\text{km/sec}^2}{g}$$

$$1 = 3.92 \times 10^{13} \frac{\text{ft/sec}^2}{\text{St.Mi./day}^2} = 2.44 \times 10^{13} \frac{\text{ft/sec}^2}{\text{Km/sec}^2}$$

Units of Angular Measure

$$1 = \frac{360}{2\pi} \text{deg./radian} = 57.2958 \text{ deg/rad.}$$

$$1 = 4.848 \times 10^{-6} \text{ rad/second} = 3600 \text{ seconds/radian.}$$

Units of Angular Velocity

$$1 = 9.549 \frac{\text{rpm}}{\text{rad/sec}} \quad 57.2958 \frac{\text{deg/sec}}{\text{rad/sec}}$$

$$1 = 15 \frac{\text{deg/hr}}{\text{ERU}} \quad 15 \frac{\text{sec/sec}}{\text{REU}}$$

(ERU = Earth Rate Unit)

Miscellaneous Physical Constants

Universal gravitational constant: $G = 6.670 \times 10^{-8} \dfrac{\text{dynes cm}^2}{\text{gm}^2}$

Velocity of light in a vacuum: $c = 299776 \times 10^{10}$ cm/sec
$= 186,272$ St.Mi./sec

Velocity of sound in Air: $v = 1088$ ft/sec $= 331.7$ M/sec.
Average noon Insolation at the earth: $p \approx 1$ Kw Hr/sq M

Index